THE RENAISSANCE OF THE TWELFTH CENTURY

THE RENAISSANCE OF THE TWELFTH CENTURY

AN EXHIBITION ORGANIZED BY STEPHEN K. SCHER

MUSEUM OF ART, RHODE ISLAND SCHOOL OF DESIGN, PROVIDENCE, RHODE ISLAND

MAY 8 — JUNE 22, 1969

CATALOGUE BY STEPHEN K. SCHER

VISITING CURATOR OF MEDIEVAL ART

MUSEUM OF ART, RHODE ISLAND SCHOOL OF DESIGN

ASSOCIATE PROFESSOR, BROWN UNIVERSITY

ESSAYS BY

PROFESSOR WALTER CAHN, YALE UNIVERSITY

PROFESSOR BRYCE LYON, BROWN UNIVERSITY

PROFESSOR STEPHEN K. SCHER, BROWN UNIVERSITY

CONTRIBUTIONS BY

DR. DOROTHY GLASS, DUMBARTON OAKS

MR. ROBERT C. MOELLER III, DUKE UNIVERSITY

PROFESSOR TANIA ROLPH, FORDHAM UNIVERSITY

PROFESSOR LINDA SEIDEL FIELD, HARVARD UNIVERSITY

FOREWORD

It is almost fifty years since Eliza Radeke and L. Earle Rowe bought the Cluny Saint Peter, one of the greatest treasures in the Museum of Art, Rhode Island School of Design. When he published the sculpture in the Museum's bulletin in 1926 Mr. Rowe could recall that not many years before, such "cathedral decorations" were considered strange, "disregarded save by a few enthusiasts." No longer, he suggested, could such stonework be dismissed without consideration, "and representative examples of this type of sculpture are being much sought by American museums."

Since 1920 the Museum's Medieval collection has grown to over one hundred and thirty pieces, augmented by several important loans. While none are so great as the Saint Peter, only a handful have received the attention they merit. Our files are full of notes, research undertaken yet often never completed by curatorial personnel pulled by equally demanding pressures in a dozen directions. Many smaller museums—and even some large ones—have had this experience; and not just with their Medieval collections.

The last systematic attempt to organize the Medieval Collection in Rhode Island's Museum was the creation in 1940 of the Medieval room by Alexander Dorner. It seemed appropriate to use this chamber as the entrance to the *Renaissance of the Twelfth Century*.

The present exhibition of sculpture represents the convergence of a number of desires, purposes, and ideas. It derives, above all, from the hope of studying and reorganizing the Medieval objects in the Museum, a task which, in the light of steady advances in scholarship, demands the attention of a specialist.

To meet these realities a successful and mutually beneficial program of visiting curatorships was established three years ago between the Museum of Art, Rhode Island School of Design, and Brown University's Art Historians.

This exhibition is the latest public manifestation of the program. Its attempt to balance scholarly aims with visual interest for the student and public coincides with the Museum's function. More than the realization of a program, however, the *Renaissance of the Twelfth Century* is due to the energetic and dedicated labors of Professor Stephen K. Scher, visiting curator of Medieval Art, whose contribution to making the Museum a better center for the study and enjoyment of art, we gratefully and pleasurably acknowledge.

DANIEL ROBBINS, *Director*

PREFACE

Although the joint program between Brown University and the Museum of Art, Rhode Island School of Design has been a major factor behind the presentation of this exhibition, it only partially explains the gathering of twelfth century sculpture in Providence at a time when exhibitions of medieval art seem suddenly to have become rather common. Being not only a visiting curator and a member of the Art Department at Brown, but also the secretary of the International Center of Medieval Art, it seemed logical to me to attempt to bring all three organizations together in a single project. When Professor Walter Cahn of Yale University visited the Museum in connection with the immensely valuable corpus of Romanesque Sculpture in American Collections that he is preparing for the International Center of Medieval Art and that he is publishing piecemeal in the journal of the Center, *Gesta,* I felt that the opportunity of mounting an exhibition based upon this compilation of material was not to be missed.

At the same time I did not feel that I was justified in asking lenders to part with what are often fragile or heavy or fairly permanently installed sculptures for an exhibition that had either no clear purpose or no significant theme. In other words, it was necessary in my mind that the exhibition fill the dual rôle of being attractive to the public and provocative to the scholar.

The specific theme chosen, "The Renaissance of the Twelfth Century," made it possible to satisfy these demands. Much that had not been seen before could be exposed; objects from the same monument that were scattered among several collections could be brought together; sculptures that were unpublished or inadequately studied could receive new attention; and finally a specific topic, the relationship between a type of sculpture defined as Romanesque and a type identified as Early Gothic, both flourishing in the twelfth century, could be examined with the possibility of arriving at new definitions.

It was necessary, therefore, that significant works be included in the exhibition and that a serious and scholarly catalogue be produced. I must accept the full responsibility for the catalogue with the hope that it will fulfill a useful purpose for the medieval art historian and the interested amateur.

In addition to my own contributions the reader will find essays by Professor Bryce Lyon of Brown University, and Professor Walter Cahn of Yale University. Professor Lyon's essay on the historiography of the Renaissance of the Twelfth Century provides a clear and very helpful introduction to the period and to the conception of a renaissance as formulated by modern historians. Professor Cahn's essay is similar in intent, but addresses itself in a highly interesting approach to the concept of the medieval artist held by subsequent ages. The contributions of both scholars do honor to the catalogue, and for their enthusiastic cooperation I wish to extend my very deepest thanks.

Since the more specific problem of the emergence of a Gothic style in art and architecture would not be fully illustrated by the exhibition and therefore not treated comprehensively in the catalogue, the possibility of a symposium suggested itself as a means of discussing this subject through a series of papers delivered by distinguished scholars as well as a general discussion in which ideas could be exchanged freely. This symposium became a reality through the generous support of The International Center of Medieval Art and Brown University, whose President, Ray L. Heffner, and Provost, Merton Stoltz, have my sincere gratitude.

In order that those who could not attend the symposium might benefit from it in conjunction with the exhibition it was decided that the papers be published in a special issue of *Gesta.* This, too, became possible when the Samuel H. Kress Foundation, which already supports the regular issue of *Gesta,* agreed to underwrite the cost of a special issue. To the Foundation and in particular to its able and charming secretary, Miss Mary Davis, I would like to offer my special thanks.

As anyone knows who has organized an exhibition, the list of people upon whose generosity and kindness such a project depends is endless. I was happily surprised in relation to the present exhibition, for the nature of the material had made me very pessimistic at the outset regarding a favorable response to loan requests. The willingness to cooperate on the part of almost all of the institutions and private collectors who were approached rapidly dispelled my pessimism.

To all of the museum directors, curators, curatorial assistants, secretaries, registrars, packers, photographers, superintendents, etc., with whom I had no direct contact, but without whose help the exhibition could not have become a reality I offer my warmest thanks.

Those with whom I did have direct contact and whose advice and help were of immense value I would like to acknowledge separately, including at the same time scholars who have given generously of their time and knowledge: Dr. Peter Bloch, Berlin-Dahlem Museum; at the Museum of Fine Arts, Boston, Dr. Hanns Swarzenski and Mr. William Young; Musée du Berry, Hôtel Cujas, Bourges, Messrs. J. Favière and P. Bailly; The Cleveland Museum of Art, Mr. William Wixom; the Fogg Art Museum, Mr. John Coolidge, former director, Miss Agnes Mongan, acting director, Mr. Henry Berg; The

Wadsworth Antheneum, Mr. Peter Marlow and Mr. Samuel Wagstaff, former curator, now in Detroit; Mr. John Hunt in Ireland; at The Metropolitan Museum of Art and the Cloisters, Mr. William Forsyth, Miss Carmen Gomez-Moreno, Mr. Thomas Miller, and Miss Bonnie Young; the Philadelphia Museum of Art, Mr. David Du-Bon; M. Léon Pressouyre, Musée national du château, Fontainebleau; at The Walters Art Gallery, Mr. Richard Randall, director; the Worcester Art Museum, Miss Louisa Dresser; at Yale University, Prof. Sumner McK. Crosby, Prof. Walter Cahn, and Mr. Andrew C. Ritchie, Director of the Yale Art Gallery; Prof. George Zarnecki, deputy director, the Courtauld Institute of Art; Dr. David Giles Carter, Director, Montreal Museum of Fine Arts; Mr. Robert C. Moeller III, Director, Museum of Art, Duke University; Mrs. Frank Robinson, Director, Wellesley College Museum.

For their encouragement and advice I would like to thank Mr. John Nicholas Brown, who has supported medieval studies so generously, and Prof. François Bucher of Princeton University, who is president of the International Center of Medieval Art.

The visual quality of this catalogue must be credited to the talents of Messrs. Malcolm Grear and David Chapman as designers in concert with the high standards of printing set by the Meriden Gravure Company. Their patience in the face of constant demands is fully appreciated.

For several of the catalogue entries scholars were approached who had devoted particular attention to objects that were to be exhibited and who would have new and perhaps controversial ideas. The response of these scholars was very gratifying, and their contributions have greatly enhanced the catalogue. In those cases where an entry was written solely by a person other than myself his signature appears alone at the end of the entry. When a person collaborated with me in the writing of an entry, their name appears first and then my initials. If I received extensive help with the research of a particular object, my initials appear first followed by the researcher's name. The responsibility for all unsigned entries is mine.

Mrs. Pearl Braude did extensive research for nos. 22, 23, 27, 37.

Miss Dorothy Glass collaborated on no. 42.

Mr. Robert C. Moeller III wrote the entries for nos. 10-19 and 47-48.

Prof. Tania Rolph wrote the entry for no. 59.

Prof. Linda Seidel Field wrote the entries for nos. 28, 31, 34-36, 45-46.

In a separate category and deserving special attention for his successful completion of a herculean task is Mr. Peter Fusco, a graduate assistant in the Art Department, Brown University. He compiled the very large bibliography included in the catalogue. By no means a pleasant task and certainly no test of his imagination, he nonetheless fulfilled it with admirable energy and devotion, and he has not only my gratitude, but that of all scholars who find the fruits of his labors useful.

Without the encouragement and irrepressible enthusiasm of Daniel Robbins I would never have been able to survive some of the more discouraging moments in the preparation of the exhibition. For any anguish I have caused him, I humbly beg his apologies. It is not every museum director who will allow his main gallery to be turned into a church.

A very special niche must be reserved for Miss Anne Booth, curatorial assistant for Antiquities, who worked with me from the very beginning on all phases of the exhibition: correspondence, loan forms, editing of the catalogue, and a thousand and one other thankless jobs. Her calmness and efficiency have been a major factor in the accomplishment of the exhibition. I wish her to know that to me, at least, none of her jobs were thankless.

Any museum director should envy Mr. Robbins the équipe he possesses. Small, tightly knit, and supremely expert and efficient in the accomplishment of their tasks, it is they who have made this exhibition a reality, and they have my deepest affection and gratitude:

Dr. Stephen E. Ostrow, Chief Curator,

Mr. Thomas Ryan, Superintendent, without whom nothing could be brought to successful completion in the museum,

Mr. Donald Dobson, Assistant Superintendent

Mr. John Hawkins, Assistant to the Superintendent

Miss Elmina Malloy, Registrar, whose efficiency keeps everything on the rails,

Miss Sofia W. Vervena, Head Extension Services

Mrs. Catharine Lantz, Membership Secretary

Mr. Robert Thornton, Photographer

Miss Janet McMichael, Executive Secretary to the Director

Miss Amy Koleman, Curatorial Assistant

The Museum owes a deep debt of gratitude as well to Mr. Harold W. Ingram Jr., Superintendent of Buildings and Grounds, Rhode Island School of Design, for his cooperation in building the "church" in the main gallery. His team of carpenters is to be congratulated on the speed and expertness with which they became medieval master-builders.

Finally, if any congratulations are to be offered, they should be offered to my wife. How she survived the effects that mounting this exhibition had upon me is beyond my comprehension. Her patience and understanding have been tested and have not weakened at any time. Any words I might use to describe my feelings would be inadequate.   STEPHEN K. SCHER

TABLE OF CONTENTS

LENDERS TO THE EXHIBITION

MUSEUMS

Amherst College, Amherst, Massachusetts

Art Museum, Duke University, Durham, North Carolina

The Art Museum, Princeton University, Princeton, New Jersey

City Art Museum of Saint Louis, Saint Louis, Missouri

Cincinnati Art Museum, Cincinnati, Ohio

The Cleveland Museum of Art, Cleveland, Ohio

Fogg Art Museum, Cambridge, Massachusetts

The Metropolitan Museum of Art, New York

The Metropolitan Museum of Art, The Cloisters Collection, New York

The Montreal Museum of Fine Arts, Montreal, Canada

Musées de la Ville de Bourges (Cher), France

Museum of Art, Rhode Island School of Design, Providence, Rhode Island

Museum of Fine Arts, Boston, Massachusetts

Philadelphia Museum of Art, Philadelphia, Pennsylvania

The Phillips Collection, Washington, D. C.

Smith College Museum of Art, Northampton, Massachusetts

The Virginia Museum of Fine Arts, Richmond, Virginia

Wadsworth Atheneum, Hartford, Connecticut

The Walters Art Gallery, Baltimore, Maryland

Wellesley College Museum, Wellesley, Massachusetts

Williams College Museum of Art, Williamstown, Massachusetts

Worcester Art Museum, Worcester, Massachusetts

Yale University Art Gallery, New Haven, Connecticut

PRIVATE LENDERS

Mr. John Nicholas Brown, Providence, Rhode Island

Mr. and Mrs. Martin Scher, New York

PHOTOGRAPH CREDITS

All photographs are courtesy of the lenders and of the following:

James Austin, Cambridge, England, (Fig. 56a)

E. Irving Blomstrann, New Britain, Connecticut, (Figs. 3, 47b)

Robert Brault, Bourges (Cher), France, (Fig. 58)

Raymond Laniepce, Paris, (Fig. 57a)

Robert C. Moeller III, Duke University, (Figs. 19a, 19b)

Tania Rolph, New York, (Fig. 58a)

Stephen K. Scher, Providence, (Figs. 38, 43, 51, 56, 59)

Robert O. Thornton, Museum of Art, Rhode Island School of Design, (Figs. 1, 7, 10, 11, 12, 20, 22, 23, 30, 37, 39, 43, 49)

Herbert P. Vose, Wellesley Hills, Massachusetts, (Fig. 27)

A. J. Wyatt, Philadelphia Museum of Art, (Fig. 21)

The Memorial Art Gallery of the University of Rochester, Rochester, New York, (Figs. 17, 18)

Archives Photographiques, Caisse National des Monuments Historiques, Service Photographique, Paris, (Fig. 44a)

Bildarchiv Foto Marburg, Germany, (Fig. 31b)

Service de Documentation photographique: Réunion des Musees Nationaux, Chateau de Versailles (Seine-et-Oise), France (Fig. 34a)

Design-Graphics, Inc., Providence, (photographic murals of Figs. 17, 18)

WAS THERE A RENAISSANCE IN THE TWELFTH CENTURY?

BRYCE LYON, *Professor of History, Brown University*

How intrigued the literate men of the twelfth century would have been to learn that their intellectual and artistic achievements were spoken of some eight centuries later by an ever increasing group of literate men with a *sympathique* for the Middle Ages as the "Renaissance of the Twelfth Century." Once the term "Renaissance" had been explained to them, they would have been delighted, for they would have felt that their own awareness and even pride in their mental and artistic accomplishments had been affirmed. Although lacking the sense of history possessed by men of later ages and although not having the means to compare the achievements of the twelfth century with those of the tenth or any other preceding century, they sensed a quickening of intellectual pace and an expansion of the traditional horizons of knowledge. The more ambitious and daring knew that change was in the air, that it was transforming western Christendom.[1] No man of the twelfth century stated or even thought that his ability, his achievements, were other than a gift from God, but men of achievement were becoming confident, were sloughing off an inferiority complex, and were learning that to live and to achieve was exciting because with their Divine given gifts they could transform, beautify, and improve God's universe. Although the twelfth century may well have been the age of Saint Bernard, and although Anselm of Bec may well have been a more profound thinker than Abelard, the confident and critical Abelard sensed that his style of life and approach to knowledge would prevail. Saint Francis of Assisi was to show how out of touch was the conservative Saint Bernard. And Abelard's *Dubitando enim ad inquisitionem venimus; inquirendo veritatem percipimus* was to prevail over Anselm's *Credo ut intelligam,* over Anselm's reiteration of Saint Augustine's dictum that "unless ye believe, ye shall not understand."

No twelfth-century artist or craftsman would have been so brash as to attribute his work to individual ability or genius. The monastic artist, Theophilus, in his treatise *Concerning the Various Arts* expressed the conviction of his colleagues when he wrote: "What God has given man as an inheritance, let man strive and work with all eagerness to attain. When this has been attained, let no one glorify himself as if it were received of himself and not another but let himself render thanks to God."[2] This is not to say, however, that the artist could not be proud of and satisfied with what he executed. The sculptor-mason Gilbert, a man with a dramatic and individual style who created between 1125 and 1135 one of the most beautiful of medieval masterpieces, the tympanum of Autun Cathedral, as well as most of the capitals throughout the church, was obviously as satisfied with his work as was the bishop because directly under the tympanum, beneath the feet of Christ in judgment, is the inscription *Gislebertus hoc fecit*.[3] Although it cannot be established that the master-mason William of Sens was associated with the construction of Sens Cathedral between 1135 and 1160, he had so great a reputation that the monks of Christ Church, Canterbury, prevailed upon him to undertake the reconstruction of Canterbury Cathedral which had been badly damaged by fire in 1174. In a *Tract on the Burning and Repair of the Church of Canterbury* the monk Gervase of Canterbury tells how diligently William supervised the reconstruction, how "he made most ingenious machines for loading and unloading ships," and how, while on the scaffolding supervising the work, he fell to the ground from a height of fifty feet and so seriously injured himself that he could no longer work. Gervase describes William as "a man active and ready" and states that the monks selected him "on account of his lively genius and good reputation."[4] No great gulf separated William of Sens from the famous architect Villard de Honnecourt who flourished early in the next century.[5]

Abbot Suger was so proud of the choir of the abbey church which he so lovingly built at Saint Denis and consecrated to the glory of God that when he dedicated it in 1144 he displayed it not only to a great assembly of prelates and abbots but also to Louis VII, king of France. Responsible for the first Gothic church in the Île de France, Suger was bothered not at all by Saint Bernard's charge that he headed a soft monastic house dedicated to vain artistic embellishment. Nor did he refrain from decorating with silver, gold, precious stones, and pearls the sardonyx cup that he had inherited from the Romans and that he used as a chalice. Adviser to both Louis VI and Louis VII of France and a kind of "prime minister," Suger labored mightily for these kings in order to make the Île de France a unified and peaceful center of a greater France with the royal church of Saint Denis as the spiritual and symbolic monument.[6]

Among all sorts of men and over all western Europe there was change in the twelfth century. The translators of Arabic and Greek texts containing the secrets of Graeco-Roman civilization and the more advanced knowledge of the Moslem world were well aware that this ancient corpus of knowledge, available in the twelfth century to the Byzantine and Moslem worlds, was new to the West and would transform what German historians of the nineteenth and twentieth centuries have been so fond of calling the *Weltanschauung*. And where were these translators?

They were in southern Italy and Sicily, areas dominated until the eleventh century by Byzantium or by Moslem emirs. They were in Barcelona, Tarazona, Segovia, León, Pamplona, Toledo, all towns close to or long under Moslem rule. There were some in northern Africa and many who lived for long periods at Constantinople, the queen of the Mediterranean, the city that the twelfth-century chronicler Odo of Deuil described as "the glory of the Greeks, rich in renown and richer still in possessions."[7] How greatly had the horizon of western Christendom expanded in the twelfth century, not alone for literate, but for all men, and this expansion had come from the efforts of western men. Long before the First Crusade at the end of the eleventh century the Latin West had shown signs of renewed political, military, and economic vigor. During the eleventh century Norman adventurers had wrested southern Italy and Sicily away from Byzantium and the Moslems and had laid the foundations for the fabulous Norman kingdom of Sicily whose rôle would be as a bridge between western and eastern culture and as a center for a new cosmopolitan culture. Meanwhile Venice had secured an economic hegemony over the Adriatic and had strengthened her position of economic dominance in trade with Constantinople. To the west the ports of Pisa and Genoa cooperated in a kind of religious-economic crusade against the Moslem. As early as 1015 they had attacked Sardinia and were soon attacking the coasts of northern Africa. So ruthlessly did soldier and merchant fight against the infidel that by 1087 the western Mediterranean was Christian and both Pisans and Genoese gave thanks to Saint Peter and the archangel Gabriel for giving them victory over the infidel.[8] The cathedral of Pisa, begun in 1063, was erected to serve as a kind of *Arc de Triomphe*.[9]

While economic and spiritual ardor pushed the Latin West back into the western Mediterranean, French feudal adventurers launched their first attacks against infidel lands in Spain, thus initiating the celebrated Reconquista of the Iberian peninsula that ended only in 1492 with the capture of Granada. As in southern Italy and Sicily another bridge was erected between eastern and western culture. These, then, were the thrusts of the West back into an area of the world denied to western men since the Early Middle Ages, these the events that must be interpreted as the military, political, economic, spiritual, and psychological antecedents of the first great western offensive against the East between 1096 and 1099. The dramatic victory of the crusaders was symbolic not only of the new western vigor and of a reformed church under a vigorous papacy, but of a new confidence. After centuries of retreat and defense the West had seized the offensive and Christian knights had demonstrated that, far from their feudal homes, they could defeat the Saracen. To both church and feudal aristocracy the First Crusade gave a psychological momentum and spurred an awakened belief in western ability. But the First Crusade must not be considered the major reason for the cultural, spiritual, and economic revival of western Europe. It was not the cause of the renaissance of the twelfth century; it was but the last in a chain of events indicative of the new western vigor. It was an economic and cultural catalyst, but no more. While the First Crusade made more westerners aware of the East and opened up more channels between East and West, to think that artistic and cultural curiosity were conspicuous attributes of the crusader knight is wholly erroneous.[10]

Wherever one looks the change in the eleventh and twelfth centuries is significant. From the middle of the eleventh century popes imbued with the desire to head a reformed and unified church were pressing claims to spiritual and secular supremacy never before demanded by a prelate. At Canossa Gregory VII won a spectacular victory over the emperor Henry IV, a victory that has remained symbolic in European history to the present. Even more important were the victories achieved by strong counts, dukes, and kings in forging effective political structures out of their feudal states. The Peace and Truce of God proclaimed by assemblies of bishops during the eleventh century, though symbolically effective, could not be translated into reality without the cooperation of such men as the counts of Flanders and of Champagne, the dukes of Normandy, the Capetian kings of France, and the Norman-Angevin kings of England, all of whom hammered out law, order, and strong political institutions capable of centralizing the government and the emerging states. Even early in the twelfth century kings such as Henry II of England were defeudalizing their kingdoms and creating institutions that were to be the girders of the modern states. To achieve these goals the rulers of western Europe had the cooperation of the new bourgeois class in the towns that had begun to rise up across western Europe during the eleventh and twelfth centuries. Although there was change even in the dreariest part of the Middle Ages between the fifth and tenth centuries, the change in the eleventh and twelfth centuries was so universal and so pronounced that it set western Europe upon new paths at quickened pace. Henceforth western Europe had that vitality, confidence, drive, and creative power which have become the trademarks of western civilization.

The intent here is not to discuss the achievements of the renaissance of the twelfth century, but simply to note them and then to tackle the fascinating problem that has long concerned medieval and Renaissance scholars: do such achievements permit the historian to speak of a renaissance of the twelfth century? In the words of Charles Homer Haskins, the distinguished medievalist primarily responsible for the concept of a renaissance in the twelfth century, this century "was in many respects an age of fresh and vigorous life. The epoch of the Crusades, of the rise of towns, and of the earliest bureaucratic states of the West, it saw the culmination of Romanesque art and the beginnings of Gothic; the emergence of the vernacular literatures; the revival of the Latin classics and of Latin poetry and Roman law; the recovery of Greek science, with its Arabic additions, and of much of Greek philosophy; and the origin of the first European universities." Anticipating the reaction of historians reared in a historiographical ambience admitting of but one Renaissance, Haskins asked: "A renaissance in the twelfth century! Do not the Middle Ages, that epoch of ignorance, stagnation, and gloom, stand in the sharpest contrast to the light and progress and freedom of the Italian Renaissance which followed?" And he answered, stating that "modern research shows us the Middle Ages less dark and less static, the Renaissance less bright and less sudden, than was once supposed . . . The Italian Renaissance was preceded by similar, if less wide-reaching movements; indeed it came out of the Middle Ages . . . the great Renaissance was not so unique or so decisive as has been supposed."[11]

This conclusion was a dramatic challenge to a cherished and well-nigh universal canon of historical thinking dating back to the fourteenth and fifteenth centuries. It was Petrarch who first divided history into ancient *(antiqua),* that period prior to the adoption of Christianity by the Roman emperors, and modern *(nova),* that period which followed and continued to his own time and which he considered barbarous and dark. In his *History of the Florentine People* Leonardo Bruni applied Petrarch's ideas to specific history and a few years later Flavio Biondo in a *History from the Decline of the Roman Empire* associated the end of the Roman Empire in the West with the sack of Rome in 410 by Alaric and his Visigoths. Thereafter historians never doubted that the golden age of classical antiquity ended with the Christianization of the Roman Empire, that the Roman Empire was destroyed by the Gothic barbarians in the fourth and fifth centuries, and that for virtually the next thousand years Europe lived in stupid ignorance and Gothic darkness.[12] Not until the nineteenth century would the Middle Ages be regarded as other than the "Dark Ages."

It was perhaps natural that Petrarch and his humanist followers of the fourteenth, fifteenth, and sixteenth centuries, convinced that they were reviving and giving birth again to culture, should have regarded the period from the fourth century to their own as a "dark intermediate period." Artists had come to the same conclusion. Publishing his *Lives of the Great Painters, Sculptors, and Architects* in 1550, Giorgio Vasari made Constantine the boundary between the good art of the ancient world and the dismal art of the period following. He believed that an artistic awakening had begun only in the thirteenth century, and especially with Giotto. From this time on artists "were able to distinguish the good from the bad, and abandoning the old style, they began to copy the ancients with all ardor and industry." According to Vasari the arts resembled human bodies; they "have their birth, growth, age, and death, and I hope by this means they will be enabled more easily to recognize the progress of the renaissance *(rinascita)* of the arts, and the perfection to which they have attained in our own time."[13] A few years later, in 1559, Jacques Amyot dedicated his translation of Plutarch to King Henry II of France and reminded Henry that his father Francis I "happily founded good letters and made them to be reborn *(renaistre)* and to flourish in this noble kingdom." So was born the French idea of the *renaissance des lettres.*[14]

This developing concept of degeneration and rebirth was reinforced by the Protestant historians who not only agreed that the Dark Ages were ignorant but castigated the church and papacy for the corruption of the Christian faith, explaining that it was necessary for such men as Luther and Calvin to restore Christianity to its pristine purity. In the sixteenth century men were beginning to agree for various reasons that the Dark Ages comprised a *media tempora.* And in 1674 with the publication by Cellarius of the *Nucleus Historiae inter Antiquam et Novam Mediae (Nucleus of Middle History between Ancient and Modern)*, the expression *medium aevum* became an accepted part of historical terminology and the famous tripartite division of history into ancient, medieval, and modern became a chronological device used from then on by all historians.[15]

Seventeenth-century historians and cultured men commonly divided history into three periods on which they made value judgments. Down to the fourth century men had been literate, capable of tremendous achievement, and acutely aware of themselves as individuals and of the world about them. Then had come those long and detested centuries of Gothic darkness devoid of knowledge and appreciation of man and the world. Finally, in the fourteenth century, had come a rebirth, a Renaissance, when cultured men not only restored antique knowledge and beauty but, inspired by the glories of the classical world, began to create beautiful literature and art.

In the eighteenth century, that age of enlightenment and reason, learned opinion merely reinforced and embellished the concept of the Renaissance. The intellectual bond between the humanists and *philosophes* was so strong that there was no reason for revision or reinterpretation; there was need only to emphasize the stupidity and superstition of medieval man as compared to the Renaissance man and especially to the enlightened man of the eighteenth century. The pastime of lettered men of the eighteenth century was to surpass each other in ridiculing the Middle Ages. In his *Essay on the Manners and the Spirit of Nations* Voltaire had ample opportunity in discussing civilization from Charlemagne to Louis XIII to heap satire upon a barbarous age. He proclaimed that it was necessary "to know the history of that age [Middle Ages] only in order to scorn it." Even late in the fifteenth century during the reign of Louis XI "barbarism, superstition, ignorance covered the face of the world, except in Italy." While throughout northern Europe there was naught but ignorance and poverty, "it was not so in the fine commercial cities of Italy: there, one lived in comfort, with opulence; it was only in their bosom that one could enjoy the pleasures of life. There, wealth and freedom finally excited genius, as it had inspired courage." Yes, "it was the age of the glory of Italy," a period distinguished by an unusual number of "extraordinary men of all kinds."[16]

In England Hume was arguing that the end of the fifteenth century saw the end of a "series of many barbarous ages" and "the dawn of civilization and science."[17] In his brilliant book *The Decline and Fall of the Roman Empire*, Edward Gibbon avowed that he was writing the history of "the triumph of barbarism and religion" and explained in elegant prose that before the revival of classic literature in Italy "the barbarians in Europe were immersed in ignorance."[18]

By what one historian has recently called "the romantic reaction," the Middle Ages were finally rehabilitated. Reaction against the age of reason, the excesses and failures of the French Revolution, and the disaster of the Napoleonic era combined with a new respect for the European past, a new awareness of the *Volksgeist* and so-called national culture, to cause men to look back to the Middle Ages and to search for indigenous and creative elements in their national pasts. While the Romantics of the nineteenth century made no attempt to minimize the achievements of the Renaissance, they forced men to admit for the first time that all that was medieval was not dark, that the Middle Ages, though different from the Renaissance, were a significant and formative period when much of what nineteenth-century Europeans regarded as typically western European had developed. Some Romantics such as Ruskin even attacked Renaissance culture, viewing it and the spirit of that age as evil. But Ruskin would not deny, no more than would his contemporaries, that there was a Renaissance. He saw in it much that he did not like, and yet he praised the old masters, those simple and unlearned men.[19]

In spite of the rehabilitation of the Middle Ages and the development of serious study of medieval records and monuments by some of the finest European historians—a development that made medieval history a respectable field of historical investigation—decades were to pass before men were convinced that the Middle Ages were not to be swept disdainfully under the rug.[20] The nineteenth century was, after all, the century of Jules Michelet, Jacob Burckhardt, and John Addington Symonds. However erratic and subjective Michelet's *History of France,* it provided one of the first synthetic treatments of medieval and Renaissance France, a kind of *Kulturgeschichte* then becoming popular in Germany. Michelet hated the Middle Ages and adored the Renaissance. All he could see in the Middle Ages was a "bizarre and monstrous condition, prodigiously artificial." When he discussed scholastic philosophy, he spoke of "the creation of a people of fools." He felt liberated when he finally came to Volume VII on the Renaissance, an age that was for him more than the "coming of a new art and the free play of imagination"; it was "the renovation of the study of antiquity"; it was "the discovery of the world and the discovery of man . . . Man refound himself"; and "he plumbed the profound depths of his nature."[21] At last the Renaissance had been defined as a total and distinct period in western civilization. The ground was prepared for Burckhardt who created the modern concept of the Renaissance.

Burckhardt's *Civilization of the Renaissance in Italy* was impressionistic *Kulturgeschichte* at its best. Describing the Middle Ages as a period when man slumbered in childish ignorance and was devoid of individuality, Burckhardt then portrayed the man of the Renaissance as a product of the particularistic history of the Italian city state, a man who not only appreciated classical culture but who, by virtue of his genius, the *Volksgeist* of the Italian people, went on to new achievements and conquests.[22] Since Burckhardt's masterpiece appeared in 1860 there has been only minor revision of its principal theses, and then only when necessitated by awareness of new evidence. The major attack upon the Burckhardtian portrait of the Italian Renaissance has come from historians in northern Europe, especially France, who have tried to show that the Renaissance in northern Europe was independent of that in Italy, that the debt of northern Europe to Italy was minuscule, and that the new northern intellectual and artistic winds may well have stirred up what happened in Italy. Much of this writing issued from the virulent nationalistic feeling of nineteenth-century Germany and France. So zealously, in fact, did the northern historian labor that he frequently ascribed to the German and French Renaissance all that he considered new and fresh in the Middle Ages.[23]

Not until the last quarter of the nineteenth century did medievalists seem to feel confident enough to launch a serious counter-attack. It began in 1885 with Henry Thode's *Francis of Assisi and the Beginning of the Art of the Renaissance in Italy* which argued that the Renaissance sprang primarily from the religious mysticism and subjectivity of the Middle Ages rather than from the rediscovery of antique culture.[24] Since then a multitude of medievalists have written studies that powerfully buttress the view that there was dynamic and creative cultural activity in the Middle Ages. They have talked about humanism, the classical revival of the twelfth century, reliance on reason, an appreciation of man and of nature, and individual gaiety and joy. Indeed, some of them have been so chauvinistic as to blot out differences between the Middle Ages and the Renaissance and to derive all good things from their favorite age.[25]

In 1927 when Haskins spoke of a renaissance of the twelfth century, he ignited spirited debate among historians. Devotees of the Renaissance have admitted, sometimes generously and other times grudgingly, that all was not stupid, superstitious, and dark in the Middle Ages; that perhaps two massive iron curtains did not isolate the Middle Ages from the Classical and Renaissance worlds; and that the Renaissance may have had antecedents in the Middle Ages. But even Wallace K. Ferguson, spokesman for the most tolerant of Renaissance scholars, has feared that the counterattack of the medievalists may cause historians to lose "sight of the very real differences between the prevailing tone of Renaissance civilization and that of the twelfth and thirteenth centuries." He has been gratified to observe in the last decade a return "toward appreciation of the originality of Renaissance culture."[26]

Some medievalists have loosely applied the concept of Renaissance to every little spurt of activity detected in the Middle Ages. Christopher Dawson, one of the most elegant and persuasive apologists of medieval civilization, has written that "though the learning of the Carolingian age may seem a poor thing to set by the side of that of the great Italian humanists, it was none the less a genuine Renaissance which had no less importance for the development of European culture than the more brilliant movement of the fifteenth century."[27] Such enthusiasm has not been shared by all medievalists. Although Henri Pirenne, the distinguished Belgian medievalist, may well have been too severe in denigrating Carolingian cultural achievements, subsequent research appears to support his conclusion that "the so-called Carolingian Renaissance is poles apart from the true Renaissance. Between them there was nothing in common except a renewal of intellectual activity. The true Renaissance, purely secular, steeped itself in antique thought. The Carolingian Renaissance, exclusively ecclesiastical and Christian, considered the classic authors merely models of style."[28] While today scholars would hesitate to view Carolingian intellectual activity as exclusively Christian, and Renaissance culture as exclusively secular, it is significant that in discussing the Carolingian renaissance Haskins admits that it was the product of a court or of a dynasty but was not a general European movement as was the renaissance of the twelfth century.[29] Most scholars agree that the so-called Carolingian renaissance dissipated itself long before the end of the ninth century and some are dubious as to the lasting results of this brief flurry, pointing out that the principal accomplishments were a sounder classical education of the clergy, the copying and preserving of Latin manuscripts, and the development of a clear and efficient style of writing.[30] Erwin Panofsky has argued that the Carolingians recognized no break between themselves and men of the classical world, that they recognized only the need for a *renovatio* of things Roman, a repair or restoration of Latin art and literature. He has called the artistic endeavors of the Carolingians a "back-to-Rome movement" and insists that the Carolingians did not think of themselves as living in a distinct or new age separated from the Roman world, that they wished merely to renovate a classical culture which seemed to them in a sad state of disrepair.[31]

Fundamental cultural achievement was inaugurated by the renaissance of the twelfth century and by the true Renaissance, but not by the Carolingian renaissance. C. R. Morey and other art historians have realistically observed that the period following this renaissance was "as barren as the seventh century" and that this barren period was followed by other short efflorescences which numerous medievalists have labelled the "Ottonian renaissance," the "Anglo-Saxon renaissance," and the "renaissance of the tenth century." Art historians are skeptical that these were renaissances because, as Panofsky states, "it was a revival in the sense of recovery, but not in the sense of a reversion to classical Antiquity." He argues that the artists of these efflorescences were inspired by what remained of early Christian and Carolingian art, and by contemporary Byzantine art, artistic motifs that were not even models for the Carolingian efflorescence, and that there was no attempt to preserve a "Graeco-Roman illusionism."[32] These observations pertain also to other cultural activity. Historians who have argued that the Ottonian renaissance was stimulated by German contact with Italy resulting from Otto the Great's renewal of the Holy Roman Empire in 962 have been singularly unsuccessful in gaining much credence for this argument.[33] And historians who speak of a renaissance of the tenth century are referring primarily to a perceptible political and economic upturn in western Europe toward the end of the century. Population increased, more land was placed under cultivation, progressive farming techniques resulted in more food, trade quickened and gave occupations to merchants who populated the nascent towns, and military anarchy gradually gave way before political stability. But to call this slight improvement in life a renaissance is unrealistic; it was but what one modern economist has called in another connotation a "take-off period" for the more spectacular and enduring achievements of the eleventh and twelfth centuries.[34]

But what about the twelfth century? Did its renaissance have the same ingredients as the Renaissance of Burckhardt and Symonds? Not even Haskins claimed that it did; he admitted that his renaissance "was a revival rather than a new birth."[35] He believed that the true Renaissance meant revival as well as birth and newness. Even Étienne Gilson, who has regarded the Middle Ages as the breeding ground for all things good, including a fully developed humanism in the thirteenth century, well understood that this humanism was of the classical variety, that it was revived by medieval men who thought that they were but restoring in spirit and form the art and literature of the Greeks and Romans.[36] Werner Jaeger, arguing that the theme of cultural birth runs through western history, states that the Renaissance "is *only* the most famous and brilliant example of a cultural rebirth."[37] Evident from these three examples is that even the most ardent defenders of a renaissance in the twelfth century hedge their conclusions by admitting continuity between classical and twelfth-century culture and by finding basic differences in the thought and psychology of twelfth-century and Renaissance men. Some contend that although humanism existed in the twelfth century it "was not at the heart of the movement [cultural revival]";[38] that while men of the twelfth century talked of *renovatio*, for "those Renaissance historians who broke away from the mediaeval scheme of history, antiquity was an age long past, separated by a thousand years from their own time"; that obviously the Middle Ages "never knew that they were mediaeval."[39] Medieval men had no thought or plan to refashion humanity in the image of classical culture; they considered themselves only continuators and restorers. In contrast, Renaissance men, examining themselves and the world, decided that they were different, that a thousand years separated them from the culture they admired. They not only revived and restored classical art, literature, and thought, but they wrought change by their creativity.

Panofsky sees a difference both in scale and structure between what he calls the "proto-Renaissance" of the twelfth century and the Renaissance. He is convinced that artists in the twelfth century began to borrow from a work of classical art or literature figures or groups which they then medievalized. Hector and Jason, for example, are always portrayed as medieval knights. Artists in the Renaissance, however, reintegrated classical form with classical content. Panofsky graphically indicates the difference in the approach to the visible world, especially regarding perspective and technique, that is obvious in a comparison of the *Lion* of Villard de Honnecourt with that of Albrecht Dürer or of Honnecourt's human figures with those of Dürer.[40]

There were, then, fundamental differences between the renaissance of the twelfth century and the Renaissance, differences that have led one medievalist to suggest that we be "satisfied to let the twelfth century stand on its own merits as a dynamic period of mediaeval culture, which made fruitful contributions to the development of modern man and the modern world without forfeiting its own essentially mediaeval character." If the twelfth century is thought of as a period of renaissance is there not the risk, this medievalist asks, of "distorting its real character" and its distinctive achievements?[41] Not so, according to Haskins and other medievalists who have contended that the strong current of *renovatio* and the remarkable cultural advances in the twelfth century have given it a place in the history of western culture so essential, even for the Renaissance, that to deprive it of a renaissance would be pedantic. To delete "renaissance of the twelfth century" from our historical vocabulary would be impractical. Admittedly the twelfth century was different from the Renaissance in spirit, form, and structure, but let us concede that its tremendous drive and vitality were essential to the formation of Romanesque and Gothic art, the university, the brilliant schoolmen, Latin and vernacular literature, and the urban ambience that was to nurture so much subsequent art and literature.

To concur with Haskins that the "wide-reaching movement" of the twelfth century can be rightly called a renaissance leads inevitably to a search for the cause of this movement.[42] It was suggested earlier that the cultural outburst of the twelfth century was dependent upon improved political conditions, the spiritual renovation of the church, the rise of population, and the economic revival. But what brought about these conditions, what explains the awakening of Europe in the eleventh century and revival of intellectual and artistic activity? Not the First Crusade, which has already been cited as a manifestation rather than a cause of this revival. Nor was it the passing of the year 1000 which supposedly marked a change in the psychological mood of men in western Europe from pessimism and despair to optimism and hope. It has been a long time since historians believed that men living around the year 1000 were convinced that the world was coming to an end and that the Day of Last Judgment was imminent. It is mere legend that men looked to the famous passage in the Apocalypse of Saint John foretelling the end of the world one thousand years after Christ's death, and that they just sat and waited for the dreadful event. It is also legend that when the year 1000 passed and the world did not end, men took heart, worked industriously, and planned for the future, thus instigating the remarkable revival of western Europe in the eleventh and twelfth centuries.[43]

The awakening of Europe in the eleventh century seems to be linked with control of the Mediterranean. It is well known that the richest and most glorious chapters of Graeco-Roman culture were written around the shores of the Mediterranean. Although it extended Graeco-Roman civilization far from the Mediterranean, the Roman Empire, however vast it became, was still centered upon this body of water that held it together militarily, politically, and economically and served as a boulevard for the interchange of ideas and the transmission of culture. Here was centered the most brilliant civilization of the western world, and as long as Rome controlled the Mediterranean, Graeco-Roman culture endured. But when Rome's control began to slip and passed in the eighth century to the Arabs, who dominated the Mediterranean until the eleventh century, this culture decayed and virtually disappeared. Certainly the Germanic occupation increased the woes of the western Empire, but the crucial blow was that the men of western Europe were pushed away from the shores of the Mediterranean and were deprived of regular economic and cultural contact with the East. The center of gravity in western Europe shifted from the Mediterranean to the new empire of the Carolingians located in western and northern Europe and nourished by a primitive agrarian economy. Trade practically ceased and the towns with their middle class inhabitants began therefore to disappear. For centuries western Europe was to be feudal and seignorial, backward and poor, its only cultural activity sustained by a weakened and disorganized church. The high points of this long period were what have been called the renaissance of the Carolingians, of the Ottonians, of the Anglo-Saxons, and of the tenth century, all, as we have seen, but paltry flurries. Deprived of full contact with the Mediterranean, Europe resembled an underdeveloped region and was so viewed by the Byzantines and Moslems.

Only in the eleventh century when western Europe returned to the shores of the Mediterranean and finally wrested control of it from the Moslems did dramatic revival come. The ensuing economic revival brought trade, towns, and a bourgeoisie; it made possible the establishment of efficient government and strong states. The new towns with their new bourgeois inhabitants soon gained social, economic, legal, and political privileges. They developed a new attitude reflective of the emancipation of men from the mentality of an agrarian society, from feudalism and seignorialism. These new centers of freedom fostered the artistic, literary, and intellectual achievements of the twelfth century. Except for the remarkable monastic art and architecture that developed mostly in a rural setting, the future lay in the towns where there were con-centrated the money, talent, and sympathetic mentality. Although, as one medievalist has argued, not all prosperous urban centers erected exquisite cathedrals or became cultural centers, it is only in the towns that cathedrals are found and around which some of the greatest universities were to develop.[44] In looking at the achievements of the renaissance of the twelfth century, one invariably is led to the Italian and Flemish communes, to the Rhenish towns, to the shores of the Mediterranean with their thriv-

NOTES

1. Singling out the twelfth century as a kind of watershed in his interpretation of medieval civilization, Henri Pirenne wrote that "Since the appearance of the bourgeoisie, civilization seemed to be waking up, to be shaking itself; it was more mobile, more nervous. From the seventh to the eleventh century the movement of history was everywhere analogous. But after the eleventh century, what variety!" (*Histoire de l'Europe des invasions au XVIᵉ siècle*, Brussels, 1936, p. 180).

2. Andrew Martindale, "The Rise of the Artist: The Changing Status of the Craftsman," in *The Flowering of the Middle Ages,* ed. Joan Evans (London, 1967), pp. 310-311. See also Wilhelm Theobald, *Technik des Kunsthandwerks im zehnten Jahrhundert des Theophilus Presbyter, Diversarum Artium Schedula* (Berlin, 1933).

3. *Ibid.*, pp. 284-285, where a section of the tympanum and inscription are reproduced. For an excellent view of the complete tympanum see *The Horizon Book of Great Cathedrals* (Boston, 1968), p. 120. For the capitals in the interior see Nikolaus Pevsner, *An Outline of European Architecture,* 6th Jubilee ed. (Baltimore, 1960), Plate 81.

4. For the relevant passages in translation see pp. 32-62 of R. Willis, *The Architectural History of Canterbury Cathedral* (London, 1845); for the Latin text see William Stubbs, *The Historical Works of Gervase of Canterbury* (London, 1879), Vol. I.

5. The standard work on Villard de Honnecourt and his famous drawings is R. H. Hahnloser, *Villard de Honnecourt* (Vienna, 1935). For some reproductions of these drawings see Pevsner, *An Outline of European Architecture,* pp. 142-143; Evans, *The Flowering of the Middle Ages,* pp. 116, 309.

6. See especially Erwin Panofsky, *Abbot Suger on the Abbey Church of St.-Denis and its Treasures* (Princeton, 1946). See also Otto von Simson, *The Gothic Cathedral* (New York, 1956), pp. 61-141; Paul Frankl, *Gothic Architecture* (Harmondsworth, 1962), pp. 226 ff. For a magnificent reproduction of the cup see William D. Wixom, *Treasures from Medieval France.* The Cleveland Museum of Art (Cleveland, 1967), p. 71. On Suger's relations with the Capetian kings see Suger, *Vie de Louis le Gros,* ed. and trans. by H. Waquet (Paris, 1929); Robert Fawtier, *The Capetian Kings of France* (London, 1960).

7. Odo of Deuil, *De Profectione Ludovici VII in Orientem (The Journey of Louis VII to the East),* ed. and trans. by Virginia G. Berry (New York, 1948), p. 62: "Constantinopolis, Graecorum gloria, fama dives et rebus ditior."

8. Charles H. Haskins, *The Normans in European History* (Boston, 1915), pp. 192-249; Henri Pirenne, *Les villes du moyen âge. Essai d'histoire économique et sociale* (Brussels, 1927), pp. 71-94.

9. Pirenne, *Economic and Social History of Medieval Europe* (New York, 1937), p. 30.

10. Henry O. Taylor, *The Mediaeval Mind,* 4th ed. (London, 1925), I, 334: "So indeed one will hesitate to regard the Crusades as the *cause* of an advance in European civilization." For similar conclusions see Haskins, *The Renaissance of the Twelfth Century* (Cambridge, Mass., 1927), pp. 14-15; Pirenne, *Histoire de l'Europe,* pp. 137-143.

11. Haskins, *The Renaissance of the Twelfth Century,* pp. vii-viii.

12. The finest study of the development of the concept of "Renaissance" and of the extensive historiography devoted to the problem is W. K. Ferguson's *The Renaissance in Historical Thought, Five Centuries of Interpretation* (Cambridge, Mass., 1948). See especially pp. 8-15 of this work, as well as his essay "The Reinterpretation of the Renaissance," in *Facets of the Renaissance* (New York, 1963), pp. 1-17; T. E. Mommsen, "Petrarch's Conception of the Dark Ages," *Speculum,* XVII (1942), 226-242; Federico Chabod, *Machiavelli and the Renaissance* (Cambridge, Mass., 1958), pp. 149-200. See also pp. 201-247 of Chabod for an extensive bibliography on Italian humanism and the Renaissance.

13. Ferguson, *Renaissance,* pp. 59-67. For a good translation of Vasari see Mrs. Jonathan Foster, *Lives of the Most Eminent Painters, Sculptors and Architects* (London, 1898-1914), 5 vols.

14. Ferguson, *Renaissance,* p. 31.

15. *Ibid.*, pp. 75-77. See also G. L. Burr, "How the Middle Ages Got Their Name," *American Historical Review,* XX (1914-15), 813-815.

16. *Ibid.*, pp. 87-96. The English translation of Voltaire's *Essai sur les moeurs et l'esprit des nations, et sur les principaux faits de l'histoire, depuis Charlemagne jusqu'à Louis XIII* (Geneva, 1756) is found in his *Works* (New York, 1901).

17. *Ibid.*, p. 100.

18. Gibbon, *The History of the Decline and Fall of the Roman Empire,* ed. J. B. Bury (New York, 1914), VII, 135. See also

ing commercial centers, and to such places as Paris, Rheims, Chartres, Laon, Orléans, and Montpellier.

And what nourished these centers? It was the Mediterranean, that boulevard for the transmission of culture. Across it came the learning and artistic inspiration from the Byzantine and Moslem East. Once the West had absorbed the superior culture of the East—which occurred mostly during the twelfth century—it was ready for the spectacular progress that has since been the trademark of western Europe. However much Henri Pirenne may have under- or overstated the evidence in the formulation of his famous theory on the rôle of the Mediterranean in the history of western Europe during the Middle Ages, he was largely justified in declaring that without Mohammed, Charlemagne is inconceivable.[45] We are equally justified in saying that without the western reconquest of the Mediterranean, the renaissance of the twelfth century is inconceivable.

the recent work by Lionel Gossman, *Medievalism and the Ideologies of the Enlightenment* (Baltimore, 1968).

19. Ferguson, *Renaissance,* pp. 113-132. For the views of Ruskin see especially Vol. XI of his *Works.*

20. For the development of medieval studies in the nineteenth century see G. P. Gooch, *History and Historians in the Nineteenth Century,* rev. ed. (London, 1952). See also Bryce Lyon, "L'oeuvre de Henri Pirenne après vingt-cinq ans," *Le Moyen Age,* LXVI (1960), 437-493; Bryce and Mary Lyon, "Maurice Prou, ami de Henri Pirenne," *Le Moyen Age,* LXXI (1965), 71-107; and the essay by Bryce Lyon, "The Golden Age of the Medievalist," to appear in a *Festschrift* for Wallace K. Ferguson.

21. Michelet's views of the Middle Ages and of the Renaissance are most forcibly expressed in Vol. VII of his *Histoire de France.*

22. See especially Part III, "The Revival of Antiquity," of Burckhardt's *The Civilization of the Renaissance in Italy.*

23. Ferguson, *Renaissance,* pp. 253-289. Johan Huizinga's interpretation of the fourteenth and fifteenth centuries in northern Europe is totally different from that of Burckhardt for the same period in Italy *(The Waning of the Middle Ages,* London, 1924).

24. One should compare the conclusions of Thode with the remarks of Vasari. Both agreed that Italian artistic developments in the thirteenth century inaugurated the break between what is medieval and Renaissance.

25. The following works are typical of those which have placed the Middle Ages in proper perspective: Emile Mâle, *Religious Art in France of the Thirteenth Century* (New York, 1913); H. O. Taylor, *The Medieval Mind. A History of the Development of Thought and Emotion in the Middle Ages,* 4th ed. (London, 1925), 2 vols.; Helen Waddell, *The Wandering Scholars,* 7th ed. rev. (London, 1934); Haskins, *The Rise of Universities* (New York, 1923); Etienne Gilson, "Humanisme médiéval et Renaissance," in *Les idées et les lettres* (Paris, 1932), and *The Spirit of Medieval Philosophy* (New York, 1936); Jacques Maritain, *True Humanism* (New York, 1938); David Knowles, *The Evolution of Medieval Thought* (New York, 1962).

26. Ferguson, in *Facets of the Renaissance,* p. 12.

27. Dawson, *The Making of Europe* (London, 1932), pp. 193-194.

28. Pirenne, *Histoire de l'Europe,* p. 54.

29. Haskins, *Renaissance of the Twelfth Century,* p. 11.

30. Erwin Panofsky, "Renaissance and Renascences," *The Kenyon Review,* VI (1944), 212.

31. *Ibid.,* pp. 208-212.

32. *Ibid.,* p. 212.

33. For example, Geoffrey Barraclough, *The Origins of Modern Germany,* rev. ed. (Oxford, 1947): "Nor can any reasonable person doubt that Germany itself derived concrete benefits as well as prestige from its association with Italy in the empire. Contact with the Mediterranean world brought on the one hand a richer culture, on the other a share in a less primitive economy" (p. 69).

34. For a sympathetic view of the tenth century see Robert S. Lopez, "Still Another Renaissance?" *American Historical Review,* LVII (1951), 1-21; and the various essays grouped under the title "Symposium of the Tenth Century," *Medievalia et Humanistica,* IX (1955), 3-29.

35. Haskins, *Renaissance of the Twelfth Century,* p. 17.

36. Gilson, in *Idées et lettres,* p. 192.

37. See the comments of William A. Nitze, "The So-Called Twelfth Century Renaissance," *Speculum,* XXIII (1948), 466.

38. Urban T. Holmes, Jr., "The Idea of a Twelfth-Century Renaissance," *Speculum,* XXVI (1951), 650.

39. Eva Matthews Sanford, "The Twelfth Century — Renaissance or Proto-Renaissance?" *Speculum,* XXVI (1951), 638; Nitze, *Speculum,* XXIII (1948), 466.

40. Panofsky, "Artist, Scientist, Genius: Notes on the 'Renaissance-Dämmerung,'" in *The Renaissance* (New York, 1962), pp. 123-182.

41. Sanford, *Speculum,* XXVI (1951), 641.

42. Haskins, *Renaissance of the Twelfth Century,* p. viii.

43. The principal source for the legend of the year 1000 is Ralph Glaber. See Maurice Prou (ed.), *Raoul Glaber, Les cinq livres de ses histoires* (Paris, 1886).

44. Lopez, "Hard Times and Investment in Culture," in *The Renaissance* (New York, 1962), pp. 29-54.

45. Pirenne, *Mohammed and Charlemagne* (London, 1939), and "Mahomet et Charlemagne," *La Revue Belge de Philologie et d'Histoire,* I (1922), 77-86.

THE ARTIST AS OUTLAW AND *APPARATCHIK:* FREEDOM AND CONSTRAINT IN THE INTERPRETATION OF MEDIEVAL ART

WALTER CAHN, *Yale University*

In the preface to his *Lives of the Most Excellent Painters,* Vasari draws a vivid contrast between the working habits of artists in Medieval times and those of his own day. Moved by the troubled atmosphere in which they lived, the artists of the period following the reign of Pope Gregory the Great (590-604) were impelled "to create works of art, not according to the rules of good art, of which they were ignorant, but with each one following his own ideas." The value placed upon improvisation and the self-validation of aesthetic judgments in the crucible of the creative act is so central to the modern experience that it has become difficult for us to form a sympathetic appreciation of the idea of wilfulness as a vice in art. Since Vasari was concerned with the art of the Renaissance, when this vice had been happily eradicated, he does not demonstrate its effect in detail. Some instances of capricious and irrational behavior, however, are given in the biographies of artists whose work tended to arouse mixed emotions in the author. Commenting on Uccello's frescoes in the *chiostro verde* of S. Maria Novella, for example, he deplores that in a monochromatic scheme, the painter should have chosen to make "his fields blue, his cities red and the buildings varied, as best pleased his fancy." Giotto and Arnolfo di Cambio, though they did much that was praiseworthy, may be censured for their failure to observe the correct measurements, proportions and design of the orders: "instead of being distinctively Doric, Corinthian, Ionic or Tuscan, they were all confused and based on some anarchic and improvised rule."

Vasari's view that the Medieval artist's propensity for impulsive and unguided action could be ascribed to the chaos visited upon the dying Roman empire by the barbarian invasions may seem somewhat surprising in view of the far from peaceful conditions which prevailed in Italy as the followers of Cimabue and Giotto were boldly carrying out their revival of the arts. The Sack of Rome (1527), it might be remembered, preceded the publication of the first edition of the *Lives* by scarcely a generation. Vasari, however, was confirmed in his account by his commitment to an evolutionary theory of cultural development, and the high excellence which he discerned in the best accomplishments of his age made necessary the assumption of a historical unfolding of the process of growth from rude beginnings to progressively higher stages of development. On this point, as for much of the theoretical foundation of his work, he was dependent on critical precepts culled from the study of antique rhetoric. From the same source derives his insistence that sound artistic practice requires an understanding and an adherence to proper rules, the argument against anarchy and improvisation in art and the basic causes to which he attributed these bad traits. Cicero noted that before the study of rhetoric was introduced in Rome the inhabitants of the city spoke in an artless manner and "did not realize that there was any value in practice or that there were any rules or system" (*De Oratore*, I, 14). The hard times of primitive existence and perpetual strife were responsible for this state of affairs. Thus, Suetonius remarks that "the study of grammar was not pursued at Rome in early days, still less held in any esteem; and naturally enough, since the state was then still uncultivated and given to war, and had as yet little leisure for liberal pursuits" (*De grammaticis*, I). In the anarchy of the Dark Ages followed by the flowering of the Renaissance, the history of Rome seemed to be repeating itself.

It is now well known that critics of the Renaissance and of the Enlightenment were by no means uniformly hostile to Medieval art. Gothic buildings were capable of arousing praise for their sound construction and structural daring. By the end of the eighteenth century, too, the association of the Medieval with the primitive had lost its injurious connotation, and Gothic architecture could be appreciated, like that of archaic Greece, as a rational response to nature by early man. But such qualified approval was not extended to the pictorial arts, which continued to be belabored in terms very similar to those used by Vasari. This division of feeling is illustrated by the position of the early eighteenth-century critic Frémin, who, while sufficiently sympathetic to Medieval architecture to propose adding to the Classical orders *"l'ordre gothique,"* could speak of decorative sculpture as "a disordered heap . . . of ugly and ill-proportioned figures." More reasoned was the response of Montesquieu. For him, too, the peculiarities of form encountered in works of the Medieval period were the consequence of improvisation in the ignorance of the rules. This was borne out by the partiality shown by Medieval artists to figures in hieratic poses. Stiffness and frontality, he felt—perhaps alluding to certain examples of Romanesque sculpture— was the natural artistic response of the untutored. Indeed, the *manière gothique* was practiced not only in the European Middle Ages, but everywhere in the world where artistic activity was carried on spontaneously, without knowledge of true principles. Thus, he could say in all consistency, if somewhat incongruously to the modern ear: "The Egyptians never moved beyond the style which we call today Gothic."

Montesquieu was further concerned to account for the unchanging quality of this "Gothic" art of Egypt in comparison to the dynamism of Greek art, repeatedly affected

in the course of its evolution by profound transformations. Plato in his well-known praise of the conservation of Egyptian art had ascribed this quality to the strict observance over the millennia of the same laws. Such devotion to rule, Montesquieu felt compelled to observe, could only occur where religious authority was closely allied to the state, as was the case in Egypt, but not, to this conscientious student of law, in Greece. To the imputation of ignorance of sound principles was thus added the charge of clerical constraint. Here was thus adumbrated the notion that the entire process of artistic growth and discovery, and ultimately even an artist's own intentions might be impeded by the rigidity and obscurantist zeal of the dominant powers of society. But did autocratic conditions, which were responsible for the *gothique* of the Egyptians, also preside over the manifestation of the European variety? Montesquieu does not make such a claim. But other writers found the idea full of promise.

The eighteenth-century picture of the Middle Ages, it hardly requires saying, was inevitably more well-rounded and many-sided than the fairly hazy historical outline available to Vasari and his contemporaries. And if the brutishness and barbarity in the medieval world stood out more clearly than ever under the searching glare of rationalist criticism, the men of the Enlightenment were no longer unanimously inclined to attribute the deplorable state of the arts to sheer turbulence and anarchy. From an enlightened or Deist position, the all-persuasive presence of a church claiming for itself alone the authority to represent the will of God on earth could not be faulted for excessive spontaneity. Thus, for Condorcet, the Roman church, assisted by an army of monks, systematically kept the populace in darkness in order to oppress it with greater ease (*Esquisse d'un tableau historique du progrès de l'esprit humain*, 1794). This "utterly corrupting system" *(système si profondément corrompteur)*, as it is described by this author, might be envisaged as an ensemble of specific measures through which native energies would be effectively misdirected, or in a less narrowly mechanistic way, as an even more radical debauchery of positive impulses by a thorough-going propagation of the values of an inherently unenlightened and unscrupulous ruling group. Yet whatever the means, the results would be as described some fifty years later and in a more even-tempered way by an English author: "The artist was not permitted to follow his own fancies or to work out his own devices, but his sole function was to execute the intentions and embody the ideas and suggestions of the ecclesiologists as derived from the writings of the fathers" (E. P. Evans, *Animal Symbolism in Ecclesiastical Architecture*, 1846).

The pre-Romantic and Romantic rehabilitation of the Middle Ages entailed a profound shift of sensibilities. Yet in this process, the old critical norms were not abandoned outright but retained under new guises. The charge of wilfulness and neglect of the rules is easy to recognize in the praise of sublimity, enthusiasm and irregularity which abounds in authors won over to the cause of Medieval art. Thus, when Ruskin, with his customary vigor, writes that ". . . Rudeness or Savageness . . . is the first element of Gothic architecture," and that true Gothic (and Romanesque to a lesser extent) cannot exist without it (*The Stones of Venice*, 1853), he means not to refute the observations of classically oriented critics but only to deny that they constitute a valid basis for complaint. Similarly, when Romantic critics of Enlightenment ideals like Friedrich Schlegel and Adam Mueller exalted in the Middle Ages the social stability and organic harmony of a society under the guidance of a universal church, they implicitly endorsed the idea of Medieval culture as an emanation of Condorcet's priest-ridden "*système corrompteur*," but they viewed the dominant role assigned to the church in this system as benign and constructive rather than malignant. Bathed in the glow of faith rather than imprisoned in darkness, the Medieval artist still remained the plaything of larger forces whose totalitarian character shaped his work in an irresistible way. Although this work was now regarded with admiration instead of being held in derision, the polarity of immoderate freedom and overwhelming constraint in the critical terminology by which it was assessed remained constant.

The conceptual foundation of Viollet-le-Duc's remarkable *Dictionnaire* exhibits unmistakable vestiges of the same polarity, albeit in a bold and original transposition. For this author, the twin poles of constraint and freedom have reference to consecutive periods in Medieval history and to the particular character and outlook of clerical and lay conditions. In the early Middle Ages and well into the twelfth century when the Church constituted the major element of stability, art took refuge in the monasteries. Hence, it was stamped with a restrictive and stereotypical quality reflecting the spirit—as Viollet-le-Duc saw it—of this milieu. "Architecture thus forced in the service of a theocratic regime not only did not tolerate innovations but reproduced more or less everywhere these same forms, without making an effort to make progress." With the rise of cities and the emergence of a bourgeoisie in the Gothic period, however, a new spirit of freedom made itself felt. Subversive and scurrilous at times, the artist now turned into a social critic: "Art, in urban society, enjoyed in the midst of a still very imperfect political system a sort of freedom of the press, an outlet for minds always ready to react against the abuses of feudal society."

Viollet-le-Duc's libertarian conception of the artist in late Medieval times shared in different ways by Victor Hugo and by Ruskin, assumes its full significance only in relation to the powerful sensations aroused by the Romantic concept of freedom. By his defiance of entrenched authority, the Gothic artist not only anticipated the Romantic insistence on freedom from the restraints of convention, but also the profound identification of leading figures of the Romantic movement with revolutionary causes. He took a vital place in the unfolding of

E. GUILLAUMOT.

the idea of liberty which, at the hands of Hegel and his followers, acquired the status of an article of faith.

The process of redefinition at one pole of the critical scale was paralleled by a similar conceptual enlargement of the notion of constraint. Instead of the rather simplistic view of the artist tyrannized into ineptitude or lulled by faith into slavish imitation, there now emerged in the historiography of Medieval art a concern for the articulation of "organic laws" and ideographic principles which, if more subtle, were no less compelling in their effect on individual effort. We mean to describe here not the analysis of form and iconography aiming, if only provisionally, to establish major lines of development, but rather that tough, triumphantly deterministic stance adopted by some writers for whom the perception of a Grand Design and the demonstration of the artist's compliance with it held a special fascination. Adolphe Napoléon Didron's striking and influential view of Medieval art as a vast encyclopedia belongs to this category of thought. What moves Didron is the conviction that artistic activity in Medieval times was controlled by adherence to an underlying pattern. "Since the philosophers, who originated ideas, and the learned men, who scrutinized facts, together fixed at that time arrangement of both, artists, whose office it is to give special and peculiar form to the impulses of the age in which they live, bowed to the prevailing influences; they could not breathe the encyclopedic atmosphere without imbibing the predominant ideas and rendering them after their manner."

Didron did not complete the truly encyclopedic task, which he had set for himself, of explicating in full the contents of this atmosphere. His ambition, however, was turned into reality in Emile Mâle's *L'art religieux du XIIIe siècle*. The opening passages of this masterful work leave no doubt as to where the author stands: "The Middle Ages had a passion for order. Its sense of organization was imposed on art as on dogma, knowledge and society." Everything having thus been neatly codified, the artists had only to submit to the inexorable. As for Didron, the encyclopedic mode—personified by Vincent of Beauvais' *Speculum majus*—was for Mâle the directing principle behind artistic activity. More than a source of subject matter, more than a programmatic basis for larger ensembles, the encyclopedia was a vast communal enterprise realizing itself out of the myriad of individual decisions as by a kind of inner necessity. The Gothic cathedral was its visual embodiment, the material counterpart of the conceptual edifice erected by the doctors of the church. In the concluding chapter of his *Mont-Saint-Michel and Chartres* (1904) Henry Adams demonstrates his sympathy for the same ideas. Art and thought are cooperative and interchangeable activities, impersonally fulfilling the same

design: "The Church Intellectual and the Church Architectural, implied not one architect, but myriads, and not one fixed, intelligent architect at the end of the series, but a vanishing vista without a beginning at any definite moment." This design is intelligible and consistent. "Compared with it all modern systems are complex and chaotic, crowded with self-contradictions, anomalies, impracticable functions and outward inheritances." As regards the artist, we are far away from Viollet-le-Duc's adventurous rebels. The Virgin Herself issued all the necessary instructions. "She was the greatest artist, as she was the greatest philosopher and musician and theologian, that ever lived on earth, except her Son . . . Her taste was infallible; her sentence eternally final."

In the deterministic constructions of Didron, Mâle, and Adams, the causal agency was located in the realm of ideas. Art materialized the ideological products of the mind. For another side of this critical position, we must turn to those theories which, by analogy with methods applied to the study of animal and plant forms after the example of Linnaeus, propounded a morphological approach to the problem of artistic development. The application of evolutionary concepts to the domain of culture encouraged another kind of determinism, based on the preeminence of formal laws rather than ideas. Morphological investigation was most at home in the sphere of abstract pattern and ornament, which were either ignored or consigned to the realm of the nonsignificant by Mâle and writers of his persuasion. In the sphere of ornament, the student committed to evolutionism could find a body of typologically connected forms, uncontaminated—or so it seemed to some—by the *zeitgeist* or by less comprehensive ideologies. The important place of ornament in Medieval art, especially in its earlier phases, guaranteed a fertile field for inquiry. The systematic classification of ornamental patterns in barbarian metalwork by B. Salin and E. Holmquist, can be cited as a very obvious illustration of the value of such an approach. Again, however, our concern is not with the localized and highly functional application of this method, but with the erection of its underlying assumptions into concepts worthy of independent contemplation. A passage from Ruskin's *Stones of Venice* is an arresting sample of this kind of intellectual stance. The author comments here on an ornamental relief of the Romanesque period decorating a house in Venice, and as one may judge, finds special satisfaction not so much in the adherence of the work to right (Ruskinian) principle, but in the discovery that the very inanimate forms which compose it should exhibit an awareness of their historical duty to perform this service. "Observe," he writes, "and this is of the utmost possible importance, that the value of this type (of ornament) does not consist in the mere shutting of the ornament into a certain space, but in the acknowledgement by the ornament of the fitness of the limitation; — of its own perfect willingness to submit to it, nay a predisposition in itself to fall into an ordained form without any direct expression of the command to do so; an anticipation of the authority, and an instant and willing submission to it, in every fibre and spray, not merely *willing* but *happy* [Ruskin's italics] submission, as being pleased rather than vexed to have so beautiful a law suggested to it, and one which to follow is so justly in accordance with its own nature."

Ruskin's enthusiasm for an art imbued with a sense of respect for formal laws should evoke a knowing response in readers broadly familiar with contemporary approaches to the interpretation of Medieval art. For the preoccupation with laws has been a major trend in scholarship devoted to the subject over the past three decades, few among the eminent men of that generation having failed at one time or another to feel the challenge presented by this issue. To be sure, little agreement was achieved on the definition of these laws of form and vigorous controversy at times enlivened the debate. In spite of differences in both substance and emphasis, however, it seems very generally to have been assumed that behind the abundant variety and complexity of the outward artistic manifestation, a few fundamental principles were operative. It was an article of the same faith that this sense of orderliness and predictability characterized the earlier phases of the Middle Ages and Romanesque art first and foremost, rather than the Medieval period as a whole. Thus, if the positivism of Viollet-le-Duc and the incantatory tone of Ruskin's prose now strike us as rather quaint, we have remained committed to the historical incarnation of the antithesis of rule and license which they gave to us.

The work of Henri Focillon is richly instructive in this regard. A lecture entitled "The Fantastic in Medieval Art" delivered in 1939 by this perceptive and eloquent observer begins auspiciously enough: "Two principles are active in the art of the Middle Ages. Each corresponds to an aspect of the human spirit and to a source of human civilization." One of these principles is represented by rationality, "a system in which every element is organized according to a studied plan in order to answer the needs of varied yet related functions." The fantastic is its opposite and necessary complement. The rational or "humanistic" principle broadly encompasses the rise of a descriptive naturalism and the concomitant and increasingly thoroughgoing exploration of visual data and psychological states in Gothic art. Although Focillon sought with insistence to avoid attaching his principles to particular historical periods, the rational strain has a connotation closely akin to Viollet-le-Duc's effervescent and emancipated art of the "société des villes," as the author himself suggests. As for the fantastic element, it must not be understood as an expression of the imagination unbridled, but in Focillon's somewhat idiosyncratic definition of terms, as the coherent product of an activity following clearly definable laws. Indeed, as formulated by Focillon and through J. Baltrusaitis' more systematic *Stylistique ornementale,* the nomenclature of these laws has acquired for students of Medieval art an almost conversational familiarity: the "law of the frame" *(loi du cadre),* the rule of ornamental schematization *(règle ornementale, dialectique ornementale),* the rule of architectural definition *(règle architecturale du décor).* The fantastic principle, rooted in the experience of peoples outside the classical orbit of the Mediterranean world came to fruition during the eleventh and twelfth centuries in Romanesque art. This was the period, it will be recalled, of Viollet-le-Duc's *régime théocratique,* whose effects on art as seen by this writer were remarkably similar to those observed by Focillon. Men of times dominated by ideals of individualism and experimentation, both thought the central problem of early Medieval art to lie in its formulaic quality. In attempting to account for this quality, deplorable to one, admirable to the other, both sought refuge in an impersonal but all-powerful agency or mechanism which would ensure conformity to its larger purpose.

Through change in taste and shifting fashion in criticism, the polarity of freedom and constraint in the interpretation of Medieval art retained a powerful appeal. In great part, the persistence of this polarity was based on the relative ease with which it proved possible to convert terms of opprobrium into words of praise: licentiousness into sublimity, rote repetitiousness into a common striving for order. This shuttling forth between extremes was rooted in the radical estrangement from the Medieval past which was the common experience of admirers and detractors alike from the Renaissance onward. While the division of opinion on the merits of this past persisted, so did the underlying agreement on the assumption that it must have been an atypical and uncharacteristic phenomenon, a product of feelings and habits of mind far removed from those of the modern spectator. Yet out of the unpromising and essentially polemical judgements of classically oriented critics, a confident and well-constructed system of values emerged. Gratuitous and perhaps utopian, the picture of complex and still only dimly understood creative processes which it sometimes engendered did much to instill a greater awareness of the problematic nature of all significant achievement in art.

THE REBIRTH OF SCULPTURE IN THE ELEVENTH AND TWELFTH CENTURIES

STEPHEN K. SCHER, *Brown University*

As is evident from the arguments that continue to surround the word, "renaissance" as a historical concept is difficult to define. According to its narrowest meaning it indicates an historical period whose values were patterned upon those of classical antiquity, and especially Republican Rome, in contrast to what was looked upon as the darkness and barbarity of a period whose values were rooted elsewhere. The purposeful resurrection of all that is classical for its own sake and as a model for the production of new forms and a new pattern of life, distinguishes this renaissance, the Italian Renaissance, from any preceding period.

The intensification of medieval studies has resulted in the attempt to deny the exclusivity of the rebirth of classical studies, art, and its attendant humanism in the fifteenth century by demonstrating that such a rebirth had occurred previously: in the twelfth century, in the eleventh century, in the tenth century, and, finally, in the ninth century. If our standard of judgment were to be restricted to the revival of classical culture, we would be forced to define more carefully these renascenses as to their purpose, scope, and accomplishments, and in the field of art history, at least, this has been admirably done by the late Erwin Panofsky.[1]

Even if the definition of "renaissance" is broadened to include the general rebirth of a civilization on a broad base in all areas—economic, social, technological, political, artistic, literary, etc.—the very term implies the prior existence of a culture that provides the basic forms for growth. The structure that Graeco-Roman civilization imposed upon the Western world was virtually demolished in the fourth and fifth centuries, and no substitute was immediately created. It was the ruins of this civilization, quite literally in the case of architecture, that served as the source of a new civilization in the West. Thus any advance that was made toward the establishment of law, stabilization of society, cultivation of art and literature, development of processes of education, or the furthering of commerce after the destruction of the Roman Empire had, of necessity, to look to the antique past for inspiration and help.

What appears as the chaos and true darkness of the Early Middle Ages is illuminated fitfully by a succession of determined, but limited, pilgrimages to the ruined shrine of classical culture. In the ninth century Charlemagne and his successors looked to Early Christian and Pre-Christian Imperial Rome with an intensity reflected in the faithfulness with which classical forms were copied, this very intensity mingling with the fervor of Christian piety to produce the extraordinary works of the school of Reims. There is no doubt that a genuine appreciation of classical forms for their own sake existed during the Carolingian *renovatio,* and such a sentiment was combined with a determined attempt to re-establish the order and stability of the Roman Empire in the midst of disorder. The results, in the end, were too limited in both time and space to effect widespread or permanent change.

The accomplishments of the Carolingian artists are awesome and mark a critical stage in the development of medieval art. The immediately succeeding period represents, as Panofsky so clearly puts it, "a kind of reaction against the Carolingian *renovatio* which, by ignoring or discarding the results of a somewhat self-conscious effort at living up to 'classical' standards, liberated the inventive and expressive powers of outstanding individuals without, however, preventing a decline of culture in general." [2]

Again the basis of reference is the specific revival of classical culture, and thus, as Panofsky points out, the so-called Ottonian and Anglo-Saxon "renascenses," dating from the latter part of the tenth to the mid-eleventh century, do not entirely merit the term. If, however, the rigidity of the definition may be relaxed, both England and Germany during this period are hosts to a resurgence of activity in the arts that is of great importance, though it does not involve a determined revival of antique forms.

What, then, of the "Renaissance of the Twelfth Century?" Acknowledging that the term is generally meant to include the second half of the eleventh century as well, in our view it is not merely the rebirth of certain aspects of a prior age, but the birth, rather than rebirth, of a Western civilization. All of its elements are outlined by Professor Lyon and can be found described in greater detail not only in Haskins' famous work, from which we have borrowed the title of this exhibition, but in any number of modern histories of the Middle Ages.[3] The opening up of the Mediterranean and the more abundant contacts with the East, the consequent growth of commerce, the rise of towns and an independent middle class, the weakening of a localized feudal structure and the strengthening of centralized authority, the Crusades, the Pilgrimage Routes, the great fairs, the wealth and universal power of the Church, the free exchange among independent thinkers probing the processes of thought in an open forum, the appearance of the universities: these and many other factors are part of the vibrant and exciting picture of the late eleventh and the twelfth century.

In his sensitive review of medieval history between 1100 and 1350, Friedrich Heer has emphasized the flexibility and openness of twelfth century civilization. There is a vitality expressed in all aspects of this period that merits

the term *naissance.* In the realm of classical studies a rebirth certainly occurs, but it is part of a far larger movement that embraces all aspects of life.

The term "renaissance," however, can certainly be applied to one particular aspect of the art of the period, monumental stone sculpture. It is no exaggeration to say that sculpture on a large scale in stone ceased to exist in the West, but for sporadic examples, for some six hundred years, and it was never a very important element in the art of the Byzantine East. The reasons for this decline in the practice of an art that was of prime importance in the classical world are complex and vary from place to place. Two basic reasons may be cited, and they are mutually interdependent: a basic distrust of sculpture, especially free-standing images of men or gods, and the lack of a tradition of stone-carving.

The basis for iconoclasm, that is, for a suspicious attitude towards imagery, runs as an unbroken thread through the Middle Ages. It is seen originally in the attitude of the early Church Fathers, who warn against the seductive powers of idols and the dangers that attend the making of images as an adjunct to worship. Only paintings and sculpture that are purely narrative or symbolic and serve a didactic purpose are allowed. The freestanding figure representing a god was considered the work of the devil and embodied the worst evils of paganism.

A more comprehensive and deep-seated avoidance of representational art in the form of three-dimensional sculpture existed in northern Europe based upon an astonishingly ancient tradition of abstract and semi-abstract art. In the relatively primitive society found among the people of the Migrations the elemental forces of a harsh Nature and values rooted in the warrior's courage and physical strength resulted in an almost total avoidance of art based upon the imitation of the forms of nature and of man, particularly for the embodiment of religious concepts. Inseparably linked with this attitude are more practical considerations. Essentially nomadic, such people developed neither sophisticated forms of architecture nor sculptural monuments on a large scale. Their energies were rather directed toward the manufacture of portable objects meant to decorate their persons. As goldsmiths and enamellers they have rarely been equalled, and their initial contributions to Western Christian art are based entirely on the type of abstract, two-dimensional, richly colored linear decoration used in their metal-work.[4]

That the revival of large-scale architectural projects did not necessarily generate corresponding activity in the field of stone carving and sculptural decoration is proven by those renascences that occurred before the mid-eleventh century. These were centered, significantly enough, far from the Mediterranean sources of a sculptural tradition and though the northern revivals established very close contacts with the south, with Italy and Byzantium, and turned for inspiration to classical forms, especially in the Carolingian period, a "renaissance" of stone carving was not forthcoming. This is due, as we have said, both to a native attitude and to Carolingian sympathy for Byzantine iconoclasm.

The Carolingian church, as a northern adaptation of Early Christian basilican forms, initiates a tradition of architecture undecorated by figural or narrative sculpture. The tradition is maintained when this particular type of architecture, built in important centers of Carolingian culture, is revived by the Saxon emperors in their domains, notably along the Rhine, and is subsequently used as the basis for Anglo-Norman churches.

If we find no significant revival of sculpture in the north in conjunction with large-scale building projects, the opposite is true in the south, for it is here, haltingly and crudely, in the early years of the eleventh century that the sculptural decoration of architecture first makes its appearance. Having no direct models except for classical remains, the early stone carvers turned to other media for inspiration. In ivory carving, metal work, textiles, and manuscript illumination the sculptors sought images to translate on a large scale into stone.

The development of this sculpture parallels the intense activity that takes place in architecture during the eleventh and twelfth centuries, clothing Europe, in the famous words of Raoul Glaber, in the "white robe of the church."[5] In southern France, Spain, and northern Italy in the centuries preceding the eleventh Roman building techniques were preserved even if on a primitive level. Against this tradition, which maintained basic methods of vaulting and masonry construction, one must see the more artificial and self-conscious revival of Early Christian architecture in the imperial churches of the Carolingian rulers and their Ottonian followers. Built on a large scale, timber-roofed, and with complicated plans and massing of spatial units, these large basilicas establish an independent line of development in the north and also serve as an important source of ideas for the south.

Because of the lack of involvement in sculptural decoration the developments in the north, in Rhenish and Anglo-Norman architecture, do not concern us here. The rebirth of sculpture in conjunction with increased building activity and more ambitious architectural programs occurs in central and southern France and in Spain. In fact, Romanesque is an art of these regions, traversed by the pilgrimage routes and bound together by a network of monastic houses. The entire area functions as a watershed for the variety of traditions that are fused to create Romanesque art: classical, Byzantine, Islamic, Carol-

ingian, Ottonian, Celtic, and Migration art, to name a few of the more important.

The once modest architecture of the area is transformed by combining its own structural techniques with the plan and scale of imperial architecture, both Carolingian and German. The result is the vaulting of large spaces and the massing of complicated plans. This appears to have occurred first in Burgundy, birthplace of the Cluniac order and a crossroads for impulses from north and south. In churches such as Saint-Philibert at Tournus (ca. 960-1120), Saint-Benigne at Dijon (1001-1018), and, above all, the second church at Cluny (ca. 955-1000) the basic experiments in large-scale architecture with vaulted spaces was carried out, Cluny II especially establishing what would become the basic Romanesque type.

Sculptural decoration on such structures was still extremely sparse. It was conceived as an application to the surface rather than as an integral part of the structure. Frieze-like reliefs carved in very shallow, successive planes, or forms indicated merely by incision are found on a variety of churches in western and southwestern France at the end of the tenth and beginning of the eleventh centuries. At Usson, Saint-Mesme-de-Chinon, Saint-Genest at Lavardin, at Saint-Benoit-sur-Loire and Selles-sur-Cher, La-Charité-sur-Loire, Vaison, Carpentras, Marcilhac, and Carennac, to name only a few, crude reliefs showing a variety of subjects decorate the walls of churches.

As a key structural element the capital is embellished with abstract ornament, animal forms, and some narrative scenes. The capitals of such monuments as Saint-Benigne at Dijon, Saint-Aignan at Orléans, Saint-Germain-d'Auxerre, and Saint-Germain-des-Prés in Paris are again only a few examples of the early stages of sculptural development as it makes its appearance in the eleventh century.

The lintel at Saint-Genis-des-Fontaines (1020-1021) and its companion at Saint-André-de-Sorède provide us with early examples of the decoration of the church portal, the area that, above all others, is the repository of the most important and most elaborate programs of sculpture.

In the eleventh century, then, techniques of sculpture production are revived. However, it is not before the end of the eleventh century that the sculptors achieve a mastery of their craft that not only releases them from dependence upon the "precious" arts, but also makes them able to cope fully with a problem that is an essential feature of Romanesque sculpture, its successful integration into an architectural scheme.

For a variety of reasons, but primarily for durability, the vaulting of the church building was considered a necessity in central and southern France and Spain. What we have called the imperial tradition, represented by Carolingian, Rhenish, and Anglo-Norman architecture and based upon Early Christian models, maintained the covering of large interior spaces with a timber roof until the last years of the eleventh and first decades of the twelfth century. In the south, the type of covering used for the central space of the nave was the barrel vault, the lower and narrower spaces of the aisles generally being covered by groin vaults. The barrel vault, often relieved by transverse arches, is a continuous and heavy unit running the entire length of the church and requiring continuous support. Its effect upon the architecture and sculpture is described in greater detail in the body of this catalogue. To summarize here, the nature of the vault, exerting heavy pressure along its entire length, required the assertion of the wall as an unbroken supporting member. No matter how much of the wall was relieved in the form of arcades and window openings, the fundamental concept of two parallel, planar masses sustaining the solid, semi-circular tunnel of the vault forms the basis of Romanesque architecture and has a profound effect upon sculpture.

Disturbance of this principle of the wall was unthinkable in those areas where vaulting was employed. The sculptural embellishment of vaulted architecture was thus severely restricted to areas where it would find a logical, and indeed integral, place in the structural system. We have already pointed out that capitals and the elements of a portal—the tympanum, archivolts, lintel, and jambs —were the primary areas of sculptural decoration. There are almost no other areas commonly chosen for such decoration except for corbels and window mouldings. In some of the churches of western France—Poitou and Angoumois—the sculpture invades other areas of the façade, but it is contained within blind arcades and composed in relation to what is still the front plane of the wall.

This insistence upon the plane of the wall and the importance of maintaining the shape of a structural member such as a capital gives Romanesque sculpture its basic character, distinct from all other styles. Romanesque sculpture emphasizes certain types of iconography more than others; it may indulge in a world of fantasy that has been evoked by few other periods in the history of art, but its most distinctive and most important characteristic is its peculiar formal life within a restrictive architectural environment. If the variety, invention, and vitality, the indescribable energy of Romanesque sculpture, is somehow symbolic of the same characteristics found in twelfth century civilization as a whole, this is due to its adaptation to architecture. Whether it be the truncated pyramid of a capital, the right angle triangle of a corbel, or the perpendicular wall planes of the portal, the sculpture, as rich and varied as its forms may be, is forced to obey the laws of the structural mass. The resulting compres-

sion and restraint resembles a collected horse in dressage; the energy returns upon itself and becomes totally contained within the limits of the basic form. This explains the choice of heraldic types of animal ornament drawn from an ancient heritage, the convolutions of foliage, the contortions and distortions practiced upon the human form, the simplification of the participants in narrative at the same time that their actions and expressions are intensified. It is this frenzy of form that is the essence of Romanesque sculpture, and, to join the legions of medievalists who have quoted his famous lines before, this is what strikes the sensitive eye and critical mind of Saint Bernard:[6] "But in the cloister, under the eyes of the Brethren who read there, what profit is there in those ridiculous monsters, in that marvellous and deformed comeliness, the comely deformity? To what purpose are those unclean apes, those fierce lions, those monstrous centaurs, those half-men, those striped tigers, those fighting knights, those hunters winding their horns? Many bodies are there seen under one head, or again, many heads to a single body. Here is a four-footed beast with a serpent's tail; there, a fish with a beast's head. Here again the forepart of a horse trails half a goat behind it, or a horned beast bears the hinder quarters of a horse. In short, so many and so marvellous are the varieties of divers shapes on every hand, that we are more tempted to read in the marble than in our books, and to spend the whole day in wondering at these things rather than in meditating the law of God. For God's sake, if men are not ashamed of these follies, why at least do they not shrink from the expense?" That the subjects described so well by Saint Bernard were common in Romanesque sculpture is demonstrated by the representation of so many of them in the present exhibition.

We have described the rebirth of sculpture and its architectural host as occurring in the earlier part of the eleventh century. The climax in both architecture and sculpture is reached in the last two decades of that century and the first two of the following. One need only name the monuments that lead the way and cite their dates to realize that the most significant achievements occurred around 1100: Santiago de Compostela, ca. 1075-1125; Saint-Sernin at Toulouse, ca. 1077-1100; the third church at Cluny, 1088-1115; La Madeleine at Vezelay, ca. 1096-1140; Saint-Étienne at Nevers, ca. 1083-1097. This represents only a partial list and points primarily to architectural leadership. The same activity was occurring at the same time in the north in architecture with the great Anglo-Norman churches, precocious and prophetic, reflecting the extraordinary character of the people who built them: Jumièges, 1037-1066; Caen, Sainte-Trinité, ca. 1062-1115 (vaulting?); Caen, Saint-Étienne, ca. 1068-

1115 (vaulting?) ; Durham, ca. 1093-1099; Ely, ca. 1090; and a host of great English cathedrals. Along the Rhine and in Lombardy significant developments also occur.

During the first half of the twelfth century these accomplishments are developed further into a mature Romanesque architecture and sculpture that spreads throughout central and southern France and Spain. Most of the sculpture in the exhibition is drawn from this period and from these areas.

In our consideration of the terms "birth" and "rebirth" we have described the eleventh and twelfth centuries as the era when a distinctly Western civilization is born and when sculpture in stone is reborn. Yet another off-spring of this fecund age remains to be noticed, and it represents perhaps the most startling and phenomenal birth of all. "One may say that the twelfth century was the great age of the Gothic experiments, just as the eleventh had been that of the Romanesque experiments."[7] It might be added that whereas southern France had fused the elements comprising Romanesque, northern France, but particularly the Île-de-France, drawing upon the accomplishments in sculpture and architecture of both north and south, became the location of a remarkable convergence of events and personalities to produce what we now call Gothic art and architecture.

The complex background of this occurrence and its initial development is described in part in the catalogue section containing the Early Gothic sculpture, but is best expounded in Otto von Simson's masterful study *The Gothic Cathedral.*[8] The grandeur of imperial architecture and the heirs to this tradition in Anglo-Norman architecture combined with the equal size and the particular articulation of southern Romanesque (both having developed sophisticated vault and support systems) to provide the architectural basis for a new style that appears in the Royal Domain of France after the third decade of the twelfth century. The entire system of this architecture is based upon the imaginative combination of elements that had already been tested and applied elsewhere: the scale, wall articulation, façade, and rib vault in Normandy and England; the pointed arch, wall articulation, scale, and façade arrangement in Burgundian and southern architecture. The two key elements are, of course, the rib vault and the pointed arch. An elaborate exposition of this system is unnecessary here. It is only important to realize that a basic change in the architecture predicated a corresponding change in sculpture.

If Romanesque architecture is based upon the principle of a supporting wall, Gothic effectively eliminated this wall. The replacement of a continuous barrel vault by a light and flexible rib vault whose reduced pressures are directed to four points of support and, eventually, to thin, arched supports located on the exterior made the continuous wall and the planar principles it fostered superfluous. The plane of wall is replaced by the bundles of piers and colonnettes whose surfaces adhere to no rigid assertion of surface. They act as the logical conclusion of the lines of force generated from the vault and also as the frame for a wall that is not a wall, but a transparent membrane of stained glass windows between the attenuated cylindrical solids, forming a seemingly immaterial plane—the very antithesis of a bearing wall.

As part of the repeated series of supports and in relation to the immense scale of a Gothic cathedral interior the application of figural sculpture seems irrelevant, and the historiated capital, so rich a source of Romanesque sculpture, is replaced by foliate decoration that seems to harmonize perfectly with the severe beauty of the structure. It is the exterior of the cathedral that becomes the recipient of elaborate sculptural programs, located almost exclusively in the portals.

Space and the limitations of a catalogue introduction forbid a detailed description of the expansion in program and iconography of Gothic portal sculpture in contrast to that of Romanesque.[9] The change in form, however, is one that is important to understand as a basis for viewing the sculpture assembled in the exhibition. The series of early Gothic heads represents a type of sculpture—the statue column—that embodies the formal changes made possible to sculpture as a result of the revolutionary changes in architecture.

The new architectural system involved the resolution by means of the vertical colonnettes and piers, of the lines of force generated from the ribs. The same system is mirrored in the Gothic portal and remains practically unchanged throughout the development of portal sculpture. Above the continuous frieze of a base and resting upon their own independent supports the statue columns or jamb statues anticipate the vertical lines on the interior. Behind and between the statues a row of colonnettes emphasizes this vertical direction. Capitals or canopies indicate the boundaries of this zone, and the latter define the spatial limits of movement allowed to the jamb statues. Finally, the vault is represented by the recession of the upper level, which is defined by the series of archivolts that reflect the form of the ribs on the interior.

To this extent the architectural control of sculpture remains unchanged and exerts its demands with an intensity equal to that of Romanesque. Beyond this point, however, the entire environment changes. The reduction of the wall to a transparent, structurally inoperative screen provides the possibility of the penetration of surface and mass on both interior and exterior. The clear organization of solid geometrical forms defined by continuous wall surfaces soberly articulated by applied decoration or lightened by the severe cutting away of window openings as found in Romanesque architecture is replaced in Gothic by an exterior that provides no plane surfaces, that allows space to penetrate and flow through the structural forms at all levels. The piercing of the structure is eventually developed to such an extent that one cannot apply the term "surface" to the exterior, which appears as an architectural skeleton. And when one finally discerns the fundamental forms of the building, they are defined not by wall surfaces, but by the external skin of the fragile glass.

As a result of the deterioration of solid mass, the portal is no longer bound by the strict planes of a wall. In imitation of the diagonal composition of a compound pier, the jambs are splayed inward diagonally, and the depth of the portal is increased. An independent pocket of space is thus created within which the sculpture may be placed. Needless to say, this new space is exploited by the sculptor. Jamb figures are no longer treated as forms in relief but assume the dimensions and physical properties of a three-dimensional body.[10] Thus begins a limited exploration of physical realism that does not move beyond the boundaries of the architectural system and is controlled as well by the concept of the type of being represented in the portals.

The first steps are taken at Saint-Denis and Chartres and progress logically from there. This progression is admirably illustrated in the exhibition by the series of heads dating from ca. 1140 to 1230 and representing practically the full span of development in the jamb figure. The portals continue to deepen; the statues lose their rigidity and become less distorted in proportion. They begin to turn and move on their central axis, and eventually they communicate with one another in the bare elements of a narrative scene. Observation of materials, textures, and realistic details increases at the same time that the decorative possibilities of graceful, independent movement are explored.

Such innovations, however, take us beyond the twelfth century and the limits of this exhibition. It has been our purpose both in the catalogue and in the exhibition, to re-emphasize and clarify the amazing qualities of that century and the half-century or so that preceded it. A century that at one and the same time could encompass the climax of Romanesque and the genesis of Gothic deserves not only our attention, but our homage.

NOTES

1. *Renaissance and Renascences in Western Art,* Stockholm, 1960.

2. *ibid.,* pg. 53.

3. Prof. Lyon's notes are helpful in this respect. cf. also the very clear survey of Renaissance studies by William Bouwsma, *The Interpretation of Renaissance Humanism,* American Historical Association, Washington, D.C., Publication no. 18, 1966. A particularly valuable survey of the development of thought in the eleventh and twelfth centuries is found in David Knowles, *The Evolution of Medieval Thought,* London, 1962, part 2.

4. Henri Focillon (*Art of the West in the Middle Ages,* Phaidon Publishers, Greenwich, Conn., and London, 1963, vol. I, *Romanesque Art,* pp. 19-20) describes the art of non-classical, northern peoples very succinctly: "An encyphered conception of the universe, rejecting the human figure as inessential or repugnant, replaces a plastic vision which had been entirely dominated by man and which had based itself on the realism and actuality of its images." This non-humanistic approach to imagery at this time predicates, of course, a total disinterest in monumental sculpture.

5. The full passage is: "Therefore, after the above-mentioned year of the millennium which is now about three years past, there occurred, throughout the world, especially in Italy and Gaul, a rebuilding of church basilicas. Notwithstanding the greater number were already well-established and not in the least in need, nevertheless each Christian people strove against the others to erect nobler ones. It was as if the whole earth, having cast off the old by shaking itself, were clothing itself everywhere in the white robe of the church. Then, at last, all the faithful altered completely most of the episcopal seats for the better, and likewise, the monasteries of the various saints as well as the lesser places of prayer in the towns . . ." cf. Elizabeth Holt, *A Documentary History of Art,* vol. I, *The Middle Ages and the Renaissance,* Doubleday Anchor Book, A 114a, Garden City, N. Y., 1957, pg. 18.

6. *ibid,* pg. 21.

7. Focillon, *op. cit.,* vol. II, *Gothic Art,* pg. 3.

8. Otto von Simson, *The Gothic Cathedral,* The Bollingen Foundation, New York, 1956.

9. In addition to von Simson, *ibid.,* cf. Adolf Katzenellenbogen, *The Sculptural Programs of Chartres Cathedral; Christ, Mary, Ecclesia,* The Johns Hopkins Press, Baltimore, 1959; and Emile Mâle, *L'Art Religieux du XIIe Siècle en France,* Paris, 1924; *idem., L'Art Religieux du XIIIe Siècle en France,* Paris, 1910 (translated and in paperback as *The Gothic Image,* Harper Torchbooks, TB344, New York, 1958.)

10. On this point cf. the lucid discussion and diagram in Panofsky, *op. cit.,* pp. 60-62.

FRANCE

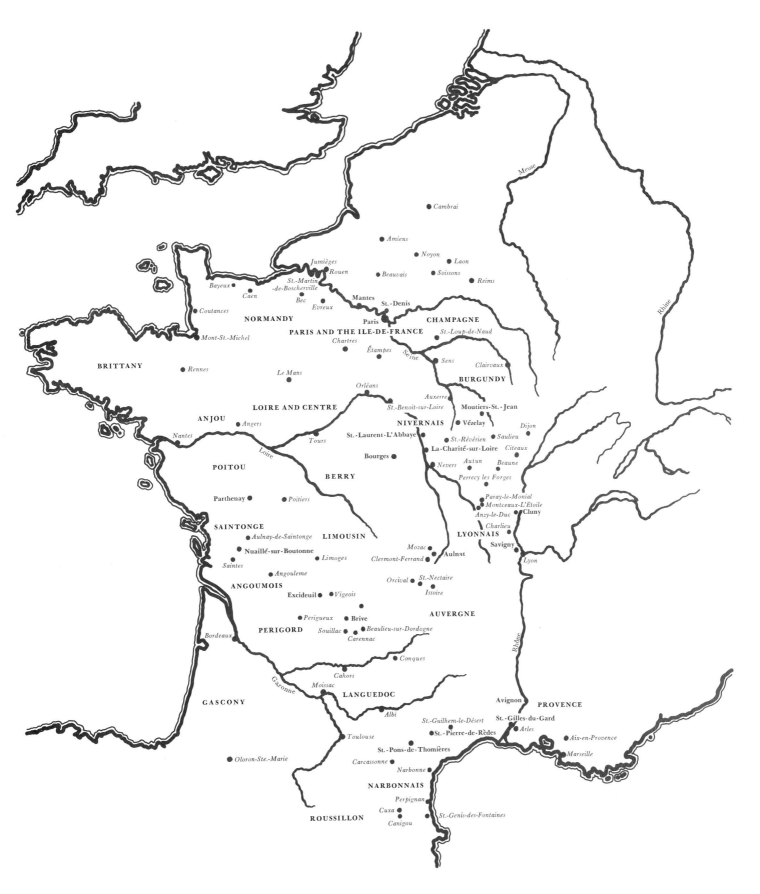

Meuse

Rhine

Cambrai

Amiens

Noyon

Laon

Jumièges

Rouen

Beauvais

Soissons

Reims

St.-Martin
-de-Boscherville

Bayeux

Caen

Bec

Evreux

Mantes

St.-Denis

Coutances

NORMANDY

Paris

CHAMPAGNE

PARIS AND THE ILE-DE-FRANCE

St.-Loup-de-Naud

Mont-St.-Michel

Chartres

Étampes

Seine

Sens

Clairvaux

BRITTANY

Rennes

Le Mans

Orléans

BURGUNDY

Auxerre

Moutiers-St.-Jean

LOIRE AND CENTRE

St.-Benoit-sur-Loire

Dijon

ANJOU

Angers

NIVERNAIS

Vézelay

Nantes

Loire

Tours

St.-Laurent-L'Abbaye

St.-Révérien

Saulieu

La-Charité-sur-Loire

Citeaux

POITOU

Bourges

BERRY

Nevers

Autun

Beaune

Perrecy les Forges

Parthenay

Poitiers

Paray-le-Monial

Montceaux-L'Étoile

Anzy-le-Duc

Cluny

SAINTONGE

LIMOUSIN

Charlieu

Aulnay-de-Saintonge

Mozac

LYONNAIS

Nuaillé-sur-Boutonne

Limoges

Clermont-Ferrand

Aulnat

Savigny

Saintes

Orcival

St.-Nectaire

Lyon

Angouleme

ANGOUMOIS

Excideuil

Vigeois

Issoire

AUVERGNE

Perigueux

Brive

Souillac

Beaulieu-sur-Dordogne

PERIGORD

Carennac

Bordeaux

Conques

Cahors

Garonne

Moissac

LANGUEDOC

Avignon

PROVENCE

GASCONY

Albi

St.-Guilhem-le-Désert

St.-Gilles-du-Gard

St.-Pierre-de-Rèdes

Arles

Aix-en-Provence

Toulouse

Marseille

Oloron-Ste.-Marie

St.-Pons-de-Thomières

Rhône

Carcassonne

Narbonne

NARBONNAIS

Perpignan

Cuxa

St.-Genis-des-Fontaines

ROUSSILLON

Canigou

Naranco
Oviedo
ASTURIAS
Lebeña (Liebana)
NAVARRE
Roncesvalles
Pamplona
Santiago
de Compostela
León
Leyre
Seo de Urgel
S. Pere de Roda
GALICIA
S. Miguel de la Escalada
S. Juan
de la Peña
ARAGON
Ripoll
Sahagun
Burgos
LEÓN
Palencia
Zaragoza
CATALONIA
Sta. Marta de Tera
Silos
R. Ebro
Zamora
Poblet
Barcelona
R. Douro
Salamanca
CASTILLE
Tarragona
Avila
Madrid
Toledo
R. Tagus
Valencia
Lisbon
R. Guadiana
R. Guadalquivir
Seville
Granada

BURGUNDY AND NIVERNAIS

1. Cluny. (Saône-et-Loire).

Third Abbey Church of Saint Peter and
Saint Paul, 1088-1130.

Saint Peter, from the north spandrel
of the west portal. 1106-1112.

Limestone, with traces of gesso and paint. h., 28½″

Museum of Art, Rhode Island School of Design. 20.254.

ex coll.: Thiebault-Sisson, Paris;
Durlacher Brothers, New York.

Besides a portion of an eagle in the Louvre (Inv. R. F. 2026) and possibly a small head in the collection of Mrs. Ernest Brummer (New York), the figure of Saint Peter is the only fragment of sculpture from the great third abbey church at Cluny that exists outside of those remains gathered in the Musée Ochier, Cluny. It is, as well, the finest piece of sculpture remaining from the west portal, which was blown up by gunpowder, along with the façade, in 1810 and totally destroyed. Such sculpture from this area that does exist was recovered between 1928 and 1936 during the course of the now famous excavations directed by Kenneth Conant with the help of Miss Helen Kleinschmidt and under the sponsorship of the Medieval Academy of America. Prior to this date the only fragments from the west façade that apparently had not passed *sous terre* were the Providence Saint Peter and the Louvre eagle.[1]

The Saint Peter was acquired by the Museum in 1920 from a New York dealer; it had previously belonged to M. Thiebault-Sisson of Paris. He had purchased the piece around 1905 from a dealer who had acquired it from yet another dealer whose memory failed him when questioned by M. Thiebault-Sisson regarding his source for the statue.

In 1920 the Museum had no idea of the precise provenance, and therefore of the extreme importance, of the

1a

Saint Peter. Indeed, since there was almost nothing precisely like it in contemporary Burgundian sculpture, its authenticity was questioned. A stylistic ambient was revealed, however, as a result of the Conant excavations at Cluny. Fragments from the lintel, archivolts, and tympanum of the west façade now in the Musée Ochier, Cluny, were unearthed which duplicated so closely the style of the Saint Peter that serious doubts as to the authenticity and original location of the piece were almost completely eliminated. The stylistic and historical evidence supporting this conclusion was presented by Helen Kleinschmidt in 1947.[2] The exact correspondence of the

details of facial structure, style of hair and beard, proportions, and drapery between a piece known at least as early as 1905 and fragments not excavated until 1928 to 1936 were described and illustrated convincingly by Miss Kleinschmidt.

Further knowledge of the original appearance of the west portal of Cluny III and the location of the Saint Peter is provided by old views and descriptions. A Dr. Dumoulin, who was physician to the monks of Cluny in the middle of the eighteenth century, described the portal in a manuscript which was later (1792) copied by a local antiquarian, Philibert Bouché.[3] Bouché's unpublished manuscript (Paris, Bib. Nat., Ms. nouv. acq. fr. 4336) also contains later notes in which he describes the destruction of the church.[4] Among the elements belonging to the great portal, Bouché mentions that in the spandrels were placed four statues, each around 4½ feet high ("Sur le cadre qui règne entre la plate-bande et la grande cintre du portail on voit de chaque coté deux statues en relief hautes d'environ 4 pieds ½").

The most reliable visual source for the original appearance of the great portal at Cluny, an engraving by Le Maître after a lost drawing by Garneray in N.-X. Willemin's *Monuments français inédits* (1839), confirms this description in a frustratingly vague fashion. Nonetheless, on the basis of the description, the Le Maître engraving, the stylistic agreements, and the correspondence in size and position, the statue in Providence can be located originally as the innermost figure of the north spandrel of the west portal (fig. 1a). Concerning the position of the Saint Peter, the figure projected from the wall at an angle as seen by the break along the left side in back and from the fact that the lines of drapery folds continue around the right side and onto the back, which at this point was free from the wall. The statue thus faced to its left and, as indicated by the engraving, must have been seated.

The fact that one of the figures was Saint Peter has led to the assumption that the other three spandrel statues were also apostles. Iconographically such a group would not be out of place in relation to the scene in the tympanum, a *Maiestas Domini*. The fact that the church at Cluny was dedicated to Saint Peter and Saint Paul is yet another reason why one might expect figures of these two apostles to be given positions of prominence.

In addition to the four apostles and the tympanum the great portal was composed of a lintel that contained, according to Conant and J. Talobre,[5] a figure of the Virgin in the center flanked by statues of the apostles looking up toward the great Christ (around nine feet high) of the tympanum. At either end of the lintel were scenes related to the central vision of the *Maiestas Domini*, so popular in Romanesque sculpture and so frequently seen composed in this way in Burgundian portals: at the north end of the lintel the Three Maries at the Tomb, and at the south end the Harrowing of Hell.

The columns flanking the portal were decorated with abstract designs, but apparently carried no figures. Of the five archivolts, one contained angels rising to a keystone figure of God the Father, and another was carved with roundels enclosing heads in profile and representing, perhaps, the Twenty-Four elders of the Apocalyptic Vision.

One question that still arises and that involves both the condition and the iconography of the Providence statue is the match between the head and the body. When the Saint Peter entered the Museum in 1920, the separation between head and body was filled and smoothed over, and the nose was restored. In 1949 these restorations were removed by Mr. James Rorimer at The Metropolitan Museum of Art, New York. It was seen then that although a restorer had corrected the areas in front to provide a smoother joint, large areas in back, especially on the left side, were missing. In addition, the head, which is mounted to the body by means of an iron dowel, at one time had been split in two and re-joined along a line running from the right rear across the lower part of the left side and including the left lower jaw with portions of the beard.

The re-setting of the head seems to give it an awkward, hunched appearance with an unlikely angle of projection from the shoulders. When imagined in its original context, however, and when looked at now from an angle approximating that context, that is, in a position some forty-five feet above the observer, the more disturbing aspects of the Saint Peter disappear. There is no question that the present joint between the head and the shoulders is not a true one, but there is also very little reason to doubt that the two were always together.

An additional factor cited as a basis for considering the two pieces separately is the supposed lack of traditionally Petrine characteristics in the head: a round face with full, curly hair and beard. That the body was from a figure of Saint Peter is obvious from the keys, but the thin face and straight beard are not those usually associated with the chief apostle. Nonetheless, this final objection can be eliminated by referring to the statue of Saint Peter on the right jamb of the central portal at Vézelay whose face is very similar in type to the same apostle from Cluny. Indeed, in context, that is, opposite the face of Saint Paul, who has just as strong a tradition of a specific facial type, the Vézelay Saint Peter manifests those characteristics associated with the saint.

While discussing condition, mention might be made here of the traces of color that can be seen on the statue —red on the lips, black on the beard, and a light ochre on the face. In her 1947 article Miss Kleinschmidt had con-sidered the colors to be a later addition. In an unpublished report written in 1936 she described in great detail the kinds of paint found on the pieces excavated in front of the site of the West portal. According to Miss Kleinschmidt and Dr. Conant (letter of May 1, 1967) the façade sculpture was repainted and white-washed several times, but especially in the fifteenth and eighteenth centuries, and both have felt for many years that the traces of color on the Providence Saint Peter are not original. On the other hand, a recent examination of the head by the Conversation Department at the Fogg Art Museum has led to some tentative expressions of a contrary opinion.

The enormous importance of the succession of churches at Cluny can never be over-exaggerated. The influence exerted by the third church in sculpture and architecture locally in Burgundy, more extensively in France, and further afield in other countries, is measured by the constant re-occurrence of motifs in sculpture and structural details in architecture that can be traced back to the colossal structure at Cluny (length, narthex portal to axial chapel wall, 587'; height, plinth to choir vault, 100').

Begun in 1088, or perhaps shortly before, under the brilliant leadership of Abbot Hugh of Semur (1024-1109), the construction of the church progressed rapidly, due, no doubt, to the generous support of King Alfonso VI of Spain and to the existence at Cluny of an experienced *chantier*. By October of 1095 five altars in the chevet had been dedicated, and by March of 1100 construction of the double transept had been completed. The west façade was built between 1106 and 1115 under the abbacy of Pons de Melgueil (d. 1125/26), and the main body of the church was dedicated on October 25, 1130.

As the result of Dr. Conant's studies and, more recently (1966), a colloquium held at Cluny by the Société Française d'Archéologie, a more precise dating of the western portal has been established. In a letter dated October 3, 1967, Dr. Conant reported that the plan of the portal was "settled about 1106, construction of the plinth, and perhaps some of the carvings prepared by 1109, completion of the portal by ca. 1112."

Although, as Dr. Conant points out in another letter (March 3, 1968), there is solid agreement on the dates of the west portal, much controversy still exists regarding the dating of the other major group of sculpture from Cluny III, the imposing capitals of the sanctuary. Disagreement over this dating, which one camp, including Dr. Conant, believes to be ca. 1092, in opposition to others who put them much later (ca. 1120), further involves the chronology of the other major Burgundian churches, Vézelay and Autun.

Combining a knowledge of the chronology of the church with stylistic evidence, a logical solution suggests itself. The eight major capitals of the sanctuary, preserved when the church was demolished, were carved under the influence of a master whose style was distinctly different from that of the master who controlled the production of the west portal decoration. Yet this second master was a member of the earlier group as can be seen in two half capitals also from the sanctuary, that are closely related in style to the portal sculptures.

According to the chronology of the construction, the sanctuary capitals were probably carved between ca. 1095 and 1100. The master responsible for the half-capitals then took over the direction of the west portal, completing the work there around 1112.

We have already mentioned the relationship between the Saint Peter figures from Cluny and Vézelay. Francis Salet in his monograph on the latter church[6] describes in some detail the specific parallels in style that exist between the two churches. Although we cannot here enter into an elaborate resumé of this material, suffice it to say that the evidence suggests that sculptors from Cluny moved to Vézelay, including, perhaps, the master of the great portal and the author of the Providence Saint Peter. Salet would date this move to around 1120-1125, but would also date the apostle figures in the jambs at Vézelay later than the major campaign of façade sculpture, putting them in the years from ca. 1130-1140. The present controversy exposed at the Cluny colloquium centers upon a re-evaluation of the chronology of Vézelay as a result of the decision regarding the dating of the two extant groups of sculpture

from Cluny. One result was the proposal of a new date of ca. 1114 for the Vézelay portals which is opposed to Salet's chronology.

The painstaking examination of the central tympanum at Vézelay in a recent article by Christian Beutler throws new light upon this question, carrying Salet's proposals one step further.[7] Beutler, in fact, has exposed more clearly the fact that the central tympanum underwent a major change in its iconographic program from a representation of the Pentecost to a more elaborate and larger description of the Mission to the Apostles (Matthew XXVIII, 18-19, and Mark, XVI, 15, 19) in conjunction with two additional, smaller flanking portals. According to Beutler, the elements of the first project were completed at the end of the 1130s.[8] The expanded composition he then dates in the mid-40s, revising Katzenellenbogen's view that the tympanum at Vézelay was a reference to the First Crusade of 1095/96.[9] Beutler feels, rather, that although Katzenellenbogen's explanation of the iconography is correct, the evidence points strongly to the fact that the central tympanum refers directly to the Second Crusade preached by Saint Bernard at Vézelay in 1146.

The point to be emphasized here is that the decoration of Cluny III, as represented in this exhibition by the statue of Saint Peter, was a source of style for the succeeding key monuments of Burgundian art: Vézelay, and, in a different manner, Autun (ca. 1130), Saulieu (ca. 1135), and an entire series of churches in this region.

NOTES

1. cf. Marcel Aubert and Michèle Beaulieu, *Description Raisonnée des Sculptures du Moyen Age*, Musée National du Louvre. Paris, 1950, art. 24, pp. 36-37.

2. *Studies*. The Museum of Art, Rhode Island School of Design, Providence, 1947, pp. 19-31.

3. *ibid.*, p. 28.

4. cf. Walter Cahn, "Romanesque Sculpture in American Collections: II. Providence and Worcester," *Gesta*, vol. VII, 1968, pg. 52.

5. "La reconstitution du portail de l'église abbatiale de Cluny," *Bulletin Monumental*, 1944, pp. 225-240.

6. *La Madeleine de Vézelay*, Melun, 1948, pp. 162-166.

7. Christian Beutler, "Das Tympanon zu Vézelay. Programm, Planwechsel und Datierung," *Wallraf-Richartz Jahrbuch*, vol. XXIX, 1967, pp. 7-30.

8. *ibid.*, pg. 29, n. 19.

9. *ibid.*, pg. 25, and Adolf Katzenellenbogen, "The Central Tympanum at Vézelay, Its Encyclopedic Meaning and Its Relation to the First Crusade," *The Art Bulletin*, vol. XXVI, September, 1944, pp. 141 ff.

BIBLIOGRAPHY

R. van Marle, "Twelfth Century Sculpture in America," *Art in America*, December, 1921, pp. 3-16.

L. Earle Rowe, "A Piece of Romanesque Sculpture," *Bulletin of the Rhode Island School of Design*, July, 1926, pp. 30-32.

J. Talobre, "La reconstitution du portail de l'église abbatiale de Cluny," *Bulletin Monumental*, 1944, pp. 225-240.

Helen Kleinschmidt, "The Cluny St. Peter," *Studies*. Museum of Art, Rhode Island School of Design. 1947, pp. 17-31.

Joan Evans, *Cluniac Art of the Romanesque Period*, Cambridge University Press, 1950, pg. 24.

William Wixom, *Treasures from Medieval France*, The Cleveland Museum of Art, 1967, pp. 61, 351-352.

Walter Cahn, "Romanesque Sculpture in American Collections. II. Providence and Worcester," *Gesta*, vol. VII, 1968, pp. 51-53.

The files of the Museum on the Saint Peter also contain much valuable material among which are an unpublished and undated paper on the relation of the head to the body by Margaret Williams, the unpublished report, dated 1936, by Miss Kleinschmidt on the color found on the sculpture excavated between 1928 and 1936, and a series of very helpful letters from Dr. Kenneth J. Conant, whose definitive study of Cluny is in press.

2. **Vézelay** (Yonne).

Sainte-Marie-Madeleine. ca. 1115/1120-1155.

Engaged capital from the narthex.

Animal, bird, and rinceaux, ca. 1150.

Limestone. h., 9.5″; top dimensions, 9.8″ x 7.4″

The Art Museum, Princeton University. 49-117.

ex coll.: Joseph Brummer.

The genealogy of this particular style of Romanesque sculpture is long and complicated. The style originates at Cluny, intermingles with that of other regions and establishes blood lines that pass on directly to the earliest sculpture of the Gothic cathedrals, notably Saint-Denis and Chartres.

It is surprising and, from the point of view of the French, rather dismaying how many of the great Romanesque and Early Gothic churches are represented in American collections. The present exhibition contains examples of sculpture from Cluny, Saint-Denis, Notre-Dame in Paris, Santiago de Compostela, La-Charité-sur-Loire, Saint-Gilles-du-Gard, and, in the present case, the famous abbey-church at Vézelay. It is indeed fortunate that this church be represented here, for the richness and fame of its sculptural decoration place it in a class occupied by very few other monuments. Its trio of tympana and large series of historiated capitals provide us with one of the climaxes of Burgundian sculpture, which had been developed first at the third church of Cluny (cat. no. 1).

Whatever resolution there may be to the controversy surrounding the dating of Cluny III and Vézelay, it is safe to state that La Madeleine was begun sometime around 1120. With the completion of the nave around 1140 work was begun immediately on a forechurch, which had been planned since 1120. Sometime between 1146 and 1152 the archbishop of Rouen blessed the altar of Saint Michael placed in the central tribune of the forechurch, which must have been completed by this time. The dating of the sculpture in this area is thus placed around 1150.

Knowledge of the Princeton capital's location in this portion of the church comes from the fact that a copy remains *in situ* in the north tribune of the forechurch. The necessity of dismounting many of the capitals and replacing them with copies came as the result both of the deterioration of age and the effects of a fire in 1819. The whole fabric of the church had fallen progressively

into disrepair during the eighteenth and early nineteenth centuries. By 1835 the building was in such a dangerous state that the famous author, Prosper Merimée, an inspector for the Monuments Historiques, in concert with the Municipal Council of Vézelay obtained funds from the State to restore the church. Through Merimée's recommendation a young man of twenty-six named Eugène Viollet-le-Duc obtained the commission in 1840 to undertake the restorations, thus beginning a phenomenal career as architect, restorer, art historian, and critic.

Between 1841 and 1859 Viollet-le-Duc brought to completion the difficult task of re-building Vézelay. It was between 1843 and 1852 that the forechurch received his attention, and it was at that time, from 1850 on, that the sculpture of this area was repaired, re-cut, or replaced by copies. The latter was certainly the case with the Princeton capital, which was placed in the Musée Lapidaire at Vézelay. It must have remained there for many years, but around 1948 it disappeared only to re-emerge a year later in the hands of the present owner, who purchased it from the Brummer collection. Knowledge of the history of this capital is particularly relevant in relation to the peculiar situation surrounding two capitals from La-Charité-sur-Loire (cat. no. 6) and a capital from Brive (cat. no. 19).

The Princeton capital shows a theme common to Romanesque sculpture: animals, birds, beasts, or human figures composed within the gyrations and meanderings of rinceaux. In this case a bird on one face and a beast of prey on the other stand within circles of vine tendrils and eat grapes from bunches that hang before their mouths.

In contrast to the style of such forms as they appear very commonly in Languedocian sculpture, the rinceaux at Vézelay are bolder and broader, allowing more space for movement. At the same time this decorative activity remains within the implicit boundaries of the block, preserving the integrity of the architectural element.

BIBLIOGRAPHY

Francis Salet, *La Madeleine de Vézelay*, Melun, 1948, pg. 201, no. 44, pl. 47.

Whitney S. Stoddard. *The West Portals of Saint-Denis and Chartres*, Harvard University Press, Cambridge, Mass., 1952, pl. XXXIV, no. 5.

3. Engaged Capital

Arion on a Dolphin (?).

Burgundy. Beginning of the second quarter
of the twelfth century.

Limestone. h., 13¼″; w., 12⅜″; d., 10″

Wadsworth Antheneum, Hartford, Connecticut.
Henry D. Miller Fund. [1949-213.]

ex coll.: Joseph Brummer.

The relationship between Cluny III and its progeny is illustrated again by this delightful capital. It has been extensively studied and published by Professor Walter Cahn, who has placed it in the diocese of Autun in the heart of Burgundy.[1] More precisely, he feels that the style of the capital is closely related to that of the master who carved the capitals and lintel of the porch and portal at Perrecy-les-Forges (Seine-et-Loire, ca. 1120-1125). Those portions of the sculpture of this church, located some twenty-four miles south of Autun, that interest us are related to the sculptural decoration of other important monuments in this region, notably Anzy-le-Duc (ca. 1115) and Montceaux-l'Étoile (ca. 1120-1125).

The question of chronology in relation to primacy of style is important in this case. As pointed out by R. and A.-M. Oursel,[2] Anzy-le-Duc was one of the most influential churches in Burgundy, in some ways superceding even Cluny. Most notably, it was apparently the first church to display a homogeneous ensemble of sculpture, beginning at a rather early date—ca. 1050 for the capitals of the chevet. The succession of styles found at Anzy in the nave capitals and the portal illustrates perfectly the complexity of stylistic growth and interchange that could occur at any given moment or in any given region. Indigenous styles, styles that evolved slowly within themselves over a period of time, and the inter-mingling of local and influential neighboring styles are all present here. It is the latter situation that is found in the portal sculpture at Anzy.

This ensemble, including a tympanum, a lintel, archivolts, and capitals, is divided into two styles. The tympanum and lintel are related to the capitals of the nave, are dated ca. 1095-1100, are unrelated to Cluny, and exercise an independent influence not only upon local churches, but perhaps also on Vézelay. The archivolts and capitals, on the other hand, were carved ca. 1115-1120 and show the influence of the great portal at Cluny and perhaps some of the sculpture at Vézelay. In addition, they are related to the portal of Montceaux-l'Étoile and the lintel and capitals of the porch of Perrecy-les-Forges.

For our purposes, therefore, the influence of Cluny either directly or indirectly, perhaps through Vézelay, is still the most important factor in determining the basic style of an area from which the Hartford capital undoubtedly came. Francis Salet has also remarked upon the consanguinity of the Cluny portal, Vézelay, Anzy-le-Duc, Perrecy-les-Forges, and Montceaux-l'Étoile. Because of his particular chronology, which dates the Vézelay portals after 1120, he is forced to date the portals of Perrecy-les-Forges and Montceaux-l'Étoile as late as 1130-1140. We must once again sidestep this prickly question, which does not, however, alter the importance of the

stylistic web that joins these monuments together. It is also interesting to observe that Autun, one of the major sculptural ensembles in Burgundy, one of the most important religious foundations in the region, and clearly dependent upon the style of Cluny III, seems to exert less influence than might be expected. In fact, the importance of Vézelay in this respect seems greater. This may be a factor in favor of a somewhat later date for the sculpture of Autun (ca. 1130), a date that would explain its relative lack of influence on neighboring churches that were either contemporary or slightly older.

Although Professor Cahn points most directly to the sculpture at Perrecy[4] as the closest relation to the Hartford capital, the style of the tympanum of the west portal at Montceaux[5] would seem to offer equal parallels. It should be noted as well that the influence of Cluny was not restricted to its own priories; Perrecy was, in fact, a dependent of another important monastery, Saint-Benoit-sur-Loire.

If the capital from Hartford exhibits the characteristically active and expressive qualities of Burgundian sculpture, it also displays a fascinating iconography. Across the two carved faces of the capital has been placed a nude male figure astride a large fish holding in his right hand a sword and in his left a stringed instrument. That the action takes place upon the ocean is revealed through the undulating lines beneath the fish. The marine rider is flanked to his right by a female head and to his left by a male head, both strangely detached and floating within what seem, despite heavy weathering and extensive chipping, to be serpentine forms. Some of these are clearly animal, but others are less precisely defined and could be variations on vegetable forms that would have composed the basic structure of a more traditionally classical capital.

In his article in the Atheneum *Bulletin,* Professor Cahn examines in great detail the possibilities for interpretation of this puzzling scene. That the scene is drawn from a classical source seems clear, but which of the many participants in sea myths may be represented here and what role he may be playing in a French twelfth century church are questions that are less easy to answer. Professor Cahn's solution points to Arion as the identity of the figure riding the fish.

In reality Arion of Lesbos was a master of the lyre and a resident of Corinth under the rule of Periander in the seventh century B.C. The myth regarding the famed musician tells of an invitation to visit Taenarus in Sicily in order to compete in a musical contest. Arion's skill won him not only the prize, but many additional gifts whose value excited the greed of the sailors who were to return him to Corinth.

Some time after the ship had put to sea Arion was informed that he was to be murdered for his prizes. Having been allowed to sing one last appeal to the gods, Arion was forced to leap into the sea. His music, however, had attracted a school of appreciative dolphins, one of whom took Arion on his back and returned him safely to Corinth. The crew of the ship, confronted by Periander with Arion, suffered a well-deserved punishment.

This story was well-known in the Middle Ages and appeared in numerous texts. Thus its appearance on a Romanesque capital is no surprise, especially in Burgundy where elements of classical decoration were commonly used at Cluny III, Autun, and Paray-le-Monial among others, and where classical myths and scenes drawn from antique art appear on several of the capitals and on the tympanum and lintel of Vezelay.

Cahn goes further in his identification of the iconography. The two disembodied heads are personifications of winds and indicate that the scene is set in the midst of a storm. The only text that mentions such conditions is the *Marriage of Mercury and Philology* by Martianus Capella, one of the basic textbooks of the medieval schools.

Either it or a commentary upon it must be the source of the Hartford capital's iconography.

True to the medieval mode of thought, this is not the mere recounting of a legend; the story of Arion was given several Christian meanings. Arion, like Orpheus, Pythagoras, and King David, made music which not only subdued the forces of nature, but embodied the principles of harmony that governed the universe. In addition, Arion's particular mode of rescue not only indicated the existence of natural miracles, but was also linked with another famous encounter between man and sea beast—Jonah and the Leviathan—and therefore became a symbolic reference to salvation. Finally, in the later Middle Ages, as Cahn points out, the story of Arion equated the miracle of Arion's salvation with the miracle of immaculate conception purely on the basis of the one being a historical precedent for the occurrence of miracles.

Although forming no iconographic parallel to the Hartford capital, it is interesting to note a capital in the north side aisle of the church at Mozac (Puy-de-Dome) that shows the story of Tobias. Formally, however, the two are quite similar, with Tobias, in this case clothed, represented riding an enormous fish.[6]

NOTES

1. See the bibliography at the end of this entry.

2. R. and A.-M. Oursel, *Les Églises Romanes de l'Autunois et du Brionnais. Cluny et sa Région.* Macon, 1956, pp. 143, 151-153.

3. *La Madeleine de Vézelay*, Melun, 1948, pp. 166-167.

4. For an illustration cf. Oursel, *op. cit.*, pls. opp. pp. 262, 264.

5. Arthur Kingsley Porter, *Romanesque Sculpture of the Pilgrimage Roads*, Boston, 1923, vol II, pls. 104, 105.

6. cf. l'Abbé Luzuy, "Mozac," *Congrès Archéologique, Moulins-Nevers*, 1913, pg. 128.

BIBLIOGRAPHY

Classical and Medieval Stone Sculptures, etc. Part III of the sale of the Joseph Brummer Collection, Parke-Bernet Galleries, New York, June 8 and 9, 1949, pg. 135, no. 571.

Wadsworth Atheneum. *Annual Report for the Year 1949.* Hartford, 1950, pg. 34.

Religious Art of the Middle Ages and Renaissance in the Collection of the Wadsworth Atheneum, Hartford, 1950, pp. 14-15, pl. II.

Walter Cahn, "Romanesque Sculpture in American Collections. I. Hartford," *Gesta*, vol. VI, January, 1967, pp. 48-49.

idem., "A Romanesque Capital from Burgundy," *Bulletin of the Wadsworth Atheneum*, Hartford, vol. III, no. 3, Winter, 1969.

4. Moutiers—Saint—Jean (Côte-d'Or) (?).

Fragment of an Angel. ca. 1133.

Limestone. h., 13¾″

The Metropolitan Museum of Art, The Cloisters
Collection, New York. 47.101.20.

ex coll.: Joseph Brummer.

The morphology of Burgundian sculpture continues to be the point at issue in this fragment of a figure, the origins of which are not entirely certain. Although it has never been published, opinions gathered in the museum files suggest plausible stylistic connections for the piece. The line of development is drawn not only through Cluny, the grandsire of most Burgundian sculpture, but in this case most clearly through Autun (ca. 1130) and Saulieu (ca. 1135). The sculptures from La-Charité-sur-Loire (ca. 1150) and Moutiers-Saint-Jean (ca. 1133) have been mentioned as more specific counterparts to the Cloisters figure, but without any serious consideration.

The sculpture at La-Charité-sur-Loire, especially that of the northern portal of the west façade, may reflect the salient characteristics of Burgundian sculpture in the facial types and the style of the drapery, but it is a much later and more sophisticated manifestation of that style and is strongly influenced by elements of Languedocian art, particularly in the southern portal, and by the early Gothic sculpture of the west façade of Chartres (ca. 1145-1155). The figures from the north portal of La-Charité are far more refined than the Cloisters fragment and must be eliminated as a possibility for a final stylistic comparison.

Moutiers-Saint-Jean is a far more likely source of style. One of the most important abbeys in Burgundy, its church was built between 1109 and 1133 and was embellished by a sculptured portal around 1150. The church was almost totally demolished during the Revolution, and elements of the sculpture were eventually dispersed, two capitals going to the Louvre in 1925 and 1929 and twelve capitals to the Fogg Art Museum in 1922. It is this material that may serve as a basis for comparison with the Cloisters relief.

This figure may be placed beside the figures in the scene of Saint Elizabeth and the Handmaiden (Fogg no. 1922. 19 (fig. 4a) and the angel in The Angel Appearing to Zacharias (Fogg no. 1922.19) as well as other angel heads for a favorable, if not exact, agreement of characteristics. The banded drapery so common in Burgundian sculpture is one feature in common and mirrors rather directly the rigidity of this manner of carving drapery at Cluny in contrast to the more elaborate and more active linear patterns found at Autun and Vézelay. Yet none of the extant pieces of Cluny sculpture has the double separation between bands that is found both in the Moutiers capitals and in the Cloisters figure. There is scarcely enough that is visible on the latter to indicate a rhythm of drapery patterns, but what does exist seems rather stiffer than that found on the Fogg capitals.

The fleshy, heavy-jawed face of the Cloisters figure is very closely related to a number of the female or angel

4a

heads on the Fogg capitals mentioned above. The pursed lips and wavy hair pulled behind the ear in several twists, and especially the enormous eyes are too close to the Fogg capitals to deny a single provenance, if not a single artist. That more than one hand may be predicated is indicated by the slight variations in the carving of drapery and in the more plastic way in which the eyes of the Cloisters fragment are carved. Its pupils, too, seem as if scooped out rather than drilled as in the eyes on the Fogg capitals.

One prototype for these heads was discovered on June 25, 1932, during the Cluny excavations and is now in the Musée Ochier, Cluny. It is the head presumably of an angel (1106-1112) and was most recently exhibited in the Congress of Europe exhibition of Romanesque art in Barcelona.[1] Although the hair is much more simply carved and the planes of the face more abruptly and severely represented, especially in the eyebrows and the eyes, the type of head, the mouth, and the large, drilled pupils establish a correspondence that does much to enhance Cluny's position as the source of a Burgundian style.

The size of the Cloisters figure, if imagined whole, would correspond to that of the larger figures on the Fogg capitals, around 22″ or 23″ high. This would suggest that it was originally part of a capital. The west portal, erected sometime later than the body of the church, is known only through an engraving in Dom Plancher's *Histoire générale et particulière de Bourgogne*,[2] and it is also possible that the fragment could have formed a part of this ensemble.

Although badly damaged to the extent that any attributes the figure may have had are missing, enough remains to suggest that it represents an angel. The halo, the youthful face, and what appear to be the remnants of a wing next to the right shoulder support this identification.

NOTES

1. *L'Art Roman.* Exhibition catalogue. Barcelona and Santiago de Compostela, 1961, pp. 276-277, no. 439, pl. XXXIX.

2. Dijon, 1739, vol. I, pp. 516-518.

5. Engaged Capital

Daniel in the Lions' Den.

Burgundy, Second quarter of the twelfth century.

Limestone. h., 13½″; w., 18½″; d., 13½″

The Cleveland Museum of Art. John L. Severance Fund.
63.477.

The localization of this capital presents difficulties that are familiar to the art historian. Undoubtedly long removed from its original location and with no record of its subsequent peregrinations having been kept, such a piece of sculpture exists as a waif whose parentage can only be discovered by a happy accident or at best inferred by means of inexact stylistic comparisons.

The Cleveland Museum has tentatively designated it as a work of the Burgundian School, drawing very cautious analogies between certain of its characteristics, such as the drilled eyes, and the work of Gislebertus of Autun. Another opinion transmitted verbally to the Museum by Professor Willibald Sauerländer places it more exactly in the region of the Nivernais. Robert Moeller of Duke University sees connections with one of at least two hands at Saulieu.

Although the capital is not of the calibre of Autun or Saulieu, its expressive strength certainly merits considerable attention. It is hoped that in this case, as in the case of a number of other objects in the present exhibition, the attention of scholars will be turned towards such unstudied works and that new solutions will be generated.

As tentative as the present opinions are concerning this capital, they seem to point to the most plausible area of origin. As Moeller pointed out in a verbal opinion, the incision splitting a ridge of drapery in half as seen in the Daniel capital is very similar to the technique used at Saulieu, as for example, on the Temptation of Christ capital.[1] Nonetheless, it should be noted that the same means of indicating folds is very common in Languedocian and related Spanish sculpture of León, which could prove nothing more than an acknowledged communication among these general regions.

The facial type in the Daniel capital, though heavier and more sharply defined, finds counterparts in the heads of Balaam and Saint Joseph at Saulieu (fig. 5a) and is the most convincingly Burgundian feature of the Cleveland capital.[2]

In other details the Daniel capital possesses its own distinctive style. The overall drapery patterns are not typical of Burgundian work and are quite individual in their treatment, combining the sweeping curves of the long sleeves and the shorter curves of the folds falling down the sides of the legs with the rigid lines of frozen cloth at the shoulders, between the knees, and at the center of the

5a

hemline. Taken together and in combination with the opposing curves, they form an extremely effective abstract pattern.

In fact, the symmetrical arrangement of linear movements, solid volumes, and deep voids is handled with considerable skill in design. The massive forms of the two lions define the limits of the capital and form a solid frame for the figure, the movement of whose outstretched arms progresses down through the curves of the sleeves to the firmly planted legs. All of these forms serve to set off the powerful head of the figure, whose upper torso is only vaguely defined as a support.

Despite the fact that their heads are broken off, the two animals flanking the central figure are clearly lions. The figure itself is described by the Museum as being merely a caryatidal figure because of his hands raised as if in support. There seems no reason not to identify this scene as a fairly common representation of Daniel in the Lions' Den. A subject that was very popular in Romanesque sculpture, and indeed in Christian art in general as a *typus* of Christ and salvation, it was developed in a variety of compositions almost all of which show Daniel as hero framed by two lions who are composed in a manner resembling heraldic supporters. Daniel is represented standing, as in an example in the Museum of Arles,[3] and even more frequently as seated. The particular gesture of the hands raised in prayer with the palms displayed is not uncommon and is found, for example, in the cloister at Moissac (ca. 1100), in the choir of Saint-Eutrope-de-Saintes (ca. 1140), and in a capital from the cloister of Sainte-Marie-la-Daurade, Toulouse (ca. 1100), now in the Musée des Augustins of that city.[4]

NOTES

1. cf. Jean Baudry et al., *Bourgogne Romane,* La Pierre qui Vire, 1958, pg. 133, fig. 8.

2. Baudry, *op. cit.,* pg. 132, fig. 7, and pg. 143, fig. 25.

3. Jean Adhémar, *Influences Antiques dans l'Art du Moyen Age Français,* London, 1939, pl. XII, no. 41.

4. Joan Evans, *Cluniac Art of the Romanesque Period,* Cambridge University Press, 1950, figs. 127b, 128c, 129a.

BIBLIOGRAPHY

The Bulletin of The Cleveland Museum of Art, December, 1963, pp. 266, 291, no. 40.

Handbook of The Cleveland Museum of Art, Cleveland, 1966, pg. 48.

6. La-Charité-sur-Loire (Nièvre).

Church of Sainte-Croix-Notre-Dame.

Engaged Capital.

Peacocks Drinking. ca. 1100.

Limestone. h., 24½″; w., 27″

Museum of Fine Arts, Boston, Gift of Mr. and Mrs. Edward Jackson Holmes. 49.534.

ex coll.: Joseph Brummer.

The problems posed by this capital and a companion piece in St. Louis[1] (fig. 6a) are similar to those generated by the capital from Brive in the Montreal Museum of Fine Arts (cat. no. 19) and are equally difficult to solve without more extensive investigation. In the famous sale of the collection of the art dealer, Joseph Brummer, in 1949 items 594 and 595 were listed as engaged capitals from the church of La-Charité-sur-Loire.[2] Number 594 was acquired by the City Art Museum, St. Louis; number 595, in the present exhibition, was bought for the Museum of Fine Arts, Boston. The problem arises from the fact that although both of these objects most certainly represent capitals from La-Charité, their exact duplicates, including all losses, have been published subsequent to the Brummer sale as being still *in situ*, while the existence of the Boston and St. Louis capitals has not been mentioned.[3]

Three possible solutions to this mystery may be offered. As was the case at Vézelay (cat. no. 2) a substitution could have been made with copies replacing the originals at the church. If this were true, the capitals in America would be the originals. It is barely possible, though highly unlikely, that the originals were merely removed without being replaced. The pictures published by Evans and Anfray would then have been based on photographs or drawings made before such a removal took place. We have been unable to determine whether such capitals are still in place at La-Charité at this moment. They are from the engaged columns of the south transept.

The final consideration is the least attractive for the American museums. It is possible that the capitals at La-Charité, if they are there, are the originals and those in this country are copies or casts. If the American examples are not the originals, they would certainly be stone casts,

since every detail is identical to the capitals published *in situ* by Evans and Anfray. In the Evans photograph as well as on the Boston capital, for example, the beak of the right-hand bird on the front face is broken off in exactly the same way. The proportions of the forms and the minutest details of carving and condition are repeated in the two sets of capitals.

It is obviously necessary to pursue this question further through stone tests and an examination of the capitals at La-Charité. If the two capitals in America are casts, they are very cleverly done. We have had the opportunity to examine at length the capital in Boston. The material and its surface markings appear to carry all the signs of authenticity. The capital in St. Louis we have seen only once and then briefly. From a photograph the surface and the carving technique seem more questionable, but we have only a drawing in Anfray to compare with it, thus rendering any opinion at this point invalid. We shall attempt to initiate tests as well as obtain reports on the capitals at La-Charité and publish the results of these investigations in the near future.

Whatever fate awaits the Boston capital, it does, after all, represent the sculpture at La-Charité. This monastery was probably the most important daughter house of the Cluniac order, one of its "cinq filles ainées" and, before being partially destroyed in 1569, it possessed a magnificent church.[4] Begun in the mid-eleventh century, construction progressed in stages and was not completed until ca. 1170. As mentioned above, the Boston capital is part of a group of capitals decorating the engaged columns of the south transept, an area that is dated around 1100.

The capital shows on its major face two peacocks drinking from a basin combined with a floral motif. Entwined around the stem that supports the basin is a serpent. On either side of the capital single peacocks also drink from basins. That the birds are peacocks is clear from the tuft of feathers rising from the head and from the differentiation of feather patterns on wings and tail.[5] An initial "O" in the First Bible of Limoges (Bib. Nat. Ms. lat. 5II, fol. 51) is composed of two similar peacocks drinking from a foliate chalice.

The association of certain animals and birds with water as an allegory of baptism or resurrection is common in Christian art from a very early period. In medieval bestiaries stories of the stag and the eagle, both of them representing the human soul, involved rejuvenation through water. The eagle, when old, was said to fly up to the sun and then, overcome with heat and thirst, to plunge into the cooling waters of a fountain from which it emerged fully restored to the powers of youth. The stag, or hart, fed upon snakes which it sucked up from their holes. The thirst resulting from such an appetite, the

6a

appetite of the human soul for evil and the subsequent thirst for redemption, drove the stag to seek a cool stream, whose waters not only allayed his thirst, but quenched the internal fires ignited by the serpents.[6]

In the case of the Boston capital the meaning seems quite explicit. The healing or redemptive waters of baptism are contained within the basin associated with a plant. It is the familiar combination of the Fountain of Living Waters and the Tree of Life. From the fountain drink two peacocks, who are symbols of immortality and often associated with Christ, though here they may refer to the soul. The serpent, of course, represents the evil of which the soul is cleansed.

The masterful design and forceful carving of this capital with the birds and fountains represented in very high relief is a reflection of the quality of the work done at La-Charité. The free space left between the figures and the vigorous movements of the peacocks conform expertly to the shape of the capital. The design is another example of the absorption into Romanesque sculpture of a tradition of stylized animals that is drawn from numerous sources in sculpture, metal-work, and textiles. The vigor of such patterns is given increased intensity by their scale and by their subordination to the form of the architectural member.

NOTES

1. St. Louis, City Art Museum, 86:49.

2. Catalogue of the sale, Part III, Parke-Bernet Galleries, New York, June 8-9, 1949.

3. cf. Joan Evans, *Cluniac Art of the Romanesque Period*, Cambridge University Press, 1950, pg. 49, fig. 88a; Marcel Anfray, *L'Architecture Religieuse du Nivernais au Moyen Age, Les Églises Romanes*, Paris, 1951, pp. 261-263, figs. 47c,d on pg. 261; Regula Raeber (*La-Charité-sur-Loire. Monographie der Romanische Kirche Notre-Dame unter spezieller Berücksichtigung der Skulpturen*. Basler Studien zur Kunstgeschichte, vol. 6, Winterthur, 1964) does not discuss this problem nor does she refer specifically to these two capitals.

4. cf. besides the study by Raeber, *op. cit.*, Philippe, *Congrès Archéologique*, Moulins-Nevers, 1913; Pierre Beaussart, *L'Église de La-Charité-sur-Loire*, La-Charité, 1929; M. Anfray, *op. cit.*, pp. 62-98, 273-287.

5. Evans, *op. cit.*, pg. 49, after describing peacocks and showing manuscript sources (fig. 85c) for them that are practically duplicates of the birds on the Boston capital, then proceeds to call these very birds eagles, whereas the eagles at La Charité are very different in form and leave no doubt as to their identity.

6. This allegory is based, of course, on the beautiful lines from Psalm 42:1, "As the hart panteth after the water brooks, so panteth my soul after thee, O God."

BIBLIOGRAPHY

Catalogue of the sale of the *Collection of Joseph Brummer*. Parke-Bernet Galleries, New York. Part III, June 8-9, 1949, no. 595.

Joan Evans, *Cluniac Art of the Romanesque Period*, Cambridge University Press, 1950, pg. 49, fig. 88a (as being at La-Charité).

Marcel Anfray, *L'Architecture Religieuse du Nivernais au Moyen Age, Les Églises Romanes*. Paris, 1951, pp. 261-263, fig. 47c (as being at La-Charité).

Bulletin of the Museum of Fine Arts, Boston, vol. LV, nos. 301-302, Autumn and Winter, 1957, pg. 54.

7-8. Saint-Laurent-l'Abbaye (Nièvre) (?).

End of the first quarter of the twelfth century.

7. *Engaged capital.*

Limestone. h., 20½″; w., 22″

Museum of Art, Rhode Island School of Design. 40.166.

8. *Engaged capital.*

Limestone. h., 21½″; w. 21½″

Philadelphia Museum of Art. The George Grey Barnard
Collection. 45-25-34.

The only unquestionable observation that has been made so far in the literature concerning these two capitals is that they are obviously from the same provenance. The flat, unadorned acanthus leaves and the scrolled corner volutes with an incised channel along the side in imitation of a Corinthian type are handled indentically in both cases. The style of carving in the heads at the center of each face of the capitals also leaves no doubt as to their common origin.

The Museum of Art, Rhode Island School of Design, possesses no information regarding its capital, but states that it is from Nevers. The capital from Philadelphia is included in the catalogue by Martin Weinberger of the George Grey Barnard Collection.[1] It is placed in the Auvergne and dated in the second half of the twelfth century. Weinberger's argument in support of this attribution has seemed quite convincing up to now and has been seconded by Walter Cahn for both the Providence and Philadelphia capitals, though he prefers a date at the end of the first quarter of the twelfth century.[2]

Both scholars point to capitals of a similar, though more elaborate, design and style at Mozac (or Mozat, Puy-de-Dôme) and especially to a capital illustrated by Louis Brehier in an article concerning the iconography of Auvergnat sculpture.[3] There is no doubt that this capital is quite close in type and even somewhat similar in style to the Philadelphia and Providence capitals. Further evidence of a stylistic connection with Mozac is seen in the fragment of a lintel from that church showing the Last Supper and now in the museum at Riom.[4]

The truth, however, seems to lie in the designation by the Museum of Art, Rhode Island School of Design, of Nevers as the place of origin of these two capitals. As the result of extensive research by M. Jacques Palet of the Musée Archéologique du Nivernais in Nevers with the cooperation of Mr. David DuBon of the Philadelphia Museum of Art, to whose great generosity we owe this information, it appears that both capitals came from the church of Saint-Laurent-l'Abbaye located just east of the Loire River and a short distance above La-Charité-sur-Loire.

The history of Saint-Laurent goes back to the sixth century. Of the Romanesque church all that remained by the beginning of this century was the transept, converted into a parish church, and the portal of the façade. The latter was sold in 1925 to an art dealer in Paris.[5] A group of capitals from the same church was sold by a dealer in Nevers directly to George Grey Barnard at the same time.[6] The portal is now in the Philadelphia Museum; the capitals were subsequently acquired by the same museum. There they remained unidentified until 1964 when M. Palet, who was studying the remains of Saint-Laurent and who was particularly interested in its portal, discovered in the course of a lengthy correspondence with Mr. DuBon that at least four capitals in the Barnard Collection were from Saint-Laurent.

This identification was made possible by the existence of an old photograph showing two of the Barnard capitals (nos. 45-25-21, 45-25-22) still in place at Saint-Laurent. These two could then be related to two others in the same collection (nos. 45-25-23, 45-25-24). Weinberger had recognized that these four capitals belonged together and had even known the old photograph of the two capitals *in situ,* but for some reason he did not know the name or location of the church in the photograph and mistakenly placed the four capitals in western France.[7]

M. Palet, having turned his eyes to the Barnard Collection in the Philadelphia Museum as a repository of Saint-Laurent material, discovered further that two other capitals, nos. 45-25-33 and 45-25-34, were also from this church. The latter is the capital on exhibit here with its mate in Providence. M. Palet's reasons for this attribution are as follows: "Par comparaison entre les mesures des emplacements vides dans les ruines de l'église et celles de certains chapiteaux non identifiés de la collection Barnard et aussi par analogie de style avec les chapiteaux restés en place, j'ai pu établir de façon certaine que les nos. 33 et 34 proviennent aussi de Saint-Laurent."

The capitals once photographed *in situ* and now in the Philadelphia Museum (nos. 45-25-21 to 24) do not resemble nos. 33 and 34, and we have not seen photographs of those capitals still *in situ* used by M. Palet to support his theory regarding nos. 33 and 34. Nonetheless, descriptions of such capitals at Saint-Laurent by Anfray mention the same kind of broad, bare leaf-forms seen in the Philadelphia and Providence capitals.[8] At the same time the collar of the Philadelphia capital with the heads (no. 34) is identical with those of the four securely identified capitals from Saint-Laurent also in Philadelphia (nos. 21-24).

There is no question, however, that some sort of analogy exists between the Auvergnat capitals seen at Mozat and those displayed here. At the same time certain aspects of the head of Daniel on the capital from Cleveland with Daniel in the Lions' Den (cat. no. 5), related to the sculpture of Saulieu and placed by Willibald Sauerländer in the Nièvre,[9] is also related to the pair of Saint-Laurent capitals. Saulieu, in the Côte-d'Or, is just to the east of the modern boundary of what is now called Nièvre. It need hardly be stated that such boundaries did not exist in the twelfth century and that the intercommunication between religious houses that were not too far distant from one another contributed greatly to an exchange of motifs and stlyes that often can upset our accepted ideas of regional styles. Thus some sort of exchange between Mozat,

Saint-Laurent, and the church that once held the Daniel capital is not beyond imagining.

The two capitals exhibited here are of impressive quality. The bare simplicity of the elements adapted from the Corinthian type of capital enhances rather than detracts from the total effect. The smooth collar of acanthus leaves on the lower half contains the powerful movement of the large corner leaves which seem to be pressed forward and out with considerable force by the thrust of the corner volutes. From the midst of the stark planes formed by the acanthus decoration emerge the equally simple and equally forceful heads that contribute most to the impressive character of these capitals.

As observed by both Jean Adhémar[10] and Brehier[11], the Corinthian capital with a human or animal head in place of the usual rosette in the center of each side is an innovation that is found in Roman capitals. Such a type was rather frequently copied by Romanesque sculptors in a variety of regions and emphasizes the important role played by antique art, whether through actual remains or through the transmission of traditions, in the art of the twelfth century. We have already noted the strength of this tradition at Cluny and in the Burgundian churches, but it is no less apparent in other areas. This particular type of capital is found, to name only a few examples, in Central France [La Berthenoux (Indre), Saint-Genou (Indre)], in the Auvergne [Mozac (Puy-de-Dôme), Me-

nat (Puy-de-Dôme)], and, quite logically, along the Mediterranean [Arles (Bouches-du-Rhône)], the cloister of Saint-Trophime; Elne (Pyrénées-Orientales), the cloister; Boule-d'Amont (Pyrénées-Orientales), cloister of the abbey of Serrabone; Prades (Pyrénées-Orientales); and Sant Pere de Roda in Catalonia (cat. no. 40).

Romanesque sculpture represents a final and climactic fusion of the accumulated traditions present in the West by the twelfth century, some of them existing in a pure state, others transmitted after having been, themselves, absorbed by the cultures of subsequent eras: Ancient Near Eastern, Classical, Gallo-Roman, Islamic, Migration, Byzantine, Carolingian, and Celtic. Preserved through the course of several chaotic centuries in the precious arts of ivory carving, manuscript illumination, and metalwork, and in the monumental arts of mosaic and fresco, these traditions flow together to create the vocabulary of forms used in the revival of monumental sculpture in the eleventh century. Adapted in a way conditioned by the specialized relationship between sculpture and Romanesque architecture, these forms were endowed with an entirely original and extremely exciting life in a new scale and material. The two capitals exhibited here are excellent examples of the continuation and adaptation of one of the strongest and most purely preserved of these sources: Classical art.

NOTES

1. Privately printed, New York, n.d., (1941), pg. 7, no. 34, pl. XI.

2. *Gesta,* vol. VII, 1968, pg. 55, fig. 7.

3. "Les Traits Originaux de l'Iconographie dans la Sculpture Romane de l'Auvergne," *Medieval Studies in Memory of Arthur Kingsley Porter,* vol. II, 1939, pg. 391, fig. 1; cf. also, l'Abbé Luzuy, "Mozac," *Congrès Archéologique, Moulins-Nevers,* 1916, pl. opp. pg. 128.

4. cf. Marcel Aubert, *La Sculpture Française au Moyen Age,* Paris, 1946, pg. 117.

5. cf. Marcel Anfray, *L'Architecture Religieuse du Nivernais au Moyen Age. Les Églises Romanes,* Paris, 1951, pp. 170-171. Commenting upon the dismemberment of Saint-Laurent, Anfray says, "Voilà ce que le vandalisme des uns, l'intérêt ou l'incurie des autres, ont fait de l'un des joyaux de l'architecture religieuse du Nivernais!"

6. Letter from Jacques Palet to David DuBon, April 30, 1964.

7. *op. cit.,* pp. 4-5, nos. 21-24.

8. Anfray, *op. cit.,* pg. 256.

9. Verbal opinion to The Cleveland Museum of Art.

10. *Influences Antiques dans l'Art du Moyen Age Français.* The Warburg Institute, London, 1939, pp. 168-175.

11. *op. cit.,* pp. 390-391.

BIBLIOGRAPHY

7. Walter Cahn, "Romanesque Sculpture in American Collections: II. Providence and Worcester," *Gesta,* vol. VII, 1968, pg. 55 and fig. 7.

8. Martin Weinberger, *The George Grey Barnard Collection,* privately printed, New York, n.d., (1941), no. 34, pg. 7, pl. XI.

Walter Cahn, *ibid.,* pg. 55.

LIMOUSIN

9. Relief.

Avarice.

Southwestern Limousin. ca. 1140-50.

Limestone. h. 24½″; w. at base, 12½″; d. 9″

Museum of Fine Arts, Boston, Charles Amos Cummings
    Fund. 48.255.

ex coll.: Joseph Brummer.

Previously placed in central France or less vaguely, but erroneously, in the region of Clermont-Ferrand, this relief bears the characteristics of the sculpture carved in a region immediately adjacent to three areas usually designated as having fostered important regional styles: Auvergne, Limousin, and Languedoc, including Quercy. The fusion of styles resulting from this proximity to major areas of development is most clearly and most importantly exemplified by the sculpture of the southern portal of Saint-Pierre at Beaulieu-sur-Dordogne (Corrèze), but is also found in varying degrees in reliefs at Saint-Sauveur in Collonges (Corrèze), Saint-Marcel at Lagraulière (Corrèze), and Saint-Georges at Ydes (Cantal).

The stylistic relationships among these churches, and including the Avarice relief, are primarily determined by the strong influence exerted by the sculpture of Languedoc and in particular by Moissac (Tarn-et-Garonne) and Souillac (Lot). The broad faces with high cheekbones, the long, pointed moustaches, the harsher, yet less complicated, linearity of the drapery in contrast to Burgundian sculpture are all prominent Languedocian characteristics found particularly at Moissac. The Boston relief may be included with the sculpture of the churches mentioned above in their dependence upon Moissac.

Although heavily weathered, the Boston relief is still very expressive, a fact which illustrates an important point regarding Romanesque sculpture. Having only a minor interest in a detailed representation of natural forms, the Romanesque sculptor was concerned primarily with the difficult task of combining dramatic narrative and successful design within the context of a powerful and dominant architecture. Relegated to specific and limited areas of this architecture, the sculpture became an integral part of the active structure and thus was forced to obey, or at least not to disturb, its laws. As a result, no matter how dense and complicated the actual ensemble of sculptural forms may become, in the best of Romanesque sculpture a clarity of organization within a severely controlled space is an absolute necessity. This, in turn, predicated the generalization and stylization of natural forms such as body structure, facial details, hair, gestures, and drapery. The reasons for this type of semi-abstraction go much further than the purely practical causes described here and involve the more basic consideration of a mode of thought. The point to be made is that even a heavily weathered or damaged work retains much of its power because its most important element—a simple and abstract compositional design—remains basically undisturbed.

The theme of the Miser or Avaricious Man was very popular in the Middle Ages. In Romanesque sculpture especially the representation of the man with a bag of money suspended from his neck and accompanied by a demon shared the honor with the image of Lust, or Luxuria, a naked women with two serpents sucking at her breasts, as being the most frequently represented of the seven deadly sins, the former being the sin of man, the latter of woman. The basic Christian disavowal of material treasures in contrast to the ultimate worth of spiritual treasures had fostered a basic aversion to usury and to those aspects of commerce that involved solely the manipulation of money or the generation of high profits. It was the greed for earthly riches as well as the satisfaction of fleshly desires that man seemed most susceptible to, and in the display of didactic imagery that was an integral part of the church the punishment for such sins was given a prominent place. In fact, the overriding theme of Romanesque sculpture, as one may see in other examples exhibited here, was Judgment. Centered upon the Apocalyptic Vision or the Last Judgment, the greater proportion of Romanesque imagery dwelt upon the terrors of the Last Day and all of its ramifications.

In the Boston relief the Avaricious Man clasps his hands over the cord that suspends the customary purse around his neck. Even in death he cannot separate himself from his treasures. The horror of his fate is apparent as he is forced to kneel upon what is probably his money chest by a hairy and grimacing demon whose sharp claws rest heavily upon the head and right shoulder of his victim.[1]

NOTES

1. What seems to be a money chest is a circular container with straps. There is a similar object on an Avarice capital in the south chapel of the apse of the church of Saint-Laurent at Blars. cf. *Dictionnaire des Églises de France*, vol. III, pg. III B 23.

10-19. Brive (Corrèze).

Saint-Martin. Second quarter of the twelfth century.

Reliefs from a destroyed Ascension group.

10. *Apostle.*

Limestone. h., 34″; w., 10″

Museum of Art, Rhode Island School of Design. 41.045.

ex coll.: Joseph Brummer.

11. *Apostle.*

Limestone. h., 32½″; w., 10½″

Museum of Art, Rhode Island School of Design. 41.046.

ex coll.: Joseph Brummer.

12. *Saint Peter.*

Limestone. h., 33″; w., 12″; d., 7″

Smith College Museum of Art. 1937:12-1.

ex coll.: Joseph Brummer.

13. *Apostle.*

Limestone. h., 35⅛″; w., 11½″

Art Museum, Duke University.

ex coll.: Ernest Brummer.

14. *Apostle.*

Limestone. h., 34½″; w., 11¾″

Art Museum, Duke University.

ex coll.: Ernest Brummer.

15. *Apostle.*

Limestone. h., 33¼″; w., 11¾″

Art Museum, Duke University.

ex coll.: Ernest Brummer.

16. *Apostle.*

Limestone. h., 33⅝″; w., 11⅝″

Art Museum, Duke University.

ex coll.: Ernest Brummer.

17. *Apostle.* (Photo-mural of original at Rochester).

Limestone. h., 34″; w., 14″

Memorial Art Gallery, University of Rochester, New York.
  R. T. Miller Fund.

18. *Angel.* (Photo-mural of original at Rochester).
Limestone. h., 33½″ ; w., 19″
Memorial Art Gallery, University of Rochester, New York.
R. T. Miller Fund.

19. *Capital.* Christ Delivering the Keys to Saint Peter.
Limestone. h., ca. 26″
The Montreal Museum of Fine Arts. Horsley and Annie
Townsend Bequest. 61.DV.4.

Disjecta membra, refugees from a once impressive sculptural complex, the two Apostle reliefs in the Museum of Art, Rhode Island School of Design, are fragmentary evidence of a significant moment in the development of Romanesque sculpture.[1] The carvings in Providence and their companions, a figure of Saint Peter at Smith College,[2] four superb carved Apostles in the Duke University Art Museum,[3] an extremely weathered figure of another apostle and that of an angel, both in the Rochester Memorial Art Gallery,[4] represent an amalgam of borrowed and local styles whose point of origin is to be found in the Department of Corrèze, France. Eight apostles and one angel, they share characteristics of style, format, and provenance.

Format, size and the fact that the apostles' poses and gestures suggest a reaction to something above, indicate that the group of reliefs was once part of a monumental sculptural complex with the Ascension as its probable theme. Peter clutches his key in one hand and raises the other upwards. Similarly, a tense, cross-legged disciple with a scroll (cat. no. 15) points over his shoulder to a now missing Christ in a mandorla. These husky, block-like figures, some with massive heads, hands, and distorted limbs, successfully convey the impression of wonder and excitement at the scene and of communication with one another. The angel, now in Rochester, indicates that a pair of winged figures served as a visual link between the Apostles and Christ, whom they once bracketed. Their very poses lent a kind of dynamic aspect to the composition—bow-like figures bent to communicate their message and to draw the attention of the apostles below.

Attribution of the angel and the eight surviving Apostles to the region of Corrèze can be justified upon the basis of the general style and pose of the figures as well as by comparison of the reconstructed composition and iconographic layout to similar sculptural programs in South Central France (Mauriac, Cahors) and more particularly at Collonges and Saint-Chamant (Corrèze). All of these monuments display a theme popular in the region: the ascending, blessing Christ, flanked by angels and attended by the Virgin and the Apostles.

Closest analogies exist between our partially reconstituted group and the portal reliefs at Saint-Chamant. This little-known sculptural program is compositionally and stylistically a simplified version of the important complex at Collonges.[5] At Saint-Chamant, angels and apostles stand upon a shelf-like "platform" which serves to separate and define the field containing Christ and angels above and apostles and Virgin below. Evidence of a similar "platform" is seen as part of the apostle and angel reliefs under discussion. Further, the Angel in Rochester compares closely to the right hand angel at Saint-Chamant in pose and gesture. A common repertoire of gestures characterizes the Saint-Chamant apostles and ours, although the application of these conventional treatments of limbs is quite different.

It has been noted that, as now presented, the rectangular shape of our angel relief would indicate that additional iconographic elements might have been inserted on either side of the attending angels, as at Cahors, for instance.[6] Saint-Chamant provides another instance of this type of compositional filling with the inclusion of a head to the outside of each angel—possibly the *viri in vestibus albis* and possibly another clue to the original aspect of our destroyed program.

If compositional and iconographic factors argue for attribution of our reliefs to South Central France, the remaining sculpture at Saint-Martin, Brive, provides the key to a more precise localization of the apostles and the angel.[7] The exterior of the chevet of Saint-Martin retains a capital depicting the appearance of the Angel to King David.[8] (Fig. 19a) The stylistic analogies between the

19a

capital and several of the apostles are so close as to warrant the conclusion that the David capital and the apostle/angel group are products of the same moment and the same workshop. The drapery surface of the capital and the larger reliefs is organized in two ways. Sets of incised lines in groups of two, three and four run vertically down the legs and arms of some of the figures. A conventional design is effected across the body by groups of two and three parallel raised ridges which tend to create sharp light and shadow contrast. The result is a kind of graphic effect applied to largely conceived sculptured masses. A comparison of the figures of David and the Angel with any of the apostles will establish the close connection.

19b

Study of the David capital at Saint-Martin will also establish that at least two stylistic modes or variants characterize the work at Brive. The figure on the left face of the David capital just behind the genuflecting king displays quite a different and more simplified drapery style than that of the companion figures. The angel in Rochester in so far as its condition permits a judgment, evidences a similar simplification of drapery convention as compared to the apostle reliefs.

Further proof of the connection of the apostle/angel group with Brive is furnished by comparison of the large reliefs with other capitals at Saint-Martin, such as that depicting Christ before Pilate[9] where the head of Christ on the capital is close in style to the head of the Smith Saint Peter and those of the apostles at Duke. On the Pilate Christ capital, the broad misshapen head of the center, crouching figure as well as that of Pilate compare with the distorted features of one of the Rhode Island figures. This diversity of figural treatment and the occurrence of the simplified drapery style noted above underlines the point already made concerning the use of modes or stylistic variants at Brive.

A capital *in situ* in the south transept at Saint-Martin (Fig. 19b) and an identical capital in the Montreal Museum of Fine Arts, wrongly attributed to Vigeois, (cat. no. 19) illustrates the *traditio clavium*.[10] Comparison of the Smith Saint Peter with the corresponding figure in the capital should dispel any doubt that the entire group of reliefs and capitals are all to be attributed to the workshop responsible for the Brive sculpture.

For the moment we must leave unanswered the question of whether the apostles and the single angel were members of an Ascension program once attached to the fabric of

Saint-Martin at Brive. Excavation and reconstruction of the porch at Saint-Martin in 1877 brought to light superb fragments of a monumental Descent into Limbo.[11] These reliefs are identical in style with the important sculpture at Souillac.[12] The original placement of the Limbo fragments is probably indicated by the fact that they were found in the western portion of the church. If one concludes, then, that the Descent into Limbo was a major theme of the west portal decoration,[13] it is difficult, though not impossible, to imagine that the Ascension group we have described was part of the same portal complex. No drawing or document yet found describes anything of the sculptural programs of Saint-Martin or gives any information regarding the decoration of any other buildings in this once important monastic establishment.

Two other suggestions could be made, then, regarding the original placement of the angel and the apostles under discussion. The first is that the group may have been part of the decoration of another monastic building at Brive. The second possibility is that the Ascension reliefs were part of the fabric of a nearby church whose sculptor-masons were the same as those responsible for the capitals of Saint-Martin at Brive. What is certain, however, is that the sculpture in the Museums at the Rhode Island School of Design, Smith College, Duke University and Rochester are of high quality. While they display stylistic links with work at Souillac and certain monuments of the Auvergne, the angel and the companion apostles are also important evidence of a fairly local regional style which plays itself out during the second quarter of the twelfth century at such sites as Vigeois, Noailles, Saillac and at Lubersac where quality and iconographic development reach a peak.

ROBERT C. MOELLER III

NOTES

1. For initial discussion of the Providence Apostles and of the related pieces discussed here, and of the questions of localization, see Robert C. Moeller III in *Sculpture and Decorative Art, Selected Works from the Brummer Collection at Duke University*, Raleigh, N. C., 1967, pp. 8-12. *Idem, College Art Journal,* winter 1967/1968, pp. 182-184.

2. E. H. P., "A Romanesque Statue of Saint Peter," *Smith College Museum Bulletin,* 1938, pp. 3-6; *Art News,* January, 1938, p. 17; Moeller, *Ibid.*, and *Idem, College Art Journal;* Walter Cahn, *Gesta,* vol. 7, January, 1968, pp. 53-54; *idem., Gesta,* vol. 8, 1969, p. 56.

3. Moeller, *Ibid.*; Cahn, *Ibid.*

4. *Memorial Art Gallery Notes,* vol. 9 #3, January/February, 1944; *Handbook of the Collection,* 1961, p. 4.

5. René Fage, "L'Église de Saint Chamant et son Portail Sculpté." *Bulletin de le Société Scientifique, Historique et Archéologique de la Corrèze,* 1941, p. 41ff. M. Chargeat, "Le Tympan du portail de Saint-Chamant et sa Place dans la Sculpture Limousine," *Ibid.*, 1943, pp. 85ff.

6. Cahn, *Gesta,* vol. 7, 1968, p. 54.

7. Moeller, *College Art Journal, op. cit.;* Cahn, *Ibid.* For Saint-Martin at Brive see: E. Lefèvre-Pontalis, "Brive" *Congrès Archéologique,* v, 84, 1921, pp. 269-291. A. de Labroderie, "L'Église Saint-Martin de Brive" *Bulletin de la Société Scientifique, Historique et Archéologique de la Corrèze,* vol. 57, 1935, pp. 12-13.

8. A. K. Porter, *Romanesque Sculpture of the Pilgrimage Roads,* Boston, 1923, vol. II, p. 356. This capital is represented by a cast now in the museum at Brive.

9. Porter, *Ibid.*, vol. II, plate 355.

10. A capital with Samson and the Lion also exists on the exterior of the chevet at Saint-Martin, Brive, and at the same time in the collection of a New York dealer. The problems posed by this situation must be carefully studied through visual and scientific analysis before a definitive study of the Brive sculpture can be completed. The situation seems to raise the same questions as the capitals at La-Charité-sur-Loire and their twins in Boston (cat. no. 6) and St. Louis.

11. L. Bonnay, "Déscription des découvertes archéologiques faites a l'église Saint-Martin de Brive." *Bulletin de la Société Scientifique, Historique et Archéologique de la Corrèze,* 1878, I, p. 234.

12. Porter was the first to discuss the connection between the Brive capitals and Souillac. *op. cit.*, vol. I, p. 200.

13. It is, of course, possible that the Limbo relief was originally carved for a position other than the west exterior—for placement in some interior context for instance.

BIBLIOGRAPHY

Since there are so many objects in this entry and since most of the reliefs are referred to together in the literature, we are listing the bibliography all together.

E. Lefèvre-Pontalis, "Brive," *Congrès Archéologique,* Limoges, vol. 84, 1921, 289-290.

Elizabeth H. Payne, "A Romanesque Statue of Saint Peter," *Bulletin of the Smith College Museum of Art,* nos. 18-19, June, 1938, pp. 3-6.

Art News, January, 1938, pg. 17.

Smith College Museum of Art. Supplement to the Catalogue of 1937. Northampton, Mass., 1941, pg. 8.

Memorial Art Gallery Notes, University of Rochester, Rochester, N.Y., vol. 9, no. 3, January/February, 1944.

Handbook of the Collection. Memorial Art Gallery, University of Rochester, Rochester, N.Y., 1961, pg. 4.

"Accessions of American and Canadian Museums," *The Art Quarterly,* Summer, 1962, pg. 166-167.

Robert C. Moeller III, *Sculpture and Decorative Art,* Selected works from the Brummer Collection at Duke University. North Carolina Museum of Art, Raleigh, N.C., 1967, pp. 8-17.

idem., The College Art Journal, Winter, 1967/1968, pp. 182-184.

Robert G. Calkins, *A Medieval Treasury.* Exhibition catalogue. Andrew Dickson White Museum of Art, Cornell University, Ithaca, N.Y., October 8–November 3, 1968; Munson-Williams-Proctor Institute, Utica, N.Y., November 10–December 8, 1968; no. 54.

Walter Cahn, "Romanesque Sculpture in American Collections: II. Providence and Worcester," *Gesta,* vol. VII, 1968, pp. 53-54.

idem., "Romanesque Sculpture in American Collections: III. New England University Museums," *Gesta,* vol. VIII, 1969, pg. 56.

WESTERN FRANCE

20. Portal

Western France (Poitou or Saintonge). Second quarter of the twelfth century.

Limestone. h., 12'8"; w., (overall), 13'10½"; opening, h., 9'8"; w., 4'10"

Museum of Art, Rhode Island School of Design. 40.014.

ex coll.: William Randolph Hearst Estate.

A handwritten note in the Museum files by Dr. Alexander Dorner, the director under whom this portal was purchased in 1940 through the Brummer Gallery, dates it around 1150 and says that it is from a region that he calls the Charente-Maritime. Walter Cahn, writing in *Gesta* includes the same region in a more general opinion of provenance.[1] He places the portal in the Loire Valley or Western France and cites examples of similar monuments in Poitou and Angoumois.

Since nothing is known about this portal, both scholars are as accurate as anyone can be under the circumstances. The portal is, indeed, typical of those found in churches in that area of western France that includes Poitou, Saintonge, and Angoumois. As represented here the characteristic features of such portals are the lack of a tympanum, and the series of stepped arches or archivolts that are severe in profile, whether heavily decorated or not, and obtrusive in weight and number. The logical resolution of these archivolts is a series of columns in the portal embrasures, and these carry capitals, which, in turn, support a continuous impost block or cornice on each side.

Cahn has attempted to link some of the decorative motifs with specific monuments in Poitou and Angoumois, but he admits that beyond a few similarities it is impossible to arrive at a precise attribution.

But for a single capital located over the innermost column on the left side, showing two birds drinking at a fountain set beneath an extremely primitive mask, reminding us in part of the capital in Boston from La-Charité-sur-Loire (cat no. 6), the remainder of the decoration is abstract, consisting of palmettes, saw-tooth, rinceaux, and flowers, and a star-like pattern formed by the bottom edges of incuse pyramids. All of this ornament is located on the capitals and impost-blocks and on a single moulding that forms a narrow outer arch framing the plain archivolts.

As a further indication that this portal probably came from some church in what was once called the Charente-Inférieur we might mention that the peculiar star-like pattern is also found in a slightly modified form at Saint-Symphorien (Deux-Sèvres), Chadennac (Charente-Maritime), Foussais (Vendée), and Melle (Deux-Sèvres).[2] The same pattern is also found in the portal of the church of Saint-Génard (Deux-Sèvres).[3]

As crude as much of the carving is, the unity of the overall architectural design and the balance in the proportions of its parts make this portal a pleasing and successful composition. Since this is the only complete architectural unit in the exhibition, and since we have frequently alluded to the crucial role played by architecture in determining the nature of Romanesque sculpture, a few general comments seem in order here. A portal, whether Romanesque or Gothic, expresses in capsule form the basic structural system of the church, preparing one visually for the interior in the same way that the sculpture of the portal prepares one spiritually and psychologically for the experience that is about to be encountered inside the building. It is a structural exemplum for the arcade and for the correspondence of bays that forms the articulation of the major interior walls.

The Museum portal provides us with a ready illustration of this principle. Resting upon simple bases, short colonnettes, in a rhythm of a,a,B on either side, moving from exterior to interior, support capitals which, through the transitional shape of the impost blocks, carry the thrust of the massive archivolts. The whole ensemble suggests the articulation of a solid wall rather than the unification of a number of separate elements to form a structural unity. It is this fact that enables one to designate the portal as Romanesque, for the integrity of the solid, planar, bearing wall has not been disturbed, but rather emphasized by the way in which the parts of this portal have been handled.

The plane of wall that would have originally surrounded this portal and that may be seen in a typical Western French façade such as Saint-Pierre at Aulnay (fig. 20a) is expressed by the outer face of the first, or outermost, archivolt, which gives way to a second, which leads to the inner arch. These are all stepped down at right angles

20a

toward the portal opening, and the resultant impression is one of the progressive cutting away of wall mass until one reaches the opening that represents the removal of a whole section of the wall. What is finally achieved is a revelation, whether actual or somewhat exaggerated, of the true thickness of the structural wall. The whole process may be called assertion by articulation, and it is a basic principle of Romanesque architecture. How much this differs from the Gothic system will become apparent when

we discuss the Early Gothic sculpture in the exhibition.

That the sculpture is, and must be, an integral part of this architectural system and that it does, indeed, underline the process of articulation is again exemplified by the Providence portal. The decoration here is relatively sober and restricted to a few areas, but even when it covers much of the surface as it does at Aulnay or Saintes in the Saintonge, it does not disturb the basic structural progression of base, column, capital, and archivolt.

NOTES

1. "Romanesque Sculpture in American Collections: II, Providence and Worcester," *Gesta,* vol. VII, 1968, pg. 53, fig. 3.

2. cf. Arthur Kingsley Porter, *Romanesque Sculpture of the Pilgrimage Roads,* vols. VII, Boston, 1923, pls. 1007, 1037, 1062, 1090

3. *Dictionnaire des Églises de France,* vol. III, Paris, 1967, pg. III C 172.

BIBLIOGRAPHY

Walter Cahn, "Romanesque Sculpture in American Collections: II, Providence and Worcester," *Gesta,* vol. VII, 1968, pg. 53, fig. 3.

21. Part of the Right Side of an Archivolt.

Six Elders of the Apocalypse.

Region of Parthenay (Deux-Sèvres), Western France.
  Mid-twelfth century.

Limestone.

  A. h., 20″; w., 11″; d., 6″

  B. h., 30″; w., 11″; d., 6″

  C. h., 11″ (half-figure) ; w., 7″; d., 6″

  D. h., 16″ (half-figure) ; w., 11″; d., 6″

  E. h., 20″; w., 11″; d., 6″

Philadelphia Museum of Art. The George Grey Barnard
  Collection. 45-25-71 A-E.

A

B

C

D

E

In the catalogue of the Barnard Collection Martin Weinberger discloses that this portion of an archivolt was said to have come from Parthenay.[1] He concludes that despite the appearance of similar elders in an archivolt of the western portal of Notre-Dame-de-la-Couldre at Parthenay (second half of the twelfth century), the Philadelphia archivolt cannot belong to that church, but must have come from another church in the neighborhood. This judgment seems quite reasonable. In general style and type the Philadelphia Elders are certainly related to those at Notre-Dame-de-la-Couldre, but in quality they are far inferior.

On the other hand, Parthenay is a town well-endowed with Romanesque churches, some of which have not avoided vandalism and the depredations of time. There is no reason, therefore, to disbelieve the old report that the archivolt came from Parthenay merely because it is not from Notre-Dame-de-la-Couldre. There is, in fact, a substantial group of sculpture that was gathered from this church and dispersed among several museums here and in France.[2] The style and quality of these fragments would underline the decision that the Philadelphia Elders are not from Notre-Dame-de-la-Couldre, but for the fact that the capitals of the central portal, though damaged, bear a certain resemblance to the Elders.[3]

There are, finally, any number of churches in Parthenay from which these figures could have come: the twelfth century church of Sainte-Croix, heavily restored; Saint-Laurent, also Romanesque in origin, but transformed later; Saint-Pierre-de-Parthenay-le-Vieux, begun after 1092 and relatively well-preserved; Saint-Jean; Saint-Sépulchre; the chapel of the Maison-Dieu, Saint-Jacques; and, on the outskirts, Saint-Paul, and the chapel of the Rosary.

Unlike the other Elder in this exhibition (cat. no. 61) whose stated origin conflicts with its composition and style, the Philadelphia Elders would not be out of place in Parthenay or its surrounding region. Archivolts with the Elders of the Apocalypse are common in western France where heavily decorated archivolts frame a portal that is generally lacking a tympanum. In connection with the other sculptures from western France included in this exhibition we have had cause to speak of the exuberance of the sculptors of this region displayed both in the variety of decorative and figural forms they employ and by the abundance of such decoration on church façades. It is a manifestation of Romanesque sculpture that Henri Focillon characterized as "baroque."[4]

Little that might be thought of as "baroque" is displayed by these timid, yet strangely appealing figures. They are, it must be admitted, not among the most accomplished products of this region. Their halting and provincial expression draws our attention, though they may not evoke the awesome vision described in the Revelation According to St. John, as do the Elders at Moissac or at Chartres:

"And immediately I was in the spirit: and, behold, a throne was set in heaven, and one sat upon the throne.

And he that sat was to look upon like a jasper and a sardine stone: And there was a rainbow round about the throne, in sight like unto an emerald.

And round about the throne were four and twenty seats: and upon the seats I saw four and twenty elders sitting, clothed in white raiment; and they had on their heads crowns of gold."

(Rev. IV: 2-4)

"And when he had taken the book, the four beasts and four and twenty elders fell down before the Lamb, having every one of them harps, and golden vials full of odours, which are the prayers of saints."

(Rev. V:8)

NOTES

1. Martin Weinberger, *The George Grey Barnard Collection*, privately printed, New York, n.d. (1941), pg. 15, no. 71 A-E.

2. There are two capitals, a relief, and two torsos in the Louvre (cf. Marcel Aubert and Michèle Beaulieu, *Description Raisonnée des Sculptures du Moyen Age*, Musée du Louvre, Paris, 1950, pp. 50-53, nos. 38-42); a relief of the Entrance Into Jerusalem and two crowned figures in the Isabella Stewart Gardner Museum, Boston (These will be published in vol. IX of *Gesta* in the Fall of 1969 by Walter Cahn); two crowned figures in the Pitcairn Collection, Bryn Athyn, Penna.; and a crowned head said to come from Notre-Dame-de-la-Couldre now in The Metropolitan Museum of Art, New York. For a more complete bibliography concerning this church see the notices in the *Description Raisonnée* by Aubert and Beaulieu. The town and its churches are described in the invaluable

Dictionnaire des Églises de France, Editions Robert Laffont, Paris, 1967, vol. III, pp. III C 122-125. Photographs of the sculptures from Notre-Dame-de-la-Couldre and Saint-Pierre-de-Parthenay-le-Vieux are found in Arthur Kingsley Porter, *Romanesque Sculpture of the Pilgrimage Roads*, Boston, 1923, vol. VII, nos. 924, 1045-1057.

3. cf. Porter, *op. cit.*, pl. 1047.

4. Henri Focillon, *The Art of the West in the Middle Ages*, vol. I, *Romanesque Art*, Phaidon, Greenwich, Conn., 1963, pp. 131-133.

BIBLIOGRAPHY

Martin Weinberger, *The George Grey Barnard Collection*, privately printed, New York, n.d., (1941), pg. 15, no. 71 A-E.

22-23. Nuaillé-Sur-Boutonne (Charente-Maritime).

Church of Saint-Pierre or Sainte-Marie. Mid-twelfth
century.

22. Corbel. *Two Hands Holding a Barrel.*

Limestone. h., 16″; w., 7½″

Museum of Art, Rhode Island School of Design. 51.316.

ex coll.: Duthil, Bordeaux; Julius Böhler, Munich;
F. A. Drey, London.

23. Corbel. *Man Blowing a Horn.*
Limestone. h., 16″; w., 7½″
Yale University Art Gallery. 1956.17.3
ex coll.: Duthil, Bordeaux; Mathais Komor, New York.

The church of Sainte-Marie or Saint-Pierre at Nuaillé-sur-Boutonne is located on the banks of the Boutonne River near the two more famous churches of Saint-Pierre at Aulnay and Saint-Jean-d'Angely. The church itself is a modest structure, but it possesses a sculptured portal that is worthy of some attention. Typical of the decorated portals of Poitou, Saintonge, and the Angoumois, the entrance at Nuaillé is composed of two archivolts heavily decorated with scenes on the outer arch of the Infancy of Christ and on the inner arch with Christ, the Apostles, and other figures difficult to identify. In addition, there are historiated capitals flanking the entrance and a carved frieze that runs across the façade. As is usual in this region there is no tympanum. What is most important is the fact that above the portal is a cornice across the façade that is now badly damaged and that once was supported by a series of corbels, the remains of which can still be seen.[1]

Nothing is said about these corbels or their eventual disposition in the literature describing the church. When, however, the two corbels in Providence and at Yale and two others, one in the Stockholm National Museum[2] (fig. 22a) and the other formerly in a private collection in London,[3] (fig. 22b) were purchased together from the Duthil Collection in Bordeaux, they were all said to have come from Nuaillé-sur-Boutonne. The loss of the corbels at that church in addition to the strong similarities that exist between the Yale Hornblower and the figural sculpture of the façade would seem to encourage belief in this provenance.

One of the distinguishing features of the rich decoration that is employed in the portals and on the façade and capitals of the churches of western France is the multiplication and development of the historiated, or figured,

22a

22b

corbel. Drawing upon an unrestricted range of topics, these corbels act in relation to the more serious sculpture of the portals in the same capacity as the marginalia in manuscripts. The selection of subject matter for the corbels seems to follow no established plan nor any integrated iconographical system. It is even questionable whether many of the images carry a specific meaning. Traditional forms are combined with local anomalies; purely decorative motifs stand side-by-side with figures whose meaning is instantly recognizable. Wry comments upon the foibles of man lighten the stern message of the portal with its warning of Judgment.

The variety of subjects used on corbels and the enthusiastic delight in exploiting this architectural member for the purposes of narrative and decoration are particularly evident in Poitou, the Saintonge, and related regions. The two corbels from Providence and Yale with their companions in Stockholm and London, representatives of a fusion of Poitevin and Saintongeais styles, are perfect examples of this decorative exuberance.

All four corbels show common subjects. On the Stockholm piece (fig. 22a) a man pulls his beard or mouth, representing anger or perhaps merely displaying the agony of a toothache. The ubiquitous image of a beast playing a musical instrument, in this case a viol, is the subject of the corbel formerly in London (fig. 22b). The ingenious composition and vigorous expression of this piece make it particularly attractive. The Providence corbel is rather bizarre. Two hands, carved with great delicacy, emerge from the block to hold an iron-bound cask with a large spout at the top. The cask is suspended by a strap from a large hook carved onto the edge of the corbel. In his short discussion of this piece Dr. Rudolf Berliner felt that it was an allegory of intemperance.[4] The representation of casks or barrels alone, supported by hands, or held by entire figures is very common in western French sculpture.[5] Whether such casks are meant to serve an admonitory purpose, whether they represent one of the more pleasant of human activities, or whether they refer to a particularly important product of the region is not always easy to determine.

The Hornblower, as seen on the Yale corbel, is as frequently encountered as the musical monster, the man pulling his beard, and the cask. Its heritage is complicated, and there are a number of possibilities for its meaning which we can only mention in passing here. The strongest and perhaps the oldest tradition links the Hornblower with a representation of the winds and, by extension, with the windiest of months, March.[6] This image of *Marcus Cornator* with one or two horns held to the mouth may be further linked with the hunter "winding his horn" or with the warrior sounding a call. The latter, then, could refer to Mars, God of War, bringing us back to March again. It is probable that the Yale corbel is simply a reference to March and its winds, though whether it was part of a series of images of the months or whether it was merely picked up as a decorative motif whose meaning was obscure to the sculptor is indeterminable.

S.K.S. AND PEARL BRAUDE

NOTES

1. For a description of this church and its sculpture cf. Charles Dangibeaud, "Le portail de l'église de Nuaillé-sur-Boutonne," *Bulletin archéologique de la Commission des travaux historiques,* Paris, 1926, pg. 40; Erik Dahl, "Nuaillé-sur-Boutonne," *Congrès Archéologique, La Rochelle,* 1956, pp. 297-303; *Dictionnaire des Églises de France,* Editions Robert Laffont, Paris, 1967, vol. III, pg. III C 119.

2. *Peintures et sculptures des écoles étrangères antérieures à l'époque moderne,* Stockholm, no. SK. 1701, pp. 275-276.

3. Mrs. M. H. Drey Coll.; cf. the exhibition catalogue, *Romanesque Art,* Manchester, England, 1959, no. 66, pg. 33.

4. "Intemperance: A Romanesque Sculptured Corbel," *Museum Notes,* Museum of Art, Rhode Island School of Design, vol. 9, no. 1, Nov., 1951.

5. cf. J. George and A. Guérin-Boutard, "Barriques, Barils et Coffinas Sculptés sur Quelques Églises Romanes de l'Angoumois," *Bulletin et Mémoires de la Société archéologique et historique de la Charente,* 1914, pp. L-LIII; R. Hallo, "Altfranzösische Barilia," *Repertorium für Kunstwissenschaft,* 1930, pp. 148-167; Elizabeth Mendell, *Romanesque Sculpture in Saintonge,* Yale University Press, New Haven, Conn., 1940, pg. 85.

6. cf. Léon Pressouyre, " 'Marcus Cornator'. Note sur un groupe de représentations médiévales du mois de Mars," *Mélanges d'Archéologie et d'Histoire.* École française de Rome, 1965, pp. 395-473. I would like to thank Prof. Linda Seidel Field of Harvard University for this reference. The further involvement of such a representation with the vast subject of the Labours of the Months in medieval art is also an important consideration. cf. Pressouyre, *op. cit.,* pg. 395, n. 1, and James C. Webster, *The Labors of the Months in Antique and Medieval Art to the End of the Twelfth Century,* Princeton University Press, 1938. For other examples of the hornblower in the sculpture of western France, cf. Mendell, *op. cit.,* pg. 84.

BIBLIOGRAPHY

22. Rudolf Berliner, "Intemperance: A Romanesque Sculptured Corbel," *Museum Notes,* Museum of Art, Rhode Island School of Design, vol. 9, no. 1, 1951.

23. Sumner McK. Crosby, "Medieval Sculpture and Jewelry," *Bulletin of the Associates in Fine Arts at Yale University,* February, 1957, pp. 12, 23.

22. and 23. Walter Cahn, "Romanesque Sculpture in American Collections: II. Providence and Worcester," *Gesta,* vol. VII, 1968, pp. 55-56.
idem., "Romanesque Sculpture in American Collections: III. New England University Museums," *Gesta,* vol. VIII, 1969, pp. 65-66.

24. Engaged Capital

Two Lions Statant-Reguardant

Poitou. ca. 1140-1150.

Limestone. h., 27″ w., 27″ d., 18″

Philadelphia Museum of Art, The George Grey
Barnard Collection. 45-25-25.

Western France, including the regions once designated as Poitou, Saintonge, Angoumois, and the Perigord, is an area particularly well-endowed with Romanesque churches. The rich decoration of these churches, whose façades, portals, and capitals are covered with a profusion of narrative scenes, foliate forms, and fantastic beasts, led Henri Focillon to apply the term "baroque Romanesque." There is an exuberance to the sculpture of western France that more than compensates for what is often seen as a lack of refinement in comparison with the best examples of Burgundian and Languedocian sculpture. Western French sculptors seem to have taken a robust delight in exploring all the possibilities of the decorative traditions available to them, as if they had resolved to counter with a vengeance the strictures of Saint Bernard against the excesses of Romanesque sculpture. It is, in fact, the architecture and sculpture of these regions that is most often brought to mind when one thinks of the essence of Romanesque.

It is a pity, therefore, that we do not know the specific origins of this capital upon whose face are carved two magnificent lions that embody all of the vigor and energy of the animal style whose ancestry stretches back several milennia before the birth of Christ and whose traditions were so perfectly adapted for translation into monumental stone sculpture in the eleventh and twelfth centuries.

As Martin Weinberger points out, the unusual quality and size of this capital and its companion piece in Philadelphia (no. 45-25-26) suggest its association with an important church.[1] Yet it finds no close stylistic counterparts in any of the most distinguished monuments in a region whose style it seems to manifest. It is the largeness of forms and the particular kind of composition that reflect the Poitevin style, and comparison with other monuments can only go as far as a very general correspondence in these areas. For example, a lion capital at Champdeniers (Deux-Sèvres) is far cruder in execution and is also composed somewhat differently, but its basic handling of the leonine forms is similar.[2] Champdeniers was a dependent of the abbey of Maillezais (Vendée) where the capitals of the portal are also vaguely reminiscent of the Philadelphia lion capital.[3] Perhaps the closest parallel, and it is only relatively close, since there are far more differences than similarities in style, exists in a capital at Saint-Amant-de-Boixe (Charente) that shows a delightful lion passant-guardant, whose wide grin, oval, drilled eyes, and configuration of snout bear some comparison with the Philadelphia capital. The remarkable quality of the latter, however, outstrips not only all the capitals we have mentioned in comparison, but a good portion of those to be found in the region. It would be valuable indeed if more accurate information could be obtained about this outstanding piece of sculpture.

NOTES

1. *The George Grey Barnard Collection,* privately printed, New York, n.d. (1941), pg. 5, no. 25, pls. VIII, IX.

2. cf. *Dictionnaire des Églises de France,* Paris, 1967, vol. III, pg. III C 37.

3. cf. Arthur Kingsley Porter, *Romanesque Sculpture of the Pilgrimage Roads,* Boston, 1923, vol. VII, pl. 963.

BIBLIOGRAPHY

F. H. Taylor, *The Pennsylvania Museum Bulletin,* vol. XXIII, pg. 21, pl. 8.

Martin Weinberger, *The George Grey Barnard Collection,* privately printed, New York, n.d. (1941), pg. 5, no. 25, pls. VIII, IX.

25. Saint-Raphaël-d'Excideuil (Dordogne).

Beginning of the second quarter of the twelfth century.

Engaged Capital.

A Scene in Hell.

Limestone. h., 22″; w., 22″ d., 14″

Williams College Museum of Art, J. O. Eaton Fund. 49.9.

ex coll.: Joseph Brummer.

The provenance of this capital is securely established. It is from the church of Saint-Raphaël near Excideuil and was seen there in the garden of the presbytery adjoining the church in the late nineteenth century.[1] The sculpture of the church has been thoroughly studied by Professor Brooks Stoddard in an unpublished thesis,[2] and this capital in particular, in addition to a torso from the same church also at Williams, has been discussed by Professor Walter Cahn.[3]

The church of Saint-Raphaël was probably built in the early part of the twelfth century and reconstructed in the late Middle Ages. All that remains of the original building are the apse, a choir with transept, and a nave of two bays. That the nave was longer and that the original façade is lost is indicated by the presence of two free-standing piers about thirty-eight feet in front of the present façade. The fragments of sculpture that exist from Saint-Raphaël undoubtedly belonged to the missing nave bays and façade. These include, among others described by Professor Stoddard, two capitals in the walls of the sacristy of the church, the torso at Williams, an angel still at Saint-Raphaël, a number of pieces in the Fogg Art Museum, Cambridge, and, according to Professor Cahn, an angel in the Philadelphia Museum of Art.[4]

The sculpture of the Perigord reflects the influences of the more distinctive schools of sculpture surrounding it, especially in Poitou and Saintonge to the west and Languedoc to the south. The sculpture from Saint-Raphaël also manifests a strong impulse from the Corrèze, an area bordering the Perigord to the east and closely linked with the sculpture of Languedoc.

The battered condition of the Williams capital makes it difficult to read the narrative in detail, but the dramatic force of the scene, repeating once again an aspect of the theme of damnation, is still potent. Standing in a fiery cauldron to which he is chained by the neck, a damned soul is subjected to particularly horrible tortures by a pair of demons, who are scarcely visible. One stabs the sinner in the abdomen or perhaps, as suggested by Walter Cahn, flays him. It is not entirely clear what the creature to the left is doing, though Cahn maintains that he is clawing the genitals of the doomed soul. Puzzling as well is the object in the figure's mouth. It is likely that it is some other instrument of torture, perhaps, as Cahn suggests, "an assault on the organ of speech."[5] The particular sin that is being punished here is no longer evident.

NOTES

1. A. de Roumejoux, "Saint-Raphael," *Bulletin de la Société historique et archéologique du Perigord,* 1890, pp. 127-130.

2. *The Romanesque Sculpture of Saint-Raphael-d'Excideuil,* unpublished M. A. thesis, The Institute of Fine Arts, New York University, 1962.

3. "Romanesque Sculpture in American Collections: III. New England University Museums," *Gesta,* vol. VIII, 1969, pp. 58-59.

4. Martin Weinberger, *The George Grey Barnard Collection,* privately printed, New York, n.d. (1941), pg. 14, no. 65, pl. XVII.

5. Cahn, *op. cit.,* pg. 58.

BIBLIOGRAPHY

A. de Roumejoux, "Saint-Raphael," *Bulletin de la Société historique et archéologique du Perigord,* 1890, pp. 127-130.

Sale of the *Joseph Brummer Collection,* catalogue, part III, Parke-Bernet Galleries, New York, June 8-9, 1949.

B. W. Stoddard, *The Romanesque Sculpture from the Church of Saint-Raphael-d'Excideuil,* unpublished M. A. thesis, The Institute of Fine Arts, New York University, 1962.

Walter Cahn, "Romanesque Sculpture in American Collections: III. New England University Museums," *Gesta,* vol. VIII, 1969, pp. 58-59.

LANGUEDOC

78

26. Double Capital

Lions and Morses (Sea Lions) *in Combat.*

Languedoc, mid-twelfth century.

Limestone. h., 15″; dimensions of the abacus:
w., 20¾″; d., 13¾″.

Mead Art Building. Amherst College,
Amherst, Massachusetts. 1942.81.

ex coll.: Joseph Brummer.

If the specific provenance of this capital is not known, its general stylistic environment is familiar. It introduces us, in fact, to one of the most important centers of Romanesque sculpture, one whose chronological precedence over Burgundian sculpture is a matter of some debate and whose identity as a distinct regional school is sufficiently complicated to cause it to be one of the chief flaws in the attempt to establish such schools.

The Amherst capital represents a type common in Languedoc and most particularly in Toulouse, which was the capital city of this general region, a major stop on the pilgrimage routes, and a leader in the development of Romanesque architecture and sculpture. Besides generating distinct and important types of architecture and sculpture, which influenced surrounding regions, it was a recipient of styles and innovations from other areas, particularly from Cluny.

The sources for the type of double capital and the style of carving exemplified by the Amherst capital are found most directly in the sculpture of Toulouse. Amherst identifies the capital as from Moissac, but there is nothing to support this label. Instead, the lions with their broad, flat heads, long mouths, and large eyes, the peculiar structure of the legs of the sea lions (or morses as they are called in heraldry), the complicated composition of the entwined forms, and the leaf pattern on the impost block all find their immediate ancestors in a number of the capitals preserved from the cloister of the great pilgrimage church of Saint-Sernin (cloister dated 1140-1150).[1] These capitals generally contain only a pair of lions or fantastic beasts addorsed and entangled in rinceaux. An earlier manifestation of this same composition was located in the cloister (ca. 1125-1130) of the cathedral of Saint-Etienne in Toulouse.[2].

The palmette frieze on the impost block, though ultimately derived from antique sources, is found commonly in Toulousan sculpture in varying degrees of sophistication, from the crisp and richly carved capitals of the ambulatory of Saint-Sernin (ca. 1100)[3] and the cloister at Moissac (ca. 1100)[4] to the flatter and cruder versions

at Saint-Sernin itself (capitals of the tribune of the north and south transept, ca. 1100)[5] and on the Amherst capital.

Walter Cahn[6] has compared the Amherst capital with several of unknown origin in the Musée des Augustins, Toulouse,[7] and though it is true that the basic types of foliate decoration and animals are the same, the style in which they are done is rather removed from the example at Amherst, whose quality is higher. In fact, the latter is far closer in style and quality to many of the capitals that are known to have come from Saint-Sernin. Cahn is accurate, however, in his comparison of the Amherst piece with a capital in The Cleveland Museum of Art (no. 16.1981).[8] Although not precisely from the same source, the Cleveland capital is clearly from the same immediate region.

The Amherst capital serves as a perfect example of another aspect of Romanesque sculpture: the endless vocabulary of animal forms, both real and fantastic, that made up the greater part of the decorative language of this style, and the particular way in which these forms were arranged upon the surface of the architectural element they decorated. Such subject matter as seen in the sculpture represents the absorption of a great variety of traditions and the adaptation of patterns and iconography from many other media: textiles, metal-working, enamel, and book illumination. These rigidly formal compositions, which are yet endowed with vigorous expression and vibrant movement within, and because of, the confining envelope of the architectural member constitute one of the most remarkable and attractive aspects of Romanesque sculpture. A capital such as the one from Amherst brings to mind, of course, the famous, and endlessly quoted, lines of Saint Bernard of Clairvaux criticizing, but at the same time describing so sensitively, Romanesque sculpture.[9]

In the present case on each of the long faces of the capital, two lions, whose bodies meet in a single head, are perched atop the backs of two morses who, at the same time, battle a pair of lions on each of the short sides. This melée of beasts is neatly composed over the surface of two capitals that are united by the abacus above with its palmette frieze, the whole being carved from one block of stone.

NOTES

1. Pierre Mesplé, *Les Sculptures Romanes, Toulouse, Musée des Augustins.* (Inventaire des Collections Publiques Françaises, 5). Paris, 1961; e.g., capitals no. 217, 218, 221, 223, and in a slightly different style, nos. 241, 242, 243.

2. Raymond Rey, *La Sculpture Romane Languedocienne,* Toulouse-Paris, 1936, pg. 234, fig. 183.

3. *Ibid.,* figs. 41, 42, 44.

4. *Ibid.,* fig. 82.

5. *Ibid.,* fig. 47, 50.

6. Walter Cahn, "Romanesque Sculpture in American Collections: III. New England University Museums," *Gesta,* vol. VIII, 1969, pg. 53.

7. Mesplé, *op. cit.,* nos. 312, 313, 314, 320, 321, 322, 324, 326, 327.

8. *Handbook of the Collection,* The Cleveland Museum of Art, 1966, pg. 47, no. 1675.16 in the handbook, but now accessioned under a new number, 16.1981.

9. cf. Elizabeth Holt, *A Documentary History of Art,* vol. I, pg. 21, and quoted in our introduction.

BIBLIOGRAPHY

S. Lane Faison, *A Guide to the Art Museums of New England,* New York, 1958, pg. 66, no. 8.

Walter Cahn, "Romanesque Sculpture in American Collections: III. New England University Museums," *Gesta,* vol. VIII, 1969, pg. 53.

27. Double Capital

Naked Figures Entwined in Rinceaux.

Languedoc or Narbonnais. Second or third quarter of the twelfth century.

Marble. h., 14½″; w., 17½″; d., 9¼″

Wellesley College Museum. Rogers Fund Purchase. Sc 49.24.

ex coll.: Joseph Brummer.

The pervasive influence of Toulousan sculpture in south-western France is further proven by the style, composition, and iconography of this capital. A number of capitals with the same relatively flat, striated rinceaux, either alone or with beasts or humans intertwined among the tendrils of the vines, are associated with at least two of the Romanesque churches of Toulouse: the cloister of the cathedral of Saint-Étienne (1120)[1] and the later friezes and capitals from Notre-Dame-de-la-Daurade (ca. 1180).[2]

In addition, as Walter Cahn has pointed out,[3] two capitals of unknown origin in the Musée des Augustins provide very close parallels in style. No. 276, though entirely different in subject matter—it displays the twelve apostles—is otherwise quite similar in several aspects. It, too, is of marble, and its dimensions are almost exactly the same as those of the Wellesley capital. The facial types of the apostles, particularly the two who are beardless, Simon and Thomas, placed on the narrow sides of the capital, bear a strong resemblance to the types seen on the Wellesley capital. Originally no. 276 in the Musée des Augustins was said to have come from Saint-Pons-de-Thomières (see cat. nos. 28, 29, 30, 31 of this exhibition), but this provenance has now been discounted with no replacement being offered.

No. 278 in the Mesplé catalogue is another rinceaux capital, with entwined nude figures, but its style, size and material do not match the Wellesley capital.

Similar facial types and capitals with heavier and cruder rinceaux are found in the sculptures at Saint-Aventin (Haute-Garonne, ca. 1150). Closer in style are certain of the capitals of the cloister of the old cathedral of Saint-Lizier (Ariége) dated either 1117 (consecration of the church) or ca. 1160 (later work in the cloister).[4] Although none of these forms an exact stylistic parallel with the Wellesley capital, all of them present a picture of provincial perpetuation of motifs and styles generated in a center such as Toulouse. Raymond Rey describes this situation most succinctly in referring to capitals such as the one exhibited here: "Ces formes attardées se répandirent dans toutes les vallées ariégeoises et dans la plus grande partie du versant pyrénéen, où d'humbles sanctuaires perpétuèrent jusqu'à la fin du moyen âge les programmes romans."[5]

The Wellesley capital and its immediate relatives and forbears perpetuate as well a tradition of classical ornament derived either from ancient remains or more indirectly through transmission in other media, particularly manuscript illumination. On all four faces of the Wellesley capital naked figures frolic within the twisting grape vines. On the main face of the capital the two figures, erroneously called Adam and Eve in the Wellesley Museum files, are engaged in no specific action. On the reverse side two wrestlers grapple with one another, but are not meant to represent Cain and Abel as the Museum states. On one of the ends of the capital a figure reaches for grapes; his counterpart at the other end stands entangled in the vines, while below him stand two birds.

The motif of putti or genii encircled by vine scrolls was a common one in Roman art and was adapted for Christian purposes in Late Antique art, the vine becoming an image of the church, the grapes of human souls. Although such an enrichment of meaning was normal, allegorical overtones should not be expected of every subject in medieval art; caprice and an independent decorative vocabulary must be given consideration when attempting to understand medieval iconography.

S.K.S. AND PEARL BRAUDE

NOTES

1. cf. particularly the side of no. 25 in P. Mesplé, *Les Sculptures Romanes. Toulouse, Musée des Augustins.* (Inventaire des Collections Publiques Françaises, 5), Paris, 1961.

2. *Ibid.,* nos. 69, 178.

3. "Romanesque Sculpture in American Collections: III. New England University Museums," *Gesta,* vol. VIII, 1969, pp. 57-58.

4. cf. *Dictionnaire des Églises de France,* vol. III, Paris, 1967, pp. III A 132-135.

5. *La Sculpture Romane Languedocienne,* Toulouse-Paris, 1936, pg. 309.

BIBLIOGRAPHY

Walter Cahn, "Romanesque Sculpture in American Collections: III. New England University Museums," *Gesta,* vol. VIII, 1969, pp. 57-58.

NARBONNAIS

28-31. Saint-Pons-de-Thomières (Hérault).

The Abbey Church.

28. *Double capital with apes and men*

1130s

Marble; h., 15″

Virginia Museum of Fine Arts. 52.19.2.

ex coll.: M. Jammes, la Pérouse.

29. *Single capital with sirens, snakes and birds*
1140s
Marble; h., 10″
Virginia Museum of Fine Arts. 52.19.3.
ex coll.: J. Sahuc, Ardouane.

30. *Single capital with sirens, snakes and birds*
1140s
Limestone; h., 10″
Williams College Museum of Art. No. 49.6.
ex coll.: Joseph Brummer.

31. *Double capital with scenes of the Emmaus Story* (Luke
  24:13-31) *and Christ's appearance to Mary Magdalene*
  (John 20:14-17)

1140s

Marble; h., 14½″

Fogg Art Museum, Gift of Professor A. Kingsley Porter.
  1922.67 (1).

ex coll.: Mme. Marty, Saint-Pons; Demotte, Paris.

The abbey church of Saint-Pons-de-Thomières, founded in 936 by the Count of Toulouse, Raymond Pons II, and his wife, Garsinde, and situated thirty miles northwest of Narbonne close to the crossroads linking Catalonia, Languedoc and Provence, flourished during the eleventh and twelfth centuries under Cluny's rule and the protection provided by the Count's descendants. The original church was rebuilt early in the eleventh century and this structure was fortified and vaulted during the 1160s.[1] A cloister, added to its south wall, bore the brunt of an attack by Roger Trencavel, Viscount of Beziers, in 1170. In an agreement signed the following year the monastery was singled out for reconstruction and, sometime thereafter, a series of capitals in developed Gothic style was added to the group that had been salvaged from Trencavel's pillaging. Repeated sackings of the monastery during the Religious Wars and the Revolution finally obliterated all traces of the cloister; more than thirty of its sculptures survive today predominantly in public collections in France (the Louvre, Toulouse, Montpellier), England (the Victoria and Albert Museum) and the United States (The Metropolitan Museum, Boston, Toledo, Richmond and the Fogg).[2] Of the four styles distinguishable in the sculptures, the two represented here reflect influences from outside the region and emphasize the cosmopolitan contacts to which the abbey was open.

28. Each long face of the capital is dominated by the figure of a bearded, wiry-haired man shown crouching astride the twin drums between a pair of squatting apes. The men appear to menace one of the animals with baton-like objects held in their right hands while they seize the outstretched arms of the second with their left hands. The heads of all six creatures are compressed under emphatic volutes which, prior to damage, combined with a drilled abacus to form a highly ornamental band around the top of the sculpture.

The capital is one of nine from the cloister[3] executed in a style indigenous to the eastern Pyrenees where marble sculptures made for the cloisters and tribunes at Cuxa and Serrabonne provide striking similarities. However, the Saint-Pons capitals are set apart by the attention given to religious representations. One capital in Toulouse juxtaposes the Crucifixion with a Madonna and Child in Glory[4] and another in Paris combines the Evangelist Symbols and Christ giving the Keys to Peter.[5] The religious figures on both of these sculptures duplicate in type and dress the men on the Virginia capital suggesting that the latter ought to be understood as specifically Christian individuals. The apes these figures restrain look toward them with backs turned to the viewer while the unsubdued animals confront the spectator with provocative poses. A similar frontal creature, paired with a multi-winged seraph,

leers at the inner angle of one of the paired tribune capitals at Serrabonne.[6] Apes are familiar as images of sin in north Spanish sculpture of the period[7] and their immobilized placement here reinforces the concept of oppression. Surely these *immundae simiae* were caveats to the monks reminding them of the constant struggle to overcome vice and not mere idle distractions whose presence in Cluniac cloisters St. Bernard condemned.

The capitals of this type from Saint-Pons were dated by Durliat in the last quarter of the eleventh century when abbot Frotoard, who served as Papal legate in Catalonia, could have acquired them in local shops there.[8] More likely, they date from the second quarter of the twelfth century when the tribunes at Cuxa and Serrabonne were under construction[9] and when the abbey, enriched by gifts from the former monk Ramiro, later King of Aragon, was in a position to undertake new construction.[10]

29. and **30.** In contrast to the compressed, menaced, forms on the Roussillonnaise sculpture, the feathered and scaled figures on the two diminutive siren capitals emerge from the drum in a series of exaggerated rhythms that convey a strong sense of animation. From a point on the astragal at the rear of the capital, the creatures' tail feathers diverge in a rising movement that sweeps across the sides of the drum and culminates in the human heads fixed in place of volutes at the front angles. The smaller birds on the sirens's backs and the pair of entwined snakes between them echo their postures, creating a decorative effect that obscures the torment of the representation. The subject is an unusual one in which sirens, described in the Physiologus as possessing a human head and the wings and tail of a bird and who are said to lure men to their doom by means of their song,[11] are themselves made the prey of other creatures. Snakes in twelfth century art were the common tormentors of those guilty of the sins of avarice and unchastity, and their association here with the siren evokes such representations.[12]

Despite surface abrasion and losses at the top and angles of both capitals, more severe in the piece from Williams, the strongly articulated abacus, neutral ground and vigorously carved ample forms suggest a familiarity with late Roman art and hint at Provence as a possible place of origin. The similarity of the shape and organization of the capitals to a group of little known sculptures in the Musée Lamourguier in Narbonne[13] and the correspondence of the decorative forms to those on a marble archivolt now in the Cloisters, New York, said to have come from Narbonne,[14] localize the pieces in the environs of the abbey. The fantastic beasts that ornament the Cloisters' sculpture assume stretching, intertwined postures similar to those of the birds and sirens on the two capitals here. The deeply undercut forms are likewise ornamented

29a

31a

there with identical repetitive patterns of beading, scales and feathery imbrications, the whole slightly more precious in effect.

Sahuc included the capital now in Virginia (cat. no. 29) with a group of sculptures he associated with the church portal at Saint-Pons, since the capital was smaller than the other cloister carvings and was scarcely carved on the fourth side.[15] A third variant of this capital decorates the fenestrated gallery on the façade of the town hall at Saint-Antonin, northwest of Saint-Pons beyond Albi (fig. 29a). The placement of this piece may hint at the original use of the two sculptures exhibited here—perhaps in a window gallery—explaining both their size and incomplete treatment on the rear face. The Williams capital (cat. no. 30) is an inferior version of the Virginia piece (cat. no. 29) in size, quality and material, typifying the repetitive shop procedures characteristic of this group and discussed further below (cat. no. 31).

31. The Emmaus story, with its strong allusions to the Pilgrimage as well as the Crusades, grew in popularity during the twelfth century and was included in the pro-

grams of southern cloisters at la Daurade, Toulouse, Santo Domingo in Silos and Saint Trophime in Arles. The story at Saint-Pons is divided into two parts. The meeting of the travelers (Luke 24:15), presented as a casual procession in which the pilgrims are undistinguished from one another, is juxtaposed with a sacramental interpretation of the Supper (Luke 24:30-31) focused on Christ's blessing and His recognition by the companions. The importance given to this theme of recognition is expressed by the insertion of another such event, the Noli me tangere, before the Supper, as a continuation of the Journey. A fortified city gate, recalling images on seals of the period and probably representing Emmaus, completes the fourth side of the sculpture.

The three Gospel scenes recall representations on separate capitals from the cloister of la Daurade so closely that the dependence of the Saint-Pons piece on that workshop cannot be doubted. The similarity in pose and costume of one of the companions at the Meal to a disciple at the Last Supper in Toulouse is characteristic of the correspondences between the sculptures (fig. 31a).[16] Absent

31b

however is the surface opulence of the la Daurade carvings which fuses figures and settings in a wealth of lively, descriptive detail. In contrast to this pictorial achievement, the Saint-Pons sculptor emphasizes the actual three-dimensionality of his forms by making them compact, differentiating them ornamentally from their surroundings and detaching them significantly from the stone. His limited vocabulary of circular or arched motifs helps to isolate the forms further at the same time conferring an overall, if somewhat static, unity on the scenes.

The seizure of Narbonne by the Count of Toulouse, Alphonse-Jordan, in 1134 may well have provided the channel through which artistic contact between the cities flowed. Although Alphonse's attempt to re-establish power over the lapsed territories once controlled by his ancestors was curtailed in 1143 when the local Viscounts forced him to withdraw,[17] it is likely that during the preceding decade Narbonne was open to numerous influences from his capital. The appearance of the lively Toulousain figure style, shorn of its elegance and transformed into a vernacular mode, on several sculptures in Narbonne (fig.

31b)[18] in the wake of Alphonse's political maneuvers, helps to explain the abrupt disappearance of the courtly idiom from the Languedoc capital after the completion of the chapterhouse of the Cathedral there.[19]

In addition to the sculptures in the Musée Lamourguier, two double capitals from the Abbey of Saint-Paul in Narbonne, with scenes from the Emmaus story and the legend of St. Nicholas, also belong to this group.[20] The Narbonne carvings are diminutive—about 10″ high—and display a particularly decorative approach to subject matter linking them with the Siren capitals (cat. nos. 29 and 30). Likewise, several of the Lamourguier pieces are carved primarily on three sides. The larger Emmaus sculpture should be grouped with the Entombment capital in the Louvre[21] and a Daniel capital in the Victoria and Albert Museum,[22] both of similar size, formality and polish, as the only surviving examples of this shop's work at Saint-Pons.

LINDA SEIDEL FIELD

NOTES

1. Marcel Durliat, "Saint-Pons-de-Thomières," *Congrès archéologique*, CVIII (1950), pp. 275-278. The basic study of the church's history and sculpture is by J. Sahuc, *L'art roman à Saint-Pons-de-Thomières* (Montpellier, 1908).

2. See Raymond Rey, *L'art des cloîtres romans* (Toulouse, 1955), pp. 116ff. for a general discussion of the sculpture.

3. Marcel Durliat, *La sculpture roussillonnaise dans la second moitié du onzième siècle,* (Perpignan, [1949]), pp. 7-13 mentions eight neglecting one included by Sahuc, (*L'art roman,* p. 55, pl. B5-6) but rightly omitting two others (*Ibid.,* pp. 61-63, pl. E3-4 and F6).

4. Paul Mesplé, *Les sculptures romanes: V, Inventaire des collections publiques françaises* (Paris, 1961), No. 264.

5. Marcel Aubert and Michèle Beaulieu, *Description raisonnée des sculptures . . . I: Moyen âge,* (Paris, 1950), No. 6, p. 22ff.

6. Marcel Durliat, *La sculpture romane en roussillon,* I, 2nd ed. (Perpignan, [1952]), p. 63, fig. 47.

7. H. W. Janson, *Apes and Ape Lore in the Middle Ages and Renaissance* (London, 1952), pp. 45-46.

8. Durliat, "Onzième siècle," pp. 14-16.

9. Marcel Durliat, "La Tribune de Saint-Michel de Cuxa," *Études roussillonnaises,* II (1952), p. 112.

10. Cf. Durliat, "Saint-Pons," p. 289.

11. Florence McCulloch, *Mediaeval Latin and French Bestiaries* (Chapel Hill, 1960), pp. 166-167. The term harpies, traditionally used for the figures on this capital, is associated in the bestiaries with a human-headed, winged quadruped.

12. Cf. Jalabert, "Les sirènes," pp. 454-456.

13. Several are described in M. Tournal, *Catalogue du Musée de Narbonne et notes historiques sur cette ville* (Narbonne, 1864), pp. 107-108. See our Fig. 31b.

14. H. S., "A Romanesque Archivolt," *The Bulletin of the Metropolitan Museum of Art,* XVIII (1923), pp. 9-10; illustrated in V.-H. Debidour, *Le bestiaire sculpté du moyen âge en France* (Paris, 1961), p. 9, fig. 1, and Richard Randall, *A Cloisters' Bestiary* (New York, 1960), pp. 34, 35, 40, 41, 45.

15. Sahuc, *L'art roman,* pp. 35, 39.

16. See Paul Mesplé, *Les sculptures romanes: Inventaire des collections publiques françaises V* (Paris, 1961), Nos. 122-154 for photographs of the la Daurade series.

17. A Grabois, "Une étape dans l'évolution vers la désagrégation de l'etat toulousain an XIIe siècle: l'intervention d'Alphonse-Jourdain à Narbonne, 1134-1143," *Annales du Midi,* LXXVIII (1966), pp. 23-35.

18. Cited by Tournal, above n. 13.

19. The traditional date for the Saint-Pons sculpture, after 1170, has never been compatible with the references to Toulousain influence. For both see Aubert, *Description,* pp. 31-32, No. 19. Kingsley Porter suggested an earlier date for the sculpture *(Fogg Notes,* 1922, p. 33), but then changed his mind and tried unsuccessfully to show a close relationship with work at Foussais in western France *(Fogg Notes,* 1923, pp. 10-15).

20. The capitals have been in the Musée des Augustins, Toulouse, since the nineteenth century. Mesplé, *Les sculptures romanes,* Nos. 262 and 263.

21. Aubert, *Description,* No. 19, and Sahuc, *L'art roman,* pp. 77-78, Pl. I 1-4.

22. *Ibid.,* pp. 74-75, Pl. F 2 and *Romanesque Art: Victoria and Albert Museum Small Picture Book No. 15,* 2nd ed. (London, 1961), Pl. 7.

BIBLIOGRAPHY

28. J. Sahuc, *L'Art roman à Saint-Pons-de-Thomières,* Montpellier, 1908, pp. 55-56, Pl. C 2-3.

Joan Evans, *Cluniac Art of the Romanesque Period,* Cambridge University Press, 1950, p. 80.

Marcel Durliat, *La sculpture roussillonnaise dans la seconde moitié du onzième siècle,* Perpignan [1949], p. 10.

Idem., La sculpture romane en roussillon: I, Perpignan, 1952, p. 90.

Arts in Virginia, I, ii, 1961, pp. 10-11.

European Art in the Virginia Museum of Fine Arts, Richmond, 1966, p. 106, No. 185.

29. J. Sahuc, *L'Art roman à Saint-Pons-de-Thomières,* Montpellier, 1908, p. 39, Pl. B 3.

Denise Jalabert, "De l'art oriental antique à l'art roman: Recherches sur la faune et la flore romane; II. Les sirènes," *Bulletin monumental,* XCV, 1936, pp. 436-437, n. 3.

European Art in the Virginia Museum of Fine Arts, Richmond, 1966, p. 106, No. 186.

Walter Cahn, "Romanesque Sculpture in American Collections, III," *Gesta,* VIII, 1969, p. 61.

30. *The Notable Art Collection belonging to the Estate of the Late Joseph Brummer,* Parke-Bernet Sale Catalogue No. 1079, June 8-9, 1949, Part III, p. 133, No. 559 (2).

Walter Cahn, "Romanesque Sculpture in American Collections, III," *Gesta,* VIII, 1969, p. 61. No. V, 5.

31. J. Sahuc, *L'Art roman à Saint-Pons-de-Thomières,* Montpellier, 1908, pp. 78-79, Pl. H 2-4.

A. Kingsley Porter, "Romanesque Capitals," *Fogg Art Museum Notes,* 1922, p. 33, figs. 17-20.

Idem., "The Avignon Capital," *Fogg Art Museum Notes,* 1923, pp. 10-15.

Jurgis Baltrusaitis, *La stylistique ornementale dans la sculpture romane,* Paris, 1931, p. 203, fig. 599.

Molly Ohl Godwin, "Medieval Cloister Arcades from St.-Pons and Pontaut," *Art Bulletin,* XV, 1933, p. 181.

Raymond Rey, *L'Art des cloîtres romans,* Toulouse, 1955, p. 125.

Louis Réau, *Iconographie de l'art chrétien,* II, ii, Paris, 1957, p. 565.

32-33. Saint-Pierre-de-Redes, de Poujol (Hérault).

Church of Saint Peter and Saint Paul. (Mid-twelfth century).

32. Relief. *An Apostle.*

Marble. h., 33¾″; w., 10¼″; d., 6½″

Museum of Fine Arts, Boston. Charles Amos Cummings Fund. 56.335.

33. Relief. *An Apostle.*

Marble. h., 33⅛″; w., 9¼″; d., 5″

Art Museum, Duke University.

ex coll.: Ernest Brummer.

A short distance to the northeast of Saint-Pons-de-Tho-mières is the old priory of Saint Peter and Saint Paul, or Saint-Pierre-de-Rèdes, in the commune of Le Poujol near Lamalou-les-Bains. The earliest reference to the church is dated 1153, but it was actually built in the first half of the twelfth century, though there exist no documents to confirm this.

There is also nothing to confirm the assertion by the Museum of Fine Arts in Boston that its Apostle relief once decorated this church. The files merely state that the relief came from the portal of Saint-Pierre-de-Rèdes and that it resembles a relief still *in situ*. We shall return to this point shortly.

Duke University had no information about its relief, nor had its knowledgeable medievalist, Robert Moeller, studied the piece. Upon seeing a photograph we immediately were reminded of the Boston relief and decided to bring the two together for comparison, grouping them tentatively under the heading of the church designated as the provenance for its relief by the Museum in Boston.

Saint-Pierre-de-Rèdes is a very simple, single-aisled church with an interior space only around seventy-five feet long composed of a nave of five bays and a choir of one bay with a semi-circular apse, and three absidioles in the thickness of the walls at the east end. The walls themselves are very heavy and are pierced only on the south side.

Twin columns attached to the walls support transverse arches applied to the pointed barrel vault, which was replaced in the mid-seventeenth century. The capitals topping these columns are decorated with very crude reliefs of animals and foliage. There are two active portals, the one to the north having been closed. The total decoration of these portals, the west and the south, consists of abstract designs surrounding a cross in the tympanum executed in vari-colored basalt and lintels with carved patterns resembling Cufic script. Nowhere does there seem to be any place from which relief sculpture could have been taken nor is such a possibility discussed in the literature.[1]

The only sculpture that exists at the church in addition to the primitive capitals is an equally primitive relief representing a pilgrim, located within the first blind arch on the south side of the apse, and a relief preserved inside the church showing Saint Peter in a bishop's robes and dating, according to Thibout, from the very end of the twelfth century.[2] It is presumably upon the basis of this relief that the Boston Museum has made its attribution.

Despite the poor quality of the illustration in the article by Thibout there actually seems to be little or no connection between the Saint Peter relief and those in Boston and at Duke. Consequently, at this point we can do noth-ing further than question the provenance given to the Boston relief.

There can be no doubt, however, that both of these reliefs come from the same region as Saint-Pierre-de-Rèdes and Saint-Pons-de-Thomières. The stylistic and typological sources for the figures are also obvious. Before investigating these points, however, it should be stated that the correspondence between the two reliefs, themselves, is not exact. Although both are almost identical in size and are carved in marble, the Boston apostle is more unified and vigorous in composition. Its drapery lines are more logical and more active, but this may be due to the position of the figure. In addition, the Boston apostle is carved in relief upon the surface, and its large feet rest upon a ledge, while the Duke figure is recessed behind the surface and therefore seems flatter.

In most other respects the similarities between the two apostles are striking. The style of the drapery with its folds defined by a ridge framed by two incised lines; the particular movement of the hem line; the decorated borders of the drapery, different in pattern, but similar in conception; the elaborate halo with its radiant pattern, again dissimilar in specific details, but with the same general treatment; the definition of the eyes, nose, and mouth, and the form of the head are all points upon which the two reliefs agree to the extent that it seems probable that they were from the same monument except for the problem of the two different kinds of relief.

That this monument was closely derived from the sculptures of the cloister of the cathedral of Saint-Étienne in Toulouse seems indisputable. Built and decorated between 1110 and 1115, the cloister was completed by 1117. It was destroyed between 1812 and 1817, and the sculptural remains are now in the Musée des Augustins, Toulouse. At the southeast corner of the cloister was located a chapter hall whose sculptural decoration has recently been studied by Linda Seidel.[3] Her relocation of the twelve apostle reliefs from what appears to have been a spurious portal arrangement concocted in the early nineteenth century to a more logical arrangement in the chapter house itself is of great interest. The dating of these reliefs is probably somewhere between 1125 and 1135.[4] This has determined our dating of the Boston and Duke apostles to mid-twelfth century because they are clearly derived from the Saint-Étienne apostles. Is it possible that the existence of such apostle reliefs in several cloister-chapter house complexes might suggest the original location of the two reliefs in the exhibition and might further suggest the loss of such a complex at Saint-Pierre-de-Rèdes, explaining away our bewilderment over the choice of that church as a provenance for the reliefs?

Allowing for the much higher quality of the Toulouse reliefs, their role as sources for the Boston and Duke figures can be seen not only in the correspondence in general types, but in the haloes, the typical Languedocian drapery ridges, the shape, details, and character of the faces, and decorated borders of the robes (cf. cat. nos. 34-36, fig. 34a). The Saint-Étienne figures, however, are of limestone and are slightly larger in size (1.16 m. or about 42″ high).

In the Boston Museum file devoted to its apostle relief there is a photograph of a sculptural fragment showing the upper portion of a figure that is undoubtedly by the same hand and from the same series. Dr. Hanns Swarzenski reported verbally that this piece was on the Paris art market in 1957, was sold in 1960 to another dealer, who in turn sold it to a Swiss collector. It measures .362 m., or about 14″, which would correspond, if it were whole, with both the Boston and Duke apostles.

NOTES

1. cf. especially, E. Bonnet, *Répertoire archéologique du département de l'Hérault,* Montpellier, 1938, pp. 48-49, *Le Poujol;* Marc Thibout, "Saint-Pierre-de Rèdes," *Congrès Archéologique,* vol. 108, 1950, pp. 261-270.

2. *op. cit.,* pg. 269.

3. Linda Seidel, "A Romantic Forgery: The Romanesque 'Portal' of Saint-Etienne in Toulouse," *The Art Bulletin,* vol. L, no. 1, March, 1968, pp. 33-42 and figs.

4. cf. Paul Mesplé, *La Sculpture Romane, Toulouse, Musée des Augustins.* (Inventaire des Collections Publiques Françaises, 5), Paris, 1961, unpaginated. The apostle figures are numbered 1, 5, 8, 11, 15, 19, 22, 24 in the catalogue.

BIBLIOGRAPHY

32. Boston Museum of Fine Arts *Calendar of Events,* December, 1956.

SPAIN

98

34-36. Santiago de Compostela.

Monastery of San Pelayo de Antealtares.

Second quarter of the twelfth century.

34. *Column with addorsed apostles above an ornamental base.*

Matthias with a book, halo inscribed + MATHIAS ∴; Jude with a book, halo inscribed ET IUDE ∴; Simon with a scroll, halo inscribed + SIMONIS.

Grey-white marble veined with black, traces of polychromy. h., 45¾″.

Fogg Art Museum. Gift of the Republic of Spain through the Museo Arqueológico Nacional and Professor A. Kingsley Porter. 1933.100.

35. *Column with addorsed apostles, unadorned base.*

Bartholomew with a book and cross; halo inscribed
+ BARTOLOMEUS; Matthew with tablets, halo
inscribed T · MATHEUS ∴; James with book, halo
inscribed + IACOBUS ⋯ FR DNI.

Cast of original in the Museo Arqueológico Nacional,
Madrid, no. 55480. h., 45¾″

Fogg Art Museum. 1933.101.

36. *Column with addorsed apostles.*

    Andrew with closed scroll, halo inscribed ANDREAS ;
        Peter with key, halo inscribed + PETRUS; Paul with
        scroll inscribed Ego Paulus cupio dissolvi et cum XPO
        EE multo melius; halo inscribed   PAULUS.

Cast of original in Museo Arqueológico Nacional,
    Madrid, no. 55479. h., 45¾″

Fogg Art Museum. 1933.102.

In 1933, in an exchange of treasures, the Spanish government gave the Fogg Art Museum one of the three columns decorated with addorsed apostles that had been removed from the church of San Pelayo de Antealtares in Santiago between 1926 and 1927.[1] The two other sculptures, casts of which are shown here, remained in the collection of the National Archeological Museum in Madrid. The columns were first mentioned in 1605, at which time four of them were described as supporting the altar in San Pelayo. The fourth column, presumably decorated with additional apostles—probably Philip, John and Thomas[2]—was separated from the group early in the eighteenth century when the altar was dismantled and replaced by a modern structure.[3]

Kingsley Porter, the first to study the columns in detail, associated them with the altar erected over the tomb of St. James in the Cathedral by his disciples and served by the monks of San Pelayo. Bishop Diego Gelmírez enlarged the altar twice during the twelfth century, and Porter theorized that the columns were carved during the first remodeling in 1105, then transferred to San Pelayo in 1135 with part of the original altar to make room in the Cathedral for a silver retable.[4] The documentary evidence supporting his arguments is slim; in fact, the first reference to the altar's presence in San Pelayo does not appear until the end of the fifteenth century.[5]

The columns are unique in altar programs in type and iconography.[6] They are tall for a table, measuring almost 46 inches without capitals, and sufficiently different in the proportion of the figures, decoration of the bases and even material,[7] to suggest that they were not planned as an intimate ensemble. Their attribution to a ciborium or baldacchino erected over St. James' tomb[8] is not supported by the description in the Pilgrim's Guide composed during the 1130s.[9] Rather, the resemblance of the Antealtares columns to the multi-figured shafts that appeared during the second half of the twelfth century in cloisters, such as those at Saint-Bertrand-de-Comminges and Châlons-sur-Marne, recommends a similar function for them.[10] Moreover the manner in which the figures are arranged indicates that the columns were planned to be viewed from two sides. When Mathias, Bartholomew and Andrew are seen dominating one face, the two other apostles in each case are paired in the opposite views. Gestures and drapery stress the relationship between the two, particularly in the cases of Peter and Paul and Simon and Jude.

This pairing of the apostles recalls the decoration of reliefs from the chapter house at Saint-Etienne in Toulouse to which the column figures from Santiago have been compared in respect to drapery and stance (Fig. 34a).[11] The large feet, usually sandaled, that curl around leafy projections on the two columns with bases recall the feet on the non-Gilabertian reliefs from the Toulouse chapterhouse. But these figures writhe in their niches, and the constrained poses and flattened forms of the column figures more closely resemble those observed on the pier reliefs at Silos (Fig. 34b).[12] Paleographic similarities be-

34a

34b

tween the inscriptions here and those on the Antealtares columns have been pointed out by Professor Schapiro.[13] These relationships with Toulouse and Silos are more convincing than those suggested with the sculpture on the south transept façade at Santiago[14] and more helpful in providing a date for the columns.

A substantial amount of building was undertaken at Santiago during the 1120s and 1130s after peace had been restored to the community.[15] It is likely that the columns were carved during this period for the cloister of the cathedral which was begun in 1124 and received a royal donation in 1137.[16] The destruction of the cloister in the sixteenth century preceded by several decades the first mention of the columns as supports for the altar in San Pelayo, a use to which they may have been adapted at that time.

LINDA SEIDEL FIELD

NOTES

1. A. Kingsley Porter, "Santiago Again," p. 100 and *Spanish Romanesque Sculpture,* II, 6.

2. Tyler, "A Spanish Romanesque Column," p. 45.

3. See Porter, "Santiago Again," p. 109, for the early history of the sculptures.

4. *Ibid.,* pp. 105-109.

5. Gaillard, "Statues-colonnes," pp. 172, 175-176.

6. Braun, "Der Altar," I, p. 165.

7. Vázquez de Parga referred to the finer quality of the marble in the baseless column (*L'art roman,* 1961, p. 570). The two in Madrid were referred to as being of calcerous stone in a report to the Governing Board of the Archeological Museum (Fogg Files, dated 17 October, 1932).

8. Carros Garcia, "Os piares," p. 13; Camps Cazorla, *Arte románico,* p. 155; Chamoso Lamas, *Santiago,* p. 138; Vázquez de Parga, *L'Art roman,* p. 570.

9. Jeanne Vielliard, *Le Guide du Pèlerin de Saint-Jacques de Compostelle,* Mâcon, 1963, pp. 108-114; Gaillard, "Statues-colonnes," pp. 174-175.

10. Porter, *Romanesque Sculpture,* I, 221 and IV, 492, X, 1487.

11. Tyler, "A Spanish Romanesque Column," p. 51; Gaillard, "Statues-colonnes," p. 177.

12. *cf.* Tyler, "A Spanish Romanesque Column," pp. 49-50 and Gaillard, "Statues-colonnes," pp. 176-177.

13. Schapiro, "Silos," p. 366.

14. *Fogg Art Museum Bulletin,* 1934, pp. 15-16 and Gaillard, "Statues-colonnes," p. 176.

15. Kenneth John Conant, *The Early Architectural History of the Cathedral of Santiago de Compostela,* Cambridge, 1926, pp. 39, 41, 42.

16. Porter initially denied any relationship with the Platerías portal and dated the columns instead 1130-40 on the basis of analogies with the figure of Oliver on the façade of the Cathedral of Verona (*Romanesque Sculpture,* I, 220).

BIBLIOGRAPHY

José María Fernandez Sanchez and Francisco Barreiro, *Santiago, Jerusalem and Roma,* I, Santiago, 1880, pp. 274-275.

Antonio Lopez Ferreiro, *Historia de la Santa A.M. Iglesia de Santiago de Compostela,* Santiago, 1898, I, 277-279.

A. K. Porter, *Romanesque Sculpture of the Pilgrimage Roads,* Boston, 1923, I, 220, VI, pl. 705-708.

idem., "Santiago Again," *Art in America,* XV, 1927, pp. 96-113.

idem., *Spanish Romanesque Sculpture,* New York, 1928, I, pl. 59 and II, 4-8.

Joseph Braun, *Der christliche Altar,* Munich, 1924, I, 165, pl. 19.

Xesus C. García, "Os piares do altar do mosteiro de San Pelayo de Sant-Yago," extr. from *Boletin de la Academia Gallega,* 1931, pp. 8-9, pl. II.

Parnassus, V, October 1933, p. 28.

Anon, "A Gift of a Romanesque Sculpture from the Spanish Government," *Bulletin of the Fogg Art Museum,* III, 1934, pp. 14-17.

E. Camps Cazorla, *El Arte románico en España,* Barcelona, 1935, p. 155, fig. 23.

Fogg Art Museum Handbook, Cambridge, 1936, p. 36.

Meyer Schapiro, "From Mozarabic to Romanesque in Silos," *Art Bulletin,* XXI, 1939, p. 354, no. 147, p. 366.

Arts of the Middle Ages: Catalogue of a Loan Exhibition, Museum of Fine Arts, Boston, 1940, no. 166, pl. XXII.

W. R. Tyler, "A Spanish Sculpture in the Fogg Museum," *Art News,* March 2, 1940, p. 13.

idem., "A Spanish Romanesque Column in the Fogg Art Museum," *Art Bulletin,* XXIII, 1941, pp. 45-52.

Hans Sedlmayer, *Die Entstehung der Kathedrale,* Zurich, 1950, p. 207.

Spanish Medieval Art: Loan Exhibition in honor of Dr. Walter W. S. Cook; the Cloisters, New York, 1954-55, No. 32, pl. IV.

Georges Gaillard, "Les statues-colonnes d'Anteltares à Saint-Jacques de Compostelle," *Bulletin de la Société nationale des Antiquaires de France,* 1957, pp. 171-179.

Manuel Chamoso Lamas, *Santigo de Compostela: Guias artisticas de España,* Barcelona, 1961, pp. 136-138.

L'Art roman; Exposition organisée par le gouvernement Espagnol sous les auspices du Conseil de l'Europe, Barcelona and Santiago 1961, Nos. 1894, 1895, pp. 569-570.

Marcel Durliat, *L'art roman en Espagne,* Paris, 1962, No. 236, pp. 85-86.

Robert G. Calkins, *A Medieval Treasury,* Ithaca, New York, 1968, No. 53, pp. 137-138.

37. Santa Marta de Tera (Zamora).

Last decade of the eleventh century.

Relief. *Christ in Majesty.*

Limestone. h., 38½″; w. 22″

Collection of Mr. John Nicholas Brown, Providence, R.I.; on loan to the Museum of Art, Rhode Island School of Design. 197.38.

The importance of the pilgrimage routes to the development of Romanesque sculpture and architecture is well enough known to require no discussion here. That the goal of all of these routes should be represented in this exhibition (cat. nos. 34-36) is appropriate and is also a necessity if we are to understand not only the general character of Romanesque sculpture, but the identity of particular stylistic groupings.

The strong ties that bound together a number of churches in the old kingdom of León and Castile in northwestern Spain and several important pilgrimage churches in Languedoc are seen in the forms of the architecture and in the close parallels that exist in the sculpture. In Spain it is the great church of Santiago, Saint James the Greater, Apostle of the West, at Compostela, that represents a center of activity. In Languedoc this position is occupied by Saint-Sernin in Toulouse. Building activities in both of these areas reach a climax at the end of the eleventh century, perhaps the most important moment in the development of Romanesque art, for it is at this time that the immense and daring third church at Cluny is being erected and that the prophetic Anglo-Norman architecture is reaching a peak of achievement.

Among those churches included in the Compostela-León group is Santa Marta de Tera, once the site of a very important shrine at which vast numbers of the infirm and handicapped were cured. The church still stands, but one piece, at least, of its decoration found its way some years ago into the hands of a prominent Providence collector. There is little known about the history of the church. Documents recording gifts are dated 1033, 1063, 1085, and 1129, but do not refer to construction. A choice of the latter two dates seems the likeliest possibility, and the weight of opinion is in favor of the years around 1085.

There is no question, however, that the relief of Christ comes from Santa Marta. It was seen and photographed *in situ* by Manuel Gomez-Moreno in 1908 and 1927 and by Arthur Kingsley Porter in 1925.[1] Porter mentions that by 1928 the relief was for sale in Madrid. It was about this time that Mr. Brown had the good fortune to acquire the piece.

The relief confirms the dating of the church to ca. 1085-1100 by its very close stylistic links with more accurately dated projects within the Compostela-León-Toulouse group. In chronological order these are the altar table and ambulatory reliefs at Saint-Sernin in Toulouse (1096), the Virgin and Child relief from San Benito, Sahagun (Museo Arqueologico Nacional, Madrid, (ca. 1100), the pier reliefs of the apostles in the cloister at Moissac (1100), the upper portions of the south transept portal, or Puerta de las Platerías, at Santiago de Compostela (ca. 1105), the portal of the south flank of the nave,

or Porte Miégeville, at Saint-Sernin, Toulouse (ca. 1110-1115), the tympana of the Puerta de las Platerías (after 1117), and the sculpture of the west and south (Puerta de Perdron) portals at San Isidoro de León. The dating of the sculpture at León, crucial to this discussion, is extremely complex and has not yet been fixed. The church itself was begun around 1071 and consecrated in 1149. Between these two dates a number of reconstructions occurred. Some of the sculpture of the west portal appears to be of the eleventh century, but the rest and that of the south transept portal probably dates around 1120-1130.

Despite certain expected and allowable variations the characteristics of this sculpture, including the Providence relief, reflect the participation in a common style. Massive proportions expressed in heavy limbs, thick, ropy hair, simple, but weighty folds of drapery, and the smooth volumes of the large head are the most prominent general features of this style. Strongly classical in feeling, much of this sculpture seems to reflect the direct influence of sixth century Constantinopolitan ivory carving as seen in the Archangel relief in the British Museum and in the figures on the front of the throne of Maximian in Ravenna. We shall see the significance of this relationship in iconography as well as style.

A number of specific works with the characteristics described above could be cited to demonstrate the close ties that existed between Santa Marta de Tera, as represented by the Providence relief, and the León-Toulouse style. The most convincing parallels may be drawn with the Adulteress with the Skull of Her Lover and the Woman Holding a Lion from the Puerta de las Platerías at Compostela;[2] with the figure of San Pelayo in the right spandrel of the west portal at San Isidoro de León;[3] to a lesser extent with the Virgin and Child from Sahagun;[4] with the relief of Saint Peter in the right spandrel of the Porte Miégeville at Saint-Sernin, Toulouse;[5] and with the relief of the two Women with the Signs of the Lamb and the Ram, also from Saint-Sernin and now in the Musée des Augustins.[6]

The Latin, Apollonic, beardless type of Christ represented on the relief from Santa Marta de Tera was in time completely overshadowed by the familiar bearded Near Eastern or Syrian type. Yet the beardless type is part of a very old tradition and is found most frequently in Roman, Early Christian and early Byzantine art. It also remains a constant type in Carolingian and Ottonian art from the ninth to the eleventh century. Numbers of ivories, manuscript illuminations, and mosaics show Christ as a youthful figure, a Sun God whose image absorbs the characteristics of Apollo. Such a parallel is particularly apt in the Providence relief where Christ holds an open book inscribed with the words EGO SUM LUX

MUNDI (John, 8:12). Enthroned in what was probably the center of a *Maiestas Domini* used to decorate a portal, the figure of Christ was probably flanked by angels and/or the four Apocalyptic beasts of the Evangelists. That the figure is indeed Christ is indicated not only by the text, but by the cruciform nimbus. The most direct model for the Providence relief is, of course, the ambulatory relief of Christ Enthroned (ca. 1096-1100) at Saint Sernin, Toulouse. The type and composition are identical, though the Toulouse relief shows another aspect of the style that we have indicated is common to Toulouse and León.

In contrast to the Toulouse *Maiestas Domini*, the Santa Marta figure wears what appears to be a chasuble, since it is worn over a robe. The shape, however, is not entirely accurate because of its squared hem. The chasuble is cut so as to fall over the arms and describe a parabolic curve front and back, which it does not appear to do in the Providence relief. If the garment is a chasuble, it would be an unusual, but, in the context of Spanish art, not a unique use of it on a figure of Christ.

The importance attached to the chasuble as the outer garment worn by priest or bishop during the Mass originates in the seventh century in Spain. It is no surprise to find, therefore, that in Spanish art Christ Himself is identified with the priest or bishop by wearing sacerdotal robes. Precedents and parallels for this aspect of the Santa Marta relief may be found in the relief showing Christ Among the Apostles on the Arca de San Felice (1090) in San Millan de la Cogolla[7] and, with mitre and crozier as well as chasuble, on the antependium from Sigueña (Huesca) of the first half of the twelfth century and now in the Lerida Museum.[8]

S.K.S. AND PEARL BRAUDE

NOTES

1. cf. the bibliography for this entry.

2. cf. Ole Naesgaard, *Saint-Jacques de Compostelle et les débuts de la grande sculpture vers 1100*, Aarhus, 1962, pp. 68, 69, 75. It is interesting to note that the subject of the Adulterous Woman with the Skull of Her Lover is found on a capital at Santa Marta de Tera.

3. cf. Manuel Gomez-Moreno, *El Arte Romanico Español*, Madrid, 1934, pl. 69.

4. cf. Arthur Kingsley Porter, *Spanish Romanesque Sculpture*, vol. I, New York, n.d., (1928 ?), pl. 46.

5. cf. Arthur Kingsley Porter, *Romanesque Sculpture of the Pilgrimage Roads*, vol. IV, Boston, 1923, pl. 312.

6. cf. William Wixom, *Treasures From Medieval France*, The Cleveland Museum of Art, 1967, pg. 55.

7. cf. Naesgaard, *op. cit.*, pg. 41.

8. cf. Porter, *Pilgrimage Roads, op. cit.*, pl. 555.

BIBLIOGRAPHY

Manuel Gomez-Moreno, "Santa Marta de Tera," *Boletín de la Sociedad Española de Excursiones*, vol. 16, 1908, pp. 81-87, esp. pg. 87 and the preceding plate.

idem., Zamora (Catalogo Monumental de España), Madrid, 1927; "Santa Marta de Tera," pp. 182-186, esp. pp. 185-186 and plate.

Arthur Kingsley Porter, *Spanish Romanesque Sculpture*, New York, n.d. (1928 ?), pg. 62, and notes 482, 483, pl. 29.

Walter Cahn, "Romanesque Sculpture in American Collections: II. Providence and Worcester," *Gesta*, vol. VII, 1968, pg. 54, fig. 6.

38. Relief.

Christ in Majesty or an Apostle.

Spanish (León?). Twelfth century.

Ivory. h., 7⅜"

Collection of Mr. John Nicholas Brown, Providence, R. I.;
on loan to the Museum of Art, Rhode Island School of
Design. 198.38.

This object has been included in an exhibition dealing only with monumental stone sculpture for three reasons: It is beautiful; it is immediately at hand; and it serves as a valuable example of another aspect of the sculpture of the twelfth century. These same three reasons governed the choice of the other two representatives of the precious or so-called minor arts (cat. nos. 59, 60).

The inter-action between monumental sculpture on the one hand and ivory and metal-work on the other is an important one to understand in relation to the development of a style and a medium. With the virtual disappearance in the West of monumental stone sculpture during the period between the fifth and the eleventh centuries visual expression was maintained in such areas as manuscript illumination, gold work, ivory carving, and, to some extent, bronze casting. Such media depended upon each other and upon the traditions that had been established for each with a possible predominance of book illumination.

By the eleventh century the development of a mature and large-scale architecture had encouraged the reappearance of sculptural decoration in stone. Without its own tradition of imagery to draw upon it was dependent upon the material provided by books, ivories, and precious objects. By the end of the eleventh century stone sculpture had reached such a point of maturity that it began to exert a counter-influence upon the other arts. At all times, of course, the exchange of impulses flowed freely, uniting within the environment of the church building all of the arts in the service of religion.

This situation is illustrated by the juxtaposition of certain of the stone sculptures with this ivory and the two bronze crucifixes. Perhaps the effect of sculpture on a large scale is seen in the fact that all three small objects are in themselves monumental. This term need not be limited to objects that are large in size, but may be applied to works of art that are powerful in their effect and therefore psychologically monumental.

The ivory figure raises a number of problems. At almost all points it satisfies the iconography of a seated figure of Christ except for the fact that the nimbus is not cruciform and the left hand holds a scroll rather than the usual book. The figure might be an apostle but for the hand raised in blessing, a gesture that, as far as this author has found, is never associated with an apostle in this position and presumably within a group of similar figures. The hand may be opened entirely or may be pointing to one side, but only Christ exercises the ultimate power to bless. Scrolls are common to both prophets and apostles, but the nimbus would eliminate the prophet. In short, a number of disparate elements appear to have been gathered together here, making the piece somewhat difficult to interpret. The strongest possibility seems to be that, despite the bestowal of a blessing, the figure represents an apostle, was part of a series, and was used to decorate a reliquary, an antependium, or a book cover.

As pointed out by Miss Carmen Gomez-Moreno, Mr. Brown's ivory figure is related to, but not from, the same hand as an ivory figure of an apostle in the Pitcairn Collection (Bryn Anthyn, Pa.).[1] There is no denying that the two are very close in style. The handling of all details of the face, including hair, eyes, nose, and mouth, and the sweeping rhythms of the drapery are so intimately related that the attribution seems to come down to a question of the same workshop, but by different hands.

Miss Gomez-Moreno summarizes the common opinion regarding the localization of the style of these pieces in León with the more specific mention of the atelier of the monastery of San Millan de la Cogolla in Logroño. The origins of this style may be seen in the Arca de San Felice (1090) and, from a different location, the remarkable Carrizo Crucifix (ca. 1063) now in the museum in León.[2] Other ivories supposedly related to the San Millan atelier, or at least to the ateliers of León, such as the plaque in The Metropolitan Museum showing the Way to Emmaeus and the Noli Me Tangere and the companion plaques of the Deposition (Oviedo, private collection) and the Three Marys at the Tomb (Leningrad, Hermitage Museum), dating in the early twelfth century,[3] do form, with the San Millan Arcas, a loosely interrelated group to which both the Brown and Pitcairn ivories belong.

Miss Gomez-Moreno suggests another highly original possibility in the existence of a connection between Mr. Brown's ivory and several relief fragments in stone of the apostles in the Musée des Antiquaires de l'Ouest, Poitiers, (ca. 1170).[4] Although there are certain superficial resemblances between the ivory and the reliefs that could indicate some form of communication between León and Poitiers along the pilgrimage roads, we do not feel that a closer relationship should be predicated.

NOTES

1. *Medieval Art From Private Collections.* A Special Exhibition at the Cloisters, New York, 1968, nos. 75, 76.

2. cf. Adolph Goldschmidt, *Die Elfenbeinskulpturen aus der Romanischen Zeit,* XI-XIII Jahrhundert. vol. IV, Berlin, 1926, nos. 98, 99, 104.

3. cf. Walter W. S. Cook and José Gudiol Ricart, *Ars Hispaniae,* vol. VI, *Pintura e Imagineria Románicas,* Madrid, 1950, pg. 291, fig. 275.

4. cf. Arthur Kingsley Porter, *Romanesque Sculpture of the Pilgrimage Roads,* vol. VII, Boston, 1923, pls. 1132, 1133.

BIBLIOGRAPHY

Arthur Kingsley Porter, *Spanish Romanesque Sculpture,* New York, n.d. (1928?), vol. I, pg. 58.

(Georg Swarzenski), *Arts of the Middle Ages,* exhibition catalogue, Boston, 1940, no. 129, pl. XIII.

Spanish Medieval Art, The Cloisters, The Metropolitan Museum of Art, New York, 1954, no. 25.

Carmen Gomez-Moreno, *Medieval Art From Private Collections.* A Special Exhibition at the Cloisters, New York, 1968, no. 76.

39. The Crucified Christ.

Aragonese Pyrenees. Second half of the twelfth century.

Oak with traces of polychromy. h., 7′1″; w., at the
   arms, 7′1″

Museum of Art, Rhode Island School of Design. 43.195.

ex coll.: Rafael Garcia Palencia (or Garcia y Palencia),
   Madrid; José Weissburger.

The most moving qualities of Romanesque sculpture are exemplified in this magnificent Christus reported to have been found in the Aragonese Pyrenees. Solemn in expression, majestic in bearing, the figure establishes an overpowering presence not only by its size, but by the heavy mass of the flattened body. With no overt expression of the physical aspects of the Passion, the face impassive, the body unscarred (although this may have been indicated by paint), the figure is a perfect image of the paradoxical fusion of divinity and humanity in the form of Christ. In a parallel fashion it epitomizes those elements that are most typical of Romanesque sculpture. In form the scale of the figure and the semi-abstract handling of its parts obey laws that are established from two realms. The ultimate spirituality of medieval thought creates a set of values based upon the abstract, the conceptual, and the immaterial. That such values should produce forms that show less concern for physical or visual reality than for the expression of spiritual truth or the embodiment of pure concepts or the description of divine beings is obvious. The Romanesque sculptor, drawing upon centuries of inherited traditions, creates figures and tells stories in a way that emphasizes not their transient, temporal existence through *mimesis,* but their exposition of immutable truths through abstraction.

Concurrently, one sees in Romanesque, and especially Burgundian, sculpture a deep awareness of and sensitivity to human emotion. With an economy of language that is astounding and that is born of his basically non-naturalistic approach, the Romanesque sculptor is able to convey the various categories of human emotion. A counterpart to this sensitivity is certainly to be found in what is commonly recognized as a pure manifestation of humanism, in the fullest sense of the word, among a large number of the greatest thinkers between 1050 and the later decades of the twelfth century.

It is this conjunction, in unequal proportions, of the temporal and the eternal that is represented not only by Christ Himself, but particularly by this Corpus. Christ Crucified, His near-naked body displayed, His humanity sacrificed, is present, but subordinate to His immortality and to His ultimate removal from pain and the perishability of the flesh, qualities that are de-emphasized in the sculpture in contrast to the images of the Crucified created in the later fourteenth and fifteenth centuries.

We have spoken of the laws of two realms that govern the forms of this Christus and have been described in brief and very general terms only one. The second realm is equally important, though far less conceptual. The body of the figure is, for the most part, flat without even a break at the knees to give it greater spatial involvement. It is very restrainedly composed of a series of broken axes: the head leaning to the right in a slightly sharper angle than the torso, whose direction is opposed by the angle given to the lower body down to the knees at which point, between knees and feet, the legs are straight. Except for the projection of the feet and the subtle forward inclination of the head with its long shape, huge eyes, flat forehead, and sharply defined zones of stylized hair and beard, contributing to its stark and immobile expression, the body itself is quite flat, and this planarity is extended to the sides, forming, in effect, three separate surfaces rather than the continuous contours of the human body.

It is in speaking of the surface and of what occurs on this surface that one becomes aware of the second realm whose laws govern Romanesque sculpture: the realm of architecture. The predominance of architecture as a conditioning environment for the other arts in the Romanesque and Gothic periods is a truth so well known as not to require further definition here. In Romanesque sculpture this environment might almost be described as tyrannical. The support of heavy, continuous barrel vaulting initially required an equally heavy and continuous wall, and no matter how sophisticated the articulation of this wall might become, the basic principle of its original planarity was preserved, particularly in the right-angle junction of any two planes.

The sculptural decoration of such architecture was forced to obey these principles. Its location was limited primarily to portals and capitals, and, to some extent, corbels or brackets, and its function as imagery was always subordinate to the form of the structural element it covered. Thus the truncated pyramidal shape of the capital determined the composition and narrative complexity or freedom of the imagery carved upon it, and the sculpture on the tympanum, lintel, archivolts, and jambs of a portal were conditioned to a great extent in form and composition, in scale and mass by the plane of the wall upon or behind which the sculpture existed.

Against such severe restraints the sculptor pitted his extraordinary abilities as a designer, drawing, as we have said above, upon a vast array of former traditions that seem to coalesce in Romanesque art. The compression of his forms within certain rigidly prescribed limits results in the unusual energy that seems to be generated by Romanesque sculpture, and in the endlessly fascinating contortions of its composition, whether of an abstract and heraldic confrontation of beasts or in the telling of a story.

The Providence Christus, though not an integral part of architecture, certainly obeys its laws. We have mentioned the planes that form its body, and we may now refer to the description of body forms and draperies upon the surface of these planes. The differentiation of the basic zones of the torso is handled as a series of layers on the surface in much the same way that a Romanesque wall is articulated by the subtraction of certain masses to form arches and windows and by what appears as an overlay of thin planes of wall or of attached supporting elements. Thus in this statue the abdomen appears as a clearly marked zone framed by the sharp edge of the rib-cage, which illogically unites with the line of the hips. The prominence of the sternum acts as a kind of dripping keystone to the arch of the rib-cage, and the ribs themselves are merely a set of very low ridges separated regularly and emphatically by shallow depressions.

The perizonium with its large, knotted sash is carved in sharp, symmetrical patterns of folds. The crisp, somewhat brittle edges of the drapery exemplify the kind of energy mentioned above as being so prominent an aspect of Romanesque sculpture.

To turn to more factual matters, the late Professor Walter W. S. Cook was told by one of the former owners of the Corpus that it was found in the Aragonese Pyrenees. Yet in type and, to some extent, in style, its closest relatives are found in north-central Spain, that is, in the old kingdom of León and Castille. Looking back as far as the justly famous ivory corpus from Carrizo (1063; now in the Muséo Arqueológico de León), one finds resemblances in the basic conception of the body, the shape of the head and the treatment of its details, and the handling of the perizonium. More contemporary in date and closer in type, though differing in specific stylistic characteristics, are two crucifixes from the same area of León and Castille. The one located in the church of Sancti-Espiritu in Salamanca is very similar in the articulation of the body and the type of the head and the perizonium. The other, now in the Cloisters Collection, New York City, and formerly in the church of the Convent of Santa Clara near Palencia (León) (fig. 39a), repeats the general composition and handling of the body, but is less closely affiliated in style. Walter Cahn also mentions another work that could be placed in this group, a crucifix at Palacios de Benaver.[1]

Although we do not propose to enter into a discussion of the subject here, for anyone familiar with the processes

of medieval thought, the dimensions of the Providence figure are provocative, since they are not only equal in height and width, but are equal in the number seven, a number whose importance and significance are well-enough known.

Neither is there space here to relate this Providence Corpus typologically to the development of this particular image. Such a history may be found in the work by Dr. Paul Thoby and involves the presence of a crown, the type of garment, the use of four nails, the expressive content of the figure, and other details.[2]

The Providence crucifix is formed of four separate pieces: the head and neck, the arms, and the remainder of the body. Although the polychromy has been lost, traces are still visible. In comparison with the figures mentioned above this Christus has a rough and weathered appearance, a feature that detracts in no way from its impressive strength.

NOTES

1. "Romanesque Sculpture in American Collections: II. Providence and Worcester," *Gesta*, vol. VII, 1968, pg. 51.

2. *Le Crucifix des Origines au Concile de Trente,* Nantes, 1959; *Supplement*, Nantes, 1963.

BIBLIOGRAPHY

Augusto Mayer, *El Estilo Romanico en España,* Madrid, 1931, pg. 74, fig. 59.

A.M.B., "A Spanish Romanesque Crucifix," *Museum Notes,* Museum of Art, Rhode Island School of Design, vol. 1, Sept., 1943.

Art News, December, 1943, pp. 26-27.

W. W. S. Cook and J. Gudiol-Ricart, *Ars Hispaniae,* vol. VI, Madrid, 1950, pg. 363, fig. 405.

Spanish Medieval Art, exhibition catalogue, The Cloisters, The Metropolitan Museum of Art, New York, 1954, no. 38.

Treasures of the Museum of Art, Rhode Island School of Design, 1956.

United Church Herald, vol. 9, no. 18, December, 1966, pg. 24.

Walter Cahn, "Romanesque Sculpture in American Collections: II. Providence and Worcester," *Gesta,* vol. VII, 1968, pg. 51, fig. 1.

40. Sant Pere de Roda (Catalonia).

Mid-twelfth century.

The Master of Cabestany. Capital.

Marble. h., 18⅛″; w., 14¾″; d., 14¾″

Worcester Art Museum. Gift of Arthur Byne. 1934.33.

The medieval art historian's concern with the identification of stylistic filiations rarely seems able to include the activities of individual personalities in the area of monumental sculpture. Our knowledge of specific artists is limited, especially in earlier periods. Names such as the famous Gislebertus of Autun, Guinamond of La Chaise-Dieu, Girbertus of Carennac, Geoffroy of Le Puy, Pierre Brun of Saint-Gilles-du-Gard, Bernardus of Conques, Bernardus Gelduinus and Gilabertus in Toulouse, and Rotbertus of Clermont-Ferrand are among the few names of sculptors that have been allowed to survive either through direct signatures or in documents.[1] If we take notice of the existence of individual artists whose names are recorded, especially those who signed a work, whether it be a section of architecture, a capital, or a whole tympanum and lintel as at Autun, we must pause before the still persistent concept of the anonymity of the medieval artist who selflessly subjected himself to the dictates of a higher authority.

At the same time the lack of recorded names or the random mention of craftsmen of varying levels of importance reflects a sense of values quite different from that obtaining in the entire period from the Renaissance of the fifteenth century to the present day. The Abbot Suger must have gathered around him the most brilliant architects and artists of his day, yet in his writings concerned with the building of the great abbey-church of Saint-Denis not one of them is mentioned. We know only of an Albricus, a mosaicist who signed mosaic medallions now in the Musée de Cluny.[2]

The way in which an artist is mentioned and the type of document in which his name is found are also important considerations. The continuing fame of the great artists of antiquity is reflected in the legends preserved by Pausanias and Pliny the Elder, and the same kind of praise of genius is what is revived in the fifteenth century in Italy. We become aware of the importance of architects and master-painters, sculptors, and illuminators in the thirteenth and fourteenth centuries north of the Alps through the impersonality of documents. In contrast with the Renaissance and antiquity we do not find the talents of such men praised by contemporaries in a special form of eulogistic literature. In the whole of Jean Froissart's (1333?-1400?) voluminous chronicles only one artist, André Beauneveu, is mentioned, and that may have been primarily because Beauneveu was also a native of Froissart's birthplace, Valenciennes.

Perhaps because of the scale of the projects—the vast complex of architecture, sculpture, and painting—the greater proportion of the work was done by what we would call craftsmen, executing the designs of masters whose personal styles were imposed upon the work as a whole.

Whether or not, by the accident of history, we can give names to these masters, the unique elements of their styles are identifiable and establish separate artistic personalities.

One such personality is represented by this capital from Worcester. Named from the tympanum of the parish church of Cabestany (Pyrénées-Orientales), a few miles to the southeast of Perpignan, the style of this master is found at a number of sites on both sides of the eastern Pyrenees in Roussillon and Catalonia: Le Boulou (Pyrénées-Orientales), certain portions of Saint-Michel-de-Cuxa (Pyrénées-Orientales), the sarcophagus of Saint Sernin at Saint-Hilaire (Aude), Rieux-Minervois (Aude), Lagrasse (Aude), Saint-Papoul (Aude), perhaps a tympanum from the church of Erroncho, and finally Sant Pere de Roda, on the coast in the northeast corner of Catalonia.

Because of the unique aspects of his style it is not difficult to follow the movements of this sculptor within a region on both sides of the Pyrenees and including portions of Languedoc and Provence, unified for a period of time under the House of Barcelona. Raymond Berenger IV (1131-1162) and Alfonso I (1162-1196) gathered under their control most of the territory along the Pyrenees and extending eastward to Nice. Within the unity of such a vast empire the free flow of communication, both artistic and otherwise, developed without hindrance.

The Master of Cabestany has been most thoroughly studied by Marcel Durliat.[3] The peculiar style of the

40a

master is best exemplified by a relief in the Musée Marès, Barcelona, from the church of Sant Pere de Roda showing the Calling of Saint Peter (fig. 40a). The Worcester capital is described by its donor as having been purchased on the site of this same church,[4] and its style is in accord not only with the Calling of Saint Peter relief, but with the other works ascribed to the master.

The most distinctive features of this style are the small, round heads with sharp edges to the jaw and cheekbones, the exaggerated slant of the eyes with their deeply drilled holes on either side of the pupil, the short, curved nose, large hands with long, slender fingers, sharply incised folds of drapery composed of hook-like lines and the edges of wide, flat, overlapping planes, and the broad, flat feet. If such characteristics are noted most clearly in the relief and capital from Sant Pere de Roda, variations in the style occur in the other churches visited by the Cabestany Master. In fact, the actual presence of his hand as distinct from the influence of his style may be due for a re-evaluation. The Cabestany tympanum, for example, varies in significant details from the Roda material, causing us to wonder whether the original appellation was correct. Most recently, as pointed out by Walter Cahn,[5] E. Junyent initially[6] and, following him, George Zarnecki[7] have suggested that the master may have come from Tuscany, citing capitals from Sant Antimo and Castelnuovo dell'Abate. If such a theory is correct, and it is widely accepted, it may explain the uniqueness of the master's style in the Roussillon and Catalonia.

Although the Worcester capital has been roughly treated, its extraordinary quality is still very evident. To illustrate the widespread influence of antique art and the similarity in various regions of a constant motif we have here the same type of modified Corinthian capital with a head in place of a rosette on one side as we saw in the capitals from Providence (cat. no. 7) and Philadelphia (cat. no. 8) originally from the Nivernais. In the Roda capital a flat network of tendrils defined by deep drilling is stretched over the surface, ending in curled knobs, most of which have been broken off. The typical Master of Cabestany head with its slightly anguished look dominates the total form.

NOTES

1. E. Lefèvre-Pontalis, "Repertoire des Architectes, Maçons, Sculpteurs, Charpentiers et Ouvriers Français au XIe et au XIIe Siècle," *Bulletin Monumental*, vol. 75, 1911, pp. 423-468.

2. *Ibid.*, pp. 424, 446.

3. *La Sculpture Romane en Roussillon*, vol. IV, 1954, pp. 6-49.

4. Walter Cahn, "Romanesque Sculpture in American Collections: II. Providence and Worcester," *Gesta*, vol. VII, 1968, pg. 60.

5. *Ibid.*, pg. 61.

6. "L'oeuvre du maître de Cabestany," *Actes du quatre-vingt-sixième Congrès des Sociétés Savantes*, Montpellier, 1961 (1962), pp. 169-178.

7. "A Sculptured Head Attributed to the Maître de Cabestany," *Burlington Magazine*, 1964, pp. 536-539.

BIBLIOGRAPHY

Worcester Art Museum Bulletin, vol. XXIV, no. 4, 1934, pg. 115.

Worcester Art Museum Annual Report, 1935, pg. 15.

Marcel Durliat, "Sculpture de marbre de l'église de Sant Pere de Roda," *La Sculpture Romane en Roussillon*, vol. III, 1950, pp. 46-64.

idem., "L'Oeuvre du 'Maître de Cabestany'," *La Sculpture Romane en Roussillon*, vol. IV, 1954, pp. 6-49, fig. 15.

Walter Cahn, "Romanesque Sculpture in American Collections: II. Providence and Worcester," *Gesta*, vol. VII, 1968, pp. 60-61, fig. 16.

41. Relief

The Annunciation to the Virgin. Navarre. Second quarter
of the twelfth century.

Limestone with traces of polychromy. h., 34¼″; w.,
27¼″; d., 7½″

Yale University Art Gallery, Maitland F. Griggs and
Leonard C. Hanna Funds. 1968.37.

ex coll.: Wildenstein and Company, New York.

Close stylistic parallels with this relief, newly acquired by Yale, are difficult to find. Walter Cahn's suggestion that it bears some resemblance to the western portal at Leyre in Navarre, especially the tympanum figures, has some merit. The parallels, however, are relatively few. Beyond the pyramidal shape of the lower draperies, the narrow, sloping shoulders, and the shape of the outer cloak as it falls between the arms and down either side of the figures, other characteristics are handled quite differently. Facial types, drapery patterns, and decorative details are dissimilar.

As at Leyre, this relief of the Annunciation to the Virgin probably formed part of a series of scenes concerned with the Infancy of Christ: the Visitation, the Nativity, and the Adoration of the Magi.[2] At Leyre, where the Annunciation is similarly composed, such scenes are set into the south spandrel of the western portal. The Yale Annunciation shows the Archangel Gabriel and the Virgin as rigid, frontal figures facing the beholder, their large, oval heads, long necks, peculiar doll-like bodies, and tiny, dangling feet giving the figures the strangely emblematic quality that is typical of much of Romanesque sculpture.

Cahn explains some of the more unusual iconographic elements in this relief. Whereas the archangel in the Leyre Annunciation gestures with one hand and raises a cross with the other, referring to the nature of Him who is conceived, the same figure in the Yale relief holds a book in the mutilated right hand, indicating, perhaps, the prophecy of Isaiah regarding the Virgin birth. The left hand, now broken away, holds a flower which either alludes to the Virgin's purity or to the act of divine conception. Cahn also mentions several precedents for the rare placement of a crown on the head of the Virgin in an Annunciation scene: Eguarte (Navarre), the cloister of Silos, and the crowned Virgin of the Visitation on the lintel of the south portal of the west façade at Chartres.

The peculiar junction between the wimple of the Virgin and the collar of her gown is not due to a break, which eliminates the suggestion that the head and the body are mismatched. It appears, rather, that the sculptor had difficulty creating a transition from the one garment to the other. A serious break can be seen running across the upper wings of the archangel and the shoulders of the Virgin, and the nose and mouth of the former are broken away.

NOTES

1. "Romanesque Sculpture in American Collections: III, New England University Museums," *Gesta,* vol. VIII, 1969, pp. 66-68.

2. *Ibid.,* pg. 67.

BIBLIOGRAPHY

Walter Cahn, "Romanesque Sculpture in American Collections: III, New England University Museums," *Gesta,* vol. VIII, 1969, pp. 66-68.

42. Engaged Capital.

Palencia. Late twelfth century.

Limestone. h., 13⅝″; w., 13½″; d., 14″

The Walters Art Gallery, Baltimore. 27.305.

ex coll.: Joseph Brummer

This unusual capital has five figures spread over its three sides. A companion piece is also in the possession of The Walters Art Gallery (no. 27.304). Both capitals present complex iconographical problems which, despite previous investigations, cannot be totally solved. The capitals appear to present certain medieval methods of solving legal problems, in this case a test for perjury and trial by combat. The one capital, no. 27.304, shows two persons taking an oath by placing their hands in the mouth of a Roman lion mask, a version of the famous Bocca della Verità in Rome. The legend connected with such a test states that the stone jaws of the mask will snap shut on the hand of a perjurer.

The capital on exhibit here shows two warriors in combat, the one on the right being now in rather poor condition. Shield to shield, sword arms raised, they prepare to hack away at one another. On the left face of the capital a coifed female figure holds the hand of a bearded, sharp-featured man who appears to have been gesturing toward the warriors. The right face of the capital is occupied by a male figure of uncertain identity.

It is extremely difficult to determine the reason the two knights have taken up arms against one another. The suggestion has been made that they are testing the virtue of a woman accused of adultery, and there is a literary tradition in Spain that could have served as a source for such imagery. The *Cantigas* of Alfonso X of Castile (il Sabio) (1221-1284), the *Libro de Buen Amor* of Juan Ruiz, and the renowned play, *Celestina*, are all works that deal with this subject. The seventh *Cantiga* of Alfonso X, for example, relates the tale of the unchaste abbess. It is elaborately illustrated in the Escorial manuscript of the *Cantigas* (Lib. Real. Biblioteca T.I.1.). The Walters capital appears to have all the necessary elements for this type of narrative.

The stylistic identity of the capital presents fewer problems. The large heads are formed by means of severe planes and sharp edges along the cheekbones, the edges of the nose, and the jawlines. The expressiveness achieved through such elements is accentuated by the bulging eyes set beneath the hard line of the brow.

The tension expressed in the faces is released as swirling energy in the draperies whose folds vary between thin, shallow ridges and overlapping or stepped planes to deep slashes and thick gatherings of cloth that fall vertically between the legs with no sense of organic unity, but with effective drama.

The dense composition with overlapping or contiguous forms and with the large heads of the figures adds the final element to the sense of excited action and internal energy generated by this capital.

Although the parallel is not exact, the Walters capitals have been compared with the capitals in the Fogg Art Museum from Santa Maria de Alabanza in Palencia, dated by an inscription to 1185 (fig. 42a). Less harsh in their definition of contours, the Alabanza capitals show much the same facial types with bulging eyes, long faces, planar cheeks, and peculiar, down-turned mouths. In the draperies, too, the swirl over the knee seen in the Alabanza Christ in Majesty and the bearded man of the Walters capital is identical in both cases, while the configuration of hem-lines and the planar folds are alike. The conclusion is that the Walters capitals were carved in the Palencia area at the end of the twelfth century.

DOROTHY GLASS AND S.K.S.

42a

BIBLIOGRAPHY

The Walters Art Gallery, *Handbook of the Collection,* Baltimore, 1936, pg. 63.

José Pijoán, *Summa Artis: Historia General del Arte,* vol. IX, *El Arte Románico Siglos XI y XII,* (2nd ed.), Madrid, 1949, pp. 534-537, figs. 843-844.

Spanish Medieval Art, Loan Exhibition in honor of Dr. Walter W. S. Cook arranged by the Alumni Association, Institute of Fine Arts, New York University, in cooperation with The Metropolitan Museum of Art, New York, 1954, no. 37.

PROVENCE AND RHÔNE VALLEY

43-44. Saint-Gilles-du-Gard (Gard).

43. *Head of a Man.*

Church of Saint-Gilles. ca. 1150 (?).

Limestone. h., 7²⁵⁄₃₂″; w., 5⁹⁄₁₆″; d., 5³⁄₃₂″

Cincinnati Art Museum. Gift of Mr. and Mrs. Philip R. Adams. 1958.548.

44. *Head of a Man.*

Church of Saint-Martin (?). ca. 1183-1190.

Limestone. h., 7″

The Phillips Collection, Washington, D. C.

Both of these heads have been accepted without question as having come from the west portals of the important Cluniac priory of Saint-Gilles at Saint-Gilles-du-Gard (Gard), and there is little reason to question the attributions. Nonetheless, the extremely complicated problems of dating, original disposition, and variety of individual styles presented by the sculpture at Saint-Gilles, when considered in relation to the styles seen at other churches in the region, has provided us with justification for re-examining these two superb fragments.

It is obvious that a very close association existed among the sculptural ateliers that worked at Saint-Gilles, at the church of Saint-Martin, also in Saint-Gilles-du-Gard, at Saint-Guilhem-le-Désert (Hérault), and at Saint-Trophime in Arles (Bouches-du-Rhône). In some cases it appears that the same atelier actually worked at several monuments.

The history of the church of Saint-Gilles is too involved to relate in detail here,[1] but a brief resumé is necessary in order to decide upon a date for the sculpture. The first church on the site was built in 725 and dedicated to Saint Peter. In the third quarter of the ninth century the remains of Saint Gilles were brought to the church, which was consequently re-dedicated. At the beginning of the eleventh century a new church was erected, but it seems that by the 1090's yet another new church was being built. The construction was continued over a number of years, the plans being changed shortly after 1116.

Discord among the monks of Saint-Gilles, the Count of Toulouse, the abbey of Cluny, and the pope delayed completion of the church, and our knowledge of its progress during the first half of the twelfth century is extremely scanty. It appears, however, that by ca. 1157 the church was close to completion. From 1157-1178 it was one of the most important stops on the pilgrimage roads.

Between 1178 and 1185 feudal warfare again disrupted the building activities, but the years between 1185 and 1195 were active and important ones for the abbey church. It was not until the first quarter of the thirteenth century that the final re-arrangements of the façade, including the piercing of the side portals, were accomplished.

The dating of the sculptural decoration itself is even more complex due to the slow construction, the changes of plan, and later restorations. The earliest work could date before 1116 and is found in the reliefs on the socles of columns of the central portal.[2] The majority of the large apostle figures and the lintel and frieze on the left side of the central portal were probably executed from ca. 1150 to ca. 1195. Two apostles, Saints Bartholomew and Matthew to the left of the central portal, are signed by a Petrus Brunus, who appears in documents at Saint-Gilles in 1157 and 1171 and at Nîmes in 1165 and 1185. Much

of the dating hangs upon this precious fragment of knowledge, but it has not led to any agreement.

Louis Grodecki, in his excellent article "La 'Première Sculpture Gothique.' Wilhelm Vöge et l'état actuel des problèmes,"[3] reviews the various opinions regarding the dates of Saint-Gilles and its sculpture. De Lasteyrie, Aubert, Gouron and most French scholars prefer a generally late date of ca. 1150-1185 for the central portal and the flanking walls. Wilhelm Vöge supported an earlier date, placing Saint-Gilles in the thirties or forties of the twelfth century.[5] Vöge's opinion was more or less seconded by Walter Horn and Meyer Shapiro who looked to the period between ca. 1129 and 1145.[6] Finally, Hamann also subscribed to an early date going to an extreme in dividing the work into two campaigns dated before 1116 and between 1116 and 1129.[7] In dating the two heads on exhibit here we have compromised to some extent by tentatively dating the head from Cincinnati around 1150. The other head requires and has received further discussion below regarding its possible provenance and date.

The tympanum of the central portal is a restoration of 1650, but is made up of some old fragments. The side portals were pierced and decorated at the beginning of the thirteenth century (ca. 1210-1220).

43a

The destruction of the heads on the façade of Saint-Gilles was systematic and thorough, providing, within the complex range of styles, little to which we may compare the Phillips and Cincinnati heads. Enough remains, however, to draw very convincing parallels. The Cincinnati head is in almost complete agreement with the first apostle to the right of the central portal, tentatively called Saint Andrew by Hamann (fig. 43a), who groups this statue, its companion, and the relief of the Archangel Michael in the niche to the left of the north portal together as reflecting strong influences from Burgundian sculpture.[8]

Another possibility for comparison, and one that appears to involve the same atelier, is a relief in the Archeological Museum, Montpellier, with five apostles from the church of Saint-Guilhem-le-Désert, built in two campaigns between ca. 1076 and ca. 1100.[9] In the second half of the twelfth century a porch was added to the façade, and it is possibly from this area that the relief comes. One head in particular (fig. 43b) compares very closely with the so-called Saint Andrew from Saint-Gilles and the Cincinnati head.[10]

The Phillips head does not seem immediately to fall into any of the stylistics groups at Saint-Gilles. From the point of view of a developing realism in sculpture, it is far more advanced with a soft expressiveness and a sub-tlety of modelling that is in contrast to the sharper treatment of surfaces and details throughout the Saint-Gilles sculpture, even that dated in the early years of the thirteenth century.

It is for this reason that we wish to advance the theory that the Phillips head may be from the church of Saint-Martin at Saint-Gilles-du-Gard. Our knowledge of the sculpture of this church is based upon a portion of a tympanum discovered in the wall of a house in Saint-Gilles in October of 1949 and exhibited in Cleveland in 1967.[11] (fig. 44a) It shows four apostles below two angels bearing instruments of the Passion and is a portion of a Last Judgment scene.

The style and dating of this fragment have caused some controversy. Gouron sees two ateliers at work, one local and involved in the carving of the bodies; the other possibly from the abbey church of Saint-Gilles nearby and responsible for the heads. He dates the work between 1183 and 1190. Hamann takes issue with this opinion, though he sees definite connections between the abbey church and Saint-Martin through an atelier that he links with certain styles seen in the west portals at Chartres Cathedral (ca. 1145-1155).[12] His major objection is to the dating, since he wishes to place the relief between Saint-Gilles and Saint-Guilhem-le-Désert or around 1152.

43b

44a

It is our feeling that because of the character of the heads Gouron's date is more accurate.

It is precisely the quality of the Saint-Martin heads, and particularly the second and fourth apostles from the left, that is reminiscent of the Phillips head—the softer modelling, the developed expressions, the gentle curving of the hair. Even the size of the Phillips head would fit the apostles on the Saint-Martin relief. We feel, therefore, that the evidence is strong enough to warrant a consideration of this attribution.

The sculpture of Saint-Gilles represents the epitome of Provençal Romanesque particularly in the region of the lower Rhône Valley. Being a late manifestation of Romanesque, the style of this area is a compound of many elements, making it difficult to define. Strong influences from major areas of Romanesque development such as Burgundy, Languedoc, and the Auvergne mingle with what is perhaps the strongest native source of Provençal style, the remains of antique sculpture. It is, in fact, this classical foundation that unifies and modifies the various impulses that combine to form the distinctive style seen at Saint-Gilles and the churches related to it stylistically; churches such as Saint-Guilhem-le-Désert (Hérault), Saint-Martin at Saint-Gilles-du-Gard, Notre-Dame-des-Pommiers at Beaucaire (Gard), Saint-Trophime at Arles (Bouches-du-Rhône), Saint-Maurice at Vienne (Isère), and Saint-Bernard in Romans-sur-Isère (Drôme).

The factor that complicates to such a great extent an understanding of Provençal sculpture of the second half of the twelfth century is the appearance in the Ile-de-France of what is called Early Gothic architecture and sculpture. Here dating is crucial, but it would seem that some sort of exchange took place at various times with perhaps the initial flow of influence proceeding from the north, as represented by such churches as Saint-Denis and Chartres, to the south during the second half of the twelfth century. Although the character of the sculpture at Saint-Gilles or Saint-Trophime is essentially different from the Portail Royal at Chartres, lacking the calmness and relative physical independence of the latter, the stylistic links are not to be denied. It is this exchange as it develops in the last two decades of the twelfth century that determines, perhaps, the remarkable quality of the Phillips head and the fragment from Saint-Martin now in the Musée de la Maison Romane, Saint-Gilles.

NOTES

1. Richard Hamann, *Die Abteikirche von St. Gilles und ihre kunstlerische Nachfolge,* Berlin, 1955; Marcel Gouron, "Saint-Gilles-du-Gard," *Congrès Archéologique,* vol. 108, Montpellier, Paris, 1951, pp. 104-119, with full bibliography.

2. Hamann, *op. cit.,* pls. 105-115.

3. *Bulletin Monumental,* vol. 117, pp. 265-289, esp. pp. 271-275.

4. R. de Lasteyrie, *Etudes sur la Sculpture française au Moyen Age (Foundation Eugène Piot, Monuments et Mémories publiés par l'Académie des Inscriptions et Belles-Lettres, t. VIII),* Paris, 1902, pp. 96, 108; Marcel Aubert, *La Sculpture Française au Moyen Age,* Paris, 1946, pg. 148; Marcel Gouron, *op. cit.,* pp. 113-118.

5. Wilhelm Vöge, *Die Anfänge des Monumentalen Stiles im Mittelalter,* Strassburg, 1894; *idem.,* "Zur provençalischen und nordfranzösischer Bildnerei des 12. Jahrhunderts," *Repertorium für Kunstwissenschaft,* 1903, pp. 512-520, reprinted in *idem., Bildhauer des Mittelalters. Gesammelte Studien.* Berlin, 1958, pp. 36-43; *idem.,* "Der Provençalische Einfluss in Italien und das Datum des Arler Porticus," *Repertorium für Kunstwissenschaft,* 1902, pp. 409-429, reprinted in *Bildhauer des Mittelalters, op. ct.,* pp. 16-35.

6. Walter Horn, *Die Fassade von St. Gilles. Eine Untersuchung zur Frage des Antikeneinflusses in der Südfranzösischen Kunst des 12 Jahrhunderts,* Hamburg, 1937; Meyer Shapiro, "New Documents on St. Gilles," *Art Bulletin,* vol. 17, 1935, pp. 415-430.

7. Hamann, *op. cit.*

8. *ibid.,* pl. 25, 26.

9. *ibid.,* fig. 303, 305.

10. *ibid.,* fig. 305.

11. Marcel Gouron, "Découverte du Tympan de l'église Saint-Martin à Saint-Gilles," *Annales du Midi,* vol. LXII, April, 1950, pp. 115-120; William Wixom, *Treasures From Medieval France,* The Cleveland Museum of Art, 1967, pp. 120-121, 359, no. III 38.

12. Hamann, *op. cit.,* pp. 251-254.

BIBLIOGRAPHY

43. *The Art Quarterly,* Autumn, 1959, pp. 273, 275.

Robert Calkins, *A Medieval Treasury,* Andrew Dickson White Museum of Art, Cornell University, October 8-November 3, 1968; Munson-Williams-Proctor Institute, Utica, New York, November 10-December 8, 1968, pg. 139, no. 55.

45-46. Avignon (Vaucluse).

Cloister of the Cathedral of Notre-Dame-des-Doms (?)

45. *Capital with Scenes from the life of Samson:*
Samson wrestling with the Lion (Judges 14:6) ; Samson Carrying off the Gates of Gaza (Judges 16:3) ; Delilah and the Philistines cutting Samson's hair (Judges 16:19) ; Samson Destroying the House of the Philistines (Judges 16:25-30).

ca. 1160

White marble. h., 12½″

Fogg Art Museum. Gift of Meta and Paul J. Sachs. 1922.132.

ex coll.: Garcin; Bernard d'Hendecourt, Paris; Paul J. Sachs, 1920.

46. *Capital with Grotesque mask, griffins and vines*

ca. 1160

Marble. h., 12 inches

The Metropolitan Museum of Art. 47.101.24.

ex coll.: Garcin at Apt; Alphonse Kahn, Paris; Joseph
    Brummer.

Towards the middle of the twelfth century, the city of Avignon was stirred by a spurt of building activity at its two most important churches, the Cathedral Notre-Dame-des-Doms up on the rock and the Abbey of Saint-Ruf just outside of town. All that remains in the city today to recall the splendid cloisters built about that time for these monuments is a group of sculptures in the local Musée Calvet. Other carvings have strayed into collections in Aix, Bordeaux, Paris, both Cambridges and New York. While there is little disagreement about the attribution of these characteristically delicate, fluid carvings to this part of Provence, their association with the cathedral, first proposed by Labande,[1] has been disputed.[2] Documentary evidence stresses the prestige of Saint-Ruf during this period, in particular the support provided by one of its previous priors, Pope Hadrian IV, for a new cloister at his former abbey.[3] In a letter written in 1156 to the canons at Pisa, he announced the visit of workers from Saint-Ruf sent by him to obtain materials for this purpose. Since most of the Avignon capitals are in fine white marble, it has been assumed that the stone was brought from Carrara and then shared with workers at the cathedral.[4] Neither assumption has been substantially supported, in fact at least two types of marble were used,[5] and the second suggestion is especially speculative. The question of attribution is complicated by the fact that the new cloister may have been built at Saint-Ruf's priory in Valence and not in Avignon.[6] A capital in a collection there representing the Judgment of Solomon with figures seen against a foliate ground, is especially close to a sculpture of the Creation now in Bordeaux.[7] Both are markedly similar in figure style to the capitals from Avignon and should be added to the group. Lastly, in favor of a Saint-Ruf designation, is the information provided by the early lists of acquisitions published by the Musée Calvet which reveal that between 1835 and 1840 six capitals, one bas-relief and one inscription from the abbey of Saint-Ruf entered the collection.[8]

45. The Samson capital is unique in its lively combination of narrative sequence and expressive detail. Decorative, turreted architecture frames each face creating a palpable space within which the figures pivot or interact with remarkable agility and the ornamented astragal serves as a stage on which they move. Fidelity to the story is revealed in the arrangement of the scenes, beginning with Samson's encounter with the lion. Although numerous angle details, such as the animal between the Gaza and Delilah scenes who serves alternately as a caryatid and a stagehand, form transitions between events, a sequential reading of the episodes is not really meaningful. Interest is clearly focused on the contrast between the two dramatic moments of Samson's greatest power and the single instant of his impotent submission. The Gaza scene is unfinished at the top and is clearly subordinated to the other events.

Von Stockhausen pointed out the reappearance of architectural motifs—such as the corbeled arch, slender pilasters, window divisions—as well as drapery patterns on several other capitals in the Avignon series.[9] Additional similarities exist such as the resemblance of the head of the sleeping Samson to the severed one of John the Baptist on a less successful capital in Aix.[10] But in composition and spirit, the Nativity capital in Avignon, with its wiry figures, environmental volutes and busy, drilled surface is most like the Fogg sculpture. The quantity of subtle, elegant detail on the Samson carving recalls that on the capitals from the chapter house of the cathedral of Toulouse. Perhaps this sculpture was similarly placed at eye level and in an equally prominent, intimate location.

46. The foliate capitals in the Avignon group present rich leafy sprouts frequently combined with ornamental bands. The Metropolitan capital recalls one of the pieces in Avignon with a faun's head and another in Paris which similarly makes use of masks.[11] With its complicated arrangement of slender forms, its avoidance of flat static surfaces, its concentrated use of the drill and its decorated astragal, the New York piece resembles the Samson sculpture to a greater degree than does a second, compact capital in the Fogg with acanthus decoration.[12]

LINDA SEIDEL FIELD

NOTES

1. Labande, "Notre-Dame-des-Doms," pp. 353-360, pl. LXXV-LXXIX.

2. Rippert, "Remarques," pp. 69-74; Benoit, "Saint-Ruf," pp. 154, 159.

3. See Labande "Notre-Dame-des-Doms," p. 359.

4. Porter, "The Avignon Capital," p. 9; Wixom, *Treasures*, p. 58.

5. Borg, "A marble capital," p. 312.

6. Charles Didelot, "Le Pape Adrien IV à Valence," *Bulletin de la Société d'archéologie et de statistique de la Drôme, XXV*, 1891, pp. 27-28; Rippert, "Remarques," 1956, p. 69.

7. Didelot, "Valence," pp. 36-46, pl. 6-9. The Bordeaux capital in the Musée Lapidaire, Marburg photos no. 35682, no. 35684, no. 35685, no. 168693 is cited by von Stockhausen, "Die Kreuzgänge II," p. 133, n. 3.

8. *Dons faits au Musée Calvet depuis sa fondation jusqu'au 31 décembre 1838*, Avignon, 1839, p. 47; *Dons faits . . . pendant l'année 1839*, Avignon, 1840, p. 5.

9. Von Stockhausen, "Die Kreuzgäng," p. 128-129.

10. For illustrations of this and the following sculpture see Borg, "A marble capital," figs. 14, 16 and 19.

11. The Avignon piece is illustrated in Borg, "A marble capital," fig. 18, and the Paris one in Aubert, *Description raisonnée*, no. 104.

12. R. de L. Brimo, "A Second Capital from Notre-Dame-des-Doms at Avignon," *Bulletin of the Fogg Art Museeum*, V, November, 1935, pp. 9-11.

BIBLIOGRAPHY

45. L.-H. Labande, "L'église Notre-Dame-des-Doms d'Avignon, des origines au XIIIe siècle," *Bulletin archéologique*, 1906, pp. 282-365, pl. LXXVI.

R. de Lasteyrie, *L'architecture religieuse en France à l'époque romane*, Paris, 1912, p. 630, fig. 642.

A. Kingsley Porter, *Romanesque Sculpture of the Pilgrimage Roads*, Boston, 1923, I, 300, IX, nos. 1342-1343.

idem., "The Avignon Capital," *Fogg Art Museum Notes*, I, January, 1923, pp. 2-10.

Paul Deschamps, *French Sculpture of the Romanesque Period*, New York, 1930, p. 88, pl. 85 B-C.

R. de L. Brimo, "A Second Capital from Notre-Dame-des-Doms at Avignon," *Bulletin of the Fogg Art Museum, Harvard University*, V, 1935-36, pp. 9-11.

Hans-Adalbert von Stockhausen, "Die romanischen Kreuzgänge der Provence, II Teil: Die Plastik," *Marburger Jahrbuch für Kunstwissenschaft*, VIII-IX, 1936, abb. 167, 168, 170, pp. 122, 127-134.

Chefs d'oeuvre de l'art français: Exposition, Palais National des Arts, Paris, 1937, I, no. 955, p. 430.

Richard Hamann-MacLean, *Frühe Kunst im westfrankischen Reich*, Leipzig, 1939, p. 24, pls. 198-199.

Arts of the Middle Ages: Catalogue of a Loan Exhibition, Museum of Fine Arts, Boston, 1940, pl. XXII, no. 165.

Werner Weisbach, *Reforma Religiosa y Arte Medieval*, trans. by Helmut Schlunk and L. Vázquez de Parga, Madrid, 1949, p. 186, fig. 82.

Marcel Aubert, *Description raisonnée des sculptures . . . I, Moyen-âge*, Paris, 1950, pp. 79, 80, 81.

Vincent Rippert, "Remarques sur l'architecture et l'art roman," *Cahiers rhodaniens*, III, 1956, p. 74.

Louis Réau, *Iconographie de l'Art Chrétien*, II, i, Paris, 1956, pp. 237, 244.

idem., Les Monuments détruits de l'art français, Paris, 1959, II, 273.

Fernand Benoit, "Provence," in *L'Art roman en France*, ed. Marcel Aubert, Paris, 1961, p. 423.

idem., "L'Abbaye de Saint-Ruf," *Congrès archéologique*, CXXI, 1963, p. 159.

Guy Barruol, "L'Église Notre-Dame-des-Doms d'Avignon au XIIe siècle," *Congrès archéologique*, 1963, p. 57.

Works of Art from the Collection of Paul J. Sachs, Cambridge, 1965, no. 84.

William D. Wixom, *Treasures from Medieval France*, The Cleveland Museum of Art, 1967, pp. 58-59, 351, no. III-6.

Alan Borg, "A Further Note on a marble capital in the Fitzwilliam Museum, Cambridge," *Burlington Magazine*, CX, June 1968, pp. 312-316.

46. Labande, L.-H. "L'église Notre-Dame-des-Doms d'Avignon," *Bulletin Archéologique*, 1906, pl. LXXVII, 2.

Stockhausen, H.A. von, "Die romanischen Kreuzgänge der Provence, II Teil: Die Plastik" *Marburger Jahrbuch für Kunstwissenschaft*, VIII-IX, 1936, p. 127.

47-48. Savigny (Rhône)

Abbey of Saint-Martin. Second quarter of the twelfth
century.

47. Capital. *Musician playing a Viol.*

Limestone. h., 12″; w., 8½″; d., 10¾″

Wellesley College Art Museum. Rogers Fund. 1949.

ex coll.: Joseph Brummer.

48. Capital. *Acrobat.*

Limestone. h., 12¾″; w., 9″

The Metropolitan Museum of Art, The Cloisters Collection. 47.101.25.

ex coll.: Joseph Brummer.

47a

47b

Perhaps some of the most intriguing and artistically rich material for study in the field of French Romanesque sculpture are those monuments situated in or near the axis, running north-south from a point just north of Lyon, west of the Saône River, down the River Rhône to its mouth in the region known as "Bouches-du-Rhône."

From the standpoint of twelfth century sculptural style, the Rhône River valley seems to act as a permeable conduit, along which the ebb and flow of innovation and reaction, in stylistic terms, occurs through the third quarter of the twelfth century. In the regions adjacent to the Rhône and its valley, the rigid definitions of "schools" fall before evidence of stylistic diversity, long range effects of certain great monuments, and the mobility of styles and sculptor-masons, forcing the conclusion that it is perhaps overly restrictive to think in terms of a Rhône valley style as opposed to a Provençal style.

As far as one can deduce from fragmentary remains, the abbey of Saint-Martin at Savigny[1] was a superb and not untypical example of an instance where a powerful monastic foundation attracted sculptor-masons representing varied styles from monuments in other regions in order to accomplish an ambitious building program. It is not unlikely, also, that craftsmen were formed here who later took their skills, techniques, and individual manners to other building campaigns.

Among the most precious pieces to survive from the 18th century destruction of the church, cloisters, and dependent buildings are three reliefs to be discussed here which may have been part of an as yet little known portal complex.

One extraordinary carving depicting King Solomon (fig. 47a) attended by a sword carrying figure, perhaps symbolizing Justice, is still to be seen among the fragments at Savigny. The King wears a crown, and an elaborately carved cloak covers his arms and shoulders. One hand is raised in a gesture of recognition or judgment while the other holds what is perhaps a scroll. The figure is applied to an architectural member which can be loosely described as a capital. The King is placed on the front face within a peculiar style of leaf work, which carries stippled decoration along its veins. Here is evidence of a modal approach to decoration, in that the leaf-work which is background for the sword carrier is not given a deluxe stippled treatment, indicating a differentiation of importance and station.

Two different systems of drapery conventions are used to suggest the folds in Solomon's cloak and tunic. The cloak displays a pattern of raised ridges defining crescent-shaped fields terminated by short incised lines. The more involved technique suggests the importance of this particular area as opposed to the drapery folds of the justice figure and other related reliefs that we shall discuss shortly that are expressed by a simple curvilinear ridge. The stonemason's drill is used lavishly not only to define form, as in the crown and in Solomon's eyes, but also to enliven the surface, to decorate certain areas of the crown and the scroll (?) which Solomon holds in his right hand. These, then, are a few of the characteristics of the style of the Savigny Solomon relief.

If a comparison is made between the relief at Savigny and two carvings of extraordinary quality included in the present exhibition, one, an acrobat lent by The Metropolitan Museum of Art, The Cloisters Collection; the other, a musician playing a viol from the Wellesley College Museum, the conclusion is inescapable that the three sculptures are virtually identical in style. The pieces are of the same format, the figures being set against the same type of leaf-work. Common to all the figures are the curvilinear ridge which organizes the drapery, the broad blocky faces, the use of the drill to define the eyes, and to embellish drapery, jewelry, shoes, and leg, the carving of the hand and the peculiar treatment of the sleeve at the wrist.

If the impressive Solomon relief now at Savigny was indeed carved for a since destroyed complex at the abbey of Saint-Martin, the Wellesley and New York pieces must also have been a part of the same sculptural program. How exactly the "jongleur" figures relate iconographically and physically to the Solomon relief is difficult to say at this moment. Additional fragments at Savigny—an "atlas" or perhaps another acrobat and a bit of drapery and leaf work identical to those features of the group under discussion (inscribed "DV . . .")—are surely part of the same program. These must rest for the moment as incompletely understood clues to the original appearance and meaning of a monument of superior quality.

Several remarks should be made concerning stylistic relationships of the Savigny work with other monuments within the Rhône Valley. In general, the style of the figures, the carving of the heads, the use of the curvilinear drapery convention is typical of early work at Vienne, such as the Emmaus reliefs immured at Saint-Maurice and the more developed apostle reliefs at Saint-Maurice and Saint-Pierre in Vienne.[2] The tympana at Saint-Alban-sur-Rhône and Condrieu, a superb, but fragmentary, shaft with scenes of the story of Samson now in the Duke University Art Museum,[3] and a battered pier relief at Hartford depicting the Evangelists,[4] (fig. 47b), are all monuments with stylistic affinities related to the Savigny reliefs.

Certain questions remain to be answered concerning the Savigny sculpture. Presently under study[5] is the implication of a close stylistic relationship between the head of Solomon from Savigny and a little known king's head at and presumably from, Charlieu, and the question of the stylistic links previously noted between the Charlieu sculpture and a Savigny capital depicting the Virgin and the Magi. This study will also include the broader problem of the connection between the vital, "baroque" Saint-Julien de Jonzy/Charlieu style and sculpture of the Savigny-Lyon-Vienne area of the first half of the twelfth century, an area which itself gives rise to a "baroque" phase of stylistic development in Vienne and Lyon in the fifth and sixth decades of the 12th century. The problematical and extremely controversial sculpture of Saint-Gilles should also be restudied in the light of its connection with monuments in the upper Rhône area, including Savigny and related monuments.[6]

ROBERT C. MOELLER III

NOTES

1. The abbey of Saint-Martin de Savigny just north and west of Lyon is the subject of an as yet unpublished thesis by Mlle. D. Cataland for the École des Chartes. See. H.M., *Bulletin historique du diocèse de Lyon,* 1924, pp. 326-7, and the brief notice of the sculpture given by L. Bégule, *Antiquités et Richesses d'art du Département du Rhône,* Lyon, 1925, pp. 139-140.

2. For Saint-Maurice at Vienne, with discussion of the related sculpture at Saint-Pierre in the same city, see Jean Vallery-Radot, "L'ancienne cathédrale Saint-Maurice de Vienne," *Bulletin Monumental,* Vol. 110, 1952, pp. 297 ff. The Saint-Maurice sculpture has a *terminus a quo* of 1107. The earliest reliefs and capitals at Saint-Maurice relate more to the work at Condrieu, Saint-Allan-sur-Rhône, the Samson shaft at Duke and the pier in Hartford than to the later capitals which precede and are connected with the dated work (1152) at Saint-André-le-Bas in Vienne. At this point it is safe to assume a date of the second quarter of the twelfth century for our three Savigny reliefs as well as for the previously noted monuments which participate in a generally related style.

3. Robert C. Moeller III, *Sculpture and Decorative Art,* Catalogue of a loan exhibition of art works from the Brummer Collection of Duke University, North Carolina Museum of Art, Raleigh, 1967, pp. 20-25.

4. Walter Cahn, *Gesta,* Vol. VI, 1967, pp. 47-48, with discussion of the possible attribution of the pier relief to Savigny.

5. The present author is preparing a detailed study of the sculpture of the Charlieu narthex, of related monuments in that region, and the question of stylistic connections with the Beaujolais-Rhône-Provence axis.

6. The basis, of course, for any re-evaluation of the development of the several styles to be seen at Saint-Gilles is Richard Hamann's *Die Abteikirche von Saint-Gilles und ihre Künstlerische Nachfolge,* Berlin, 1955.

   It is to be hoped that the study of Saint-Gilles and provençal sculpture by Professor Whitney Stoddard may throw considerable light on a monument and area of great interest to historians of twelfth century French sculpture.

BIBLIOGRAPHY

47. *The Joseph Brummer Collection.* Sale catalogue. Parke-Bernet Gallery, June 8-9, 1949, Part III, pg. 101, no. 475.

47. and 48. Walter Cahn, "Romanesque Sculpture in American Collections: III. New England University Museums," *Gesta,* vol. VIII, 1969, pg. 57, fig. 7.

Robert G. Calkins, *A Medieval Treasury,* exhibition catalogue, The Andrew Dickson White Museum of Art, Cornell University, Ithaca, New York, 1968, no. 51.

NORTHERN FRANCE AND THE VALLEY OF THE MEUSE

49. Capital

The Adoration of the Shepherds.

Ile-de-France or Northern France (?). Late twelfth century.

Limestone. h., 11½″; w., 10″; d., 10″

Williams College Museum of Art. Gift of James J. Rorimer. 49.5.

ex coll.: Joseph Brummer.

We follow here the judgment of Walter Cahn regarding the general regional provenance, since we have been no more successful than he in finding any specific stylistic parallels.[1] Cahn makes a cautious comparison with the crypt capitals of Saint-Denis and with the sculpture of the chapter house of Saint-George-de-Boscherville. The severe damage to the heads of the figures has eliminated one of the most important criteria of stylistic comparison. The draperies are extremely simple, being described only by rough incisions in the surface. The type of monster, technically a rather long-tailed wyvern, and the foliage are too common to suggest any specific region.

The damage to the capital does not obscure the key elements of the scene represented. It is an Adoration of the Shepherds, showing two shepherds with their dog accompanied by a small flock of five sheep. One of the shepherds is holding a staff; the other, a horn.

The constant theme of the concordance of the Old and New Testaments is repeated here with the presence of the figure in the *clipeus* who is probably Isaiah, referring to his prophecy of the miraculous birth (7:17). The portrait in a *clipeus* is drawn directly from a classical source, and in this case Isaiah is presented in the guise of a philosopher. The *clipeus* itself is framed by the long tail of the wyvern, whose body fills the space below. Other ex-amples of the representation of Isaiah in conjunction with scenes of the Infancy Cycle are described by Cahn.[2]

Despite its battered appearance, this capital has been included in the exhibition as a representative of an area that does not offer much to Romanesque sculpture. Although the architecture of Normandy in combination with that of England in the eleventh and twelfth centuries is extremely important both as a major style within what is defined as Romanesque architecture and as the primary source of Gothic architecture, sculpture production in the north, including Brittany, Normandy, and the Ile-de-France, was not distinguished and could in no way compare with the flourishing of Romanesque sculpture in central and southern France. Yet by 1150 a remarkable fusion of many of the elements of Romanesque with a distinctly new approach to both sculpture and architecture occurred in the Ile-de-France. Within this new style the historiated capital was rejected and replaced by relatively uniform capitals decorated at first with stylized and sub-sequently with rather realistic foliate ornament. That the use of historiated capitals did not die swiftly is proven by their presence at Saint-Denis, in the north tower and on the west portals of Chartres, at Étampes, and by the Williams capital.

NOTES

1. Walter Cahn, "Romanesque Sculpture in American Collections: III. New England University Museums," *Gesta,* vol. VIII, 1969, pg. 62, figs. 15 a, b.

2. *ibid.*

BIBLIOGRAPHY

The Notable Art Collection belonging to the Estate of the late Joseph Brummer. Part I, pg. 139, no. 553. Parke-Bernet Galleries, New York, June 8-9, 1949.

Walter Cahn, "Romanesque Sculpture in American Collections: III. New England University Museums," *Gesta,* vol. VIII, 1969, pg. 62.

50. Engaged Capital.

Crouching Woman and Two Heads.

Northwestern France (?). End of the twelfth century (?).

Limestone. h., 15″; w., 20″; d., 16″

Philadelphia Museum of Art, The George Grey
Barnard Collection. 45-25-50.

This intriguing capital is included in the exhibition as both a curiosity and a problem. Martin Weinberger's opinion that it came from Northern France is probably accurate, though a more precise location in Normandy or Brittany might also be suggested.[1] It is the date that must be considered first before discussing provenance. In the Barnard catalogue it is dated in the second half of the thirteenth century, yet Weinberger describes it as "early Gothic in character." At the same time, in certain records the Philadelphia Museum lists the capital in the second half of the twelfth century. The latter date is more logical and suggests that the date published in the catalogue of the Barnard Collection is a misprint.

Sifting this information, and with little else to use as a guide, it would make more sense to locate the capital in northwestern France and to date it at the end of the twelfth century. It seems an abuse of the term to call the capital Early Gothic. The sculptural traditions in Brittany especially, but also in Normandy and even in the Ile-de-France during the eleventh and the early part of the twelfth century were weak, reflecting none of the inventiveness, vigor, and quality of those regions to the south and east normally associated with the flourishing of Romanesque sculpture.

Brittany proper developed little in the way of Romanesque and Gothic architecture and sculpture.[2] Its products in the field of sculpture are astonishingly backward and make this capital from Philadelphia, as bare as it is, look rather accomplished in comparison. Normandy, while it did not develop a strong tradition of sculpture, fostered achievements in architecture from the mid-eleventh century on that were of major importance not only within the period called Romanesque, but also as direct forerunners of the Gothic cathedral.

In the Ile-de-France until the second or third decade of the twelfth century the development of architecture and sculpture was of little note, but at that moment and for reasons already described in the Introduction, the impetus was given to the establishment of a new mode of building and a new approach to sculpture that were to generate in turn a style that would, in one way or another, captivate western Europe. Within this style the effectiveness of the historiated capital was eliminated.

The rough charm and simplicity of this capital are reminiscent of the products of the general area of northwestern France including the three regions mentioned above. In the center of the front face of the capital a naked woman crouches, hands upon knees. Her grinning, round mask of a face is joined in mirth by a human head at each corner of the capital.

NOTES

1. Martin Weinberger, *The George Grey Barnard Collection,* Privately printed, New York, n.d. (1941), pg. 10, no. 50.

2. For examples of the primitive state of sculpture and architecture in Brittany during the Romanesque period cf. Roger Grand, *L'Art Roman en Bretagne,* Paris, 1958.

BIBLIOGRAPHY

Martin Weinberger, *The George Grey Barnard Collection,* privately printed, New York, n.d. (1941), pg. 10, no. 50.

51. The Crucified Christ.

Valley of the Meuse or the Lower Rhine. Second half
of the twelfth century.

Bronze. h., 8 11/16"; w., at arms, 8"

Museum of Art, Rhode Island School of Design. 49.371.

The reasons that were offered for including **Mr. Brown's**
ivory relief (cat. no. 38) in an exhibition of monumental
sculpture may be applied with equal force to this Corpus
and to the other bronze Corpus on exhibition (cat. no. 59).
Such objects have a crucial relevance to the study of
sculpture and painting that has often not been acknowledged with the result that entire areas of medieval art
have been neglected.[1]

One such area in particular is the bronze Corpus Christi
that exists in numerous examples and that was obviously
an object of great importance. One must delve into museum catalogues, catalogues of private collections and exhibitions, and the occasional book or article that may list
or discuss a few figures. In most of these works the same
general terminology is applied without any satisfactory
analysis of the characteristics that have led the authors to
arrive at their conclusions; Mosan, French, Spanish, Rhenish, German, English are attributions that are met with
so frequently without the kind of convincing qualifications
that would give such designations meaning. A body of
literature, in short, that would approach such objects systematically and with a careful categorization of styles is
lacking.

A valuable, but not exhaustive, typological study of the
crucifix has been provided by Dr. Paul Thoby,[2] but the
most valuable contribution will be made by Dr. Peter
Bloch of the Berlin-Dahlem Museum who has taken in
hand the work begun by Otto von Falke and Erich Meyer
on medieval bronze objects.[3] Dr. Bloch is now engaged in
preparing Erich Meyer's corpus of over 600 bronze Christus figures for publication, and this, when it appears.
would provide the foundation for any further study.

Fortunately, the Providence Christus falls into a group
that is easily recognizable, if not always fully defined. In
attributing it to a Mosan or lower Rhenish area we have
referred to two very similar figures exhibited recently in

medieval exhibitions in this country. This attribution has subsequently been confirmed by Dr. Bloch who found that the Providence Christus existed in Dr. Meyer's files and was designated as Mosan from the second half of the twelfth century.

A Christus from the Princeton Art Museum exhibited at Cornell and Utica,[4] and most particularly a figure from the collection of Mr. and Mrs. Jack Linsky included in an exhibition at The Cloisters, New York,[5] are clearly related to the Providence figure. In both cases an attribution is made to a German or Mosan area. From Calkins' discussion of the particular characteristics of Christus figures from the Meuse Valley as distinct from the figures produced farther east along the Rhine and in Northern Germany, and from the extremely close relationship between the Providence and Linsky figures, the latter being generally placed in Saxony or the lower Rhine, we would favor such an area as the place of origin for the Providence figure.

The softness evident in the Princeton Corpus and described as a characteristic of Mosan work is in contrast to the hardness of forms and the sharpness of details, especially in the drapery folds, that distinguish the Providence and Linsky figures. Yet Calkins' observation that the Princeton figure may ultimately be related to the Werden and Bernward of Hildesheim crucifixes is a valid one. The probability is that such prominent Ottonian eleventh century works represent basic models that were maintained in those areas of Germany and along the Meuse where bronze casting was a major activity. The changes which developed during the course of the twelfth century were due to local tastes and perhaps to new influences from other quarters.

The characteristics that join together the Providence and Linsky figures are the round shape of the head with a roll of hair at the forehead, ropy locks falling onto the shoulders, and a short beard with a sharp edge and incised lines. The torso is more detailed and more subtly modelled in the Linsky figure in contrast to the more abstractly divided zones of chest and abdomen seen on the Providence Corpus. The configuration of the perizonium with its large knot on the right side, the resultant harsh and, in the Providence Corpus, extremely sharp folds, and the roll of cloth over the waistband are also areas of strong correspondence. Whereas the Linsky perizonium is stippled, the Providence perizonium is plain with a patterned band running down both the left side and the fall of drapery beneath the knot. The legs are basically the same and rest upon a *suppedaneum* that is also of the same general type, although the Providence support is a more elaborate, floral design.

Miss Gomez-Moreno is justified in suggesting that metallurgical and other analytical studies be carried out to aid in the understanding of the stylistic distribution of Romanesque bronze Christus figures. It is hoped that Dr. Block will include such material in his study of the subject. In the interest of such a project we might add to our description of the Providence figure that it is still covered with gilding which in turn has a patchy covering of a rather odd, dark patina that does not seem natural, but induced or added artifically. The fabric of the bronze is very thick, making the piece quite heavy. There is a roughly oblong cavity in the back where more specific details of the casting process may be seen. Our own experience with such objects has been too limited to enable us to comment upon the evidence which, to the trained eye, must be there for the taking. The figure would originally, of course, have been attached either to a wooden cross covered with repoussé bronze plates or a flat bronze cross also decorated with enamels, niello work, or simple incised lines.

NOTES

1. cf. On this subject the lucid introduction by Hanns Swarzenski, *Monuments of Romanesque Art,* London and Chicago, 1954.

2. *Le Crucifix des Origines au Concile de Trente,* Nantes, 1959; *Supplément,* Nantes, 1963.

3. *Bronzegeräte des Mittelalters,* vol. I: *Romanische Leuchter und Gefässe, Giessegefässe der Gotik,* Berlin, 1935.

4. Robert Calkins, *A Medieval Treasury,* Cornell, 1968, pp. 131-132, no. 45.

5. Carmen Gomez-Moreno, *Medieval Art in Private Collections,* The Cloisters, New York, 1968, no. 92.

EARLY GOTHIC

52-53. Saint Denis. Abbey Church.

52. *Head of a King.*

West portals, jamb statue. 1137-1140.

Limestone. h., 13¾″; w., of crown, 8″

The Walters Art Gallery, Baltimore. 27.22.

ex coll.: Kelekian, Henry Walters.

53. *Head of a King.*

West portals, jamb statue. 1137-1140.

Limestone. h., 16¾″; w., 9½″

Fogg Art Museum, Harvard University. Wetzel Bequest. 1920.30.

52a

The period between around 1130 and 1160 is of critical importance to the study of Romanesque and Gothic architecture and sculpture. During this span of years most of the major Romanesque monuments were built, following the lead of the great innovative churches of the late eleventh century. At the same time there appears in the Ile-de-France a series of churches that state for the first time new structural, stylistic, and iconographic principles that become the basis for a style of architecture and sculpture destined to dominate the art of Western Europe for at least the next three hundred years. It is this style that has been called Gothic, following the terminology, if not the motivation, of Vasari.

The six heads brought together in this exhibition and discussed in this and the following four entries represent the earliest stages of the development of Gothic sculpture and provide us with a set of problems as difficult to solve as any faced by the art historian and museum curator.

In 1940 Marvin C. Ross, then curator at The Walters Art Gallery, published in the *Journal* of the Gallery an article of great importance in which he identified two heads (figs. 52, 52a) purchased in Paris in 1911 by Mr. Henry Walters and a head that entered the Fogg Art Museum in 1920 as having come originally from the statue columns that decorated the west portals of the abbey church of Saint-Denis just north of Paris. The importance of this discovery can only be appreciated when one is aware of the key position assumed by the church at Saint-Denis in the development of Gothic architecture and sculpture and of the fate of its sculptural decoration.

Very seldom, if ever, in the history of art can one point to a specific place and name a precise date for the birth of a style. Such an occurrence seems totally illogical when one considers the complex movements and the span of time required for the normal evolution of a style. Yet it is not impossible that with the elements at hand and with the ideas already partially developed in a disconnected way a catalyst can appear in the form of a single artist or a happy combination of artist and patron that can cause the rapid and even instant precipitation of the basic principles of a new style.

Just such a miraculous birth occurred at Saint-Denis. Taking some liberties, we might say that the date of birth was June 11, 1144, the day of the consecration of the new choir. The names of the artists and architects have been lost to us, but the moving force behind these anonymous and obviously brilliant men is very well-known as the Abbot Suger of Saint-Denis, one of the most powerful, influential, and able men of his time. It is really he who "created" Gothic architecture in more than an indirect way. The remarkable maturity and sophistication of the ambulatory of Saint-Denis, which is all that remains of the twelfth century choir above the crypt level, are ultimately due to the abilities and desires of Suger, to whom is due, also, the equally new and equally influential characteristics of the west façade with its triple portals, which are the source of the sculptural fragments discussed here.

The career and character of the Abbot Suger and his phenomenal achievements have been brilliantly described in recent years,[1] allowing us to mention in passing those events relevant to an understanding of his church and its sculptural decoration. A man of extraordinary administrative talents and of deep sensitivity to beauty, devoted to his abbey and to the Capetian monarchy, both of which he served with skill and loyalty throughout his active life, Suger was born in 1081 of humble parents. Placed in the school at Saint-Denis, he became a close friend of the royal prince who was to become Louis VI, thus beginning a long and mutually beneficial association with the French royal house, a factor of some importance to the birth and growth of Gothic architecture and sculpture.

After displaying his unusual abilities in a succession of posts connected with the abbey and its dependencies, the Papacy, and the French monarchy, Suger was elected to the abbacy of Saint-Denis in 1122. This immediately made him one of the foremost churchmen in Europe, for Saint-Denis was among the most important of all monasteries, possessing great power and prestige. This prominence was especially evident in France where the connections between the monarchy and the abbey since Merovingian times had been extremely close, not only because it was the chosen burial place of the kings of the Merovingian, Carolingian, and Capetian houses, but also because it was the shrine of the patron saint of France and the location of an important school.

The church inherited by Suger had been built in the latter part of the eighth century and consecrated in 775. With the exception of the addition of a chapel to the east end around 832 and a tower to the north transept in the latter part of the eleventh century, few changes had been made in the eighth century church. For a variety of reasons the new abbot decided that a building more worthy of the Apostle of France should replace the old structure. Suger reports in his *De Administratione* that because of their age the walls of the church were near ruin.[2] In addition, he expresses dismay over the small size of the old church (around 203 feet long by around 67 feet in overall width) and its inadequacy in the face of the large crowds who entered on feast days.

There were, however, other reasons that were to Suger, perhaps, the most important ones. Despite the venerability of the old abbey church and its legendary association with a dim, but awesome, past, its size and condition hardly matched its prestige. In addition, this prestige had received a new lustre through the close association of the abbey and of Suger himself with a monarchy that was asserting its own secular power and at the same time acting as a champion of the church. It was only fitting that the size and splendor of the church of Saint-Denis match not only its spiritual rôle as an embodiment of the Heavenly Jerusalem and therefore as the palace of celestial monarchy, but also its rôle as the French Royal abbey and as the symbol of the joint terrestrial monarchy of church and state.

Suger's plans for the re-building of the abbey date from ca. 1125. Actual construction did not begin until 1137, when the foundations were laid for a monumental new façade. It is this portion of his church that interests us, for it was in the three portals of this western façade that the statues were located from which came the two heads on exhibition. This portion of the building was completed up to the towers by 1140, at which time construction of the chevet was begun.

That Suger should have begun construction at the west rather than the east end, as was customary, is significant, especially in relation to the nature of the royal heads that survive from the jamb statues.

The portals of Saint-Denis and its whole façade are meant to signify the gate of Heaven and derive ultimately from the idea of a city gate. Parallel with this meaning is the association of the western portion of the church, as developed in the West in Carolingian architecture, with the

secular ruler. It is ultimately derived from the Carolingian *westwerk* and is thus inseparably linked with the idea of kingship, both heavenly and earthly. What better symbol of the rôle of Saint-Denis and of Suger himself in the growth of royal power in the heartland of the Capetian domain than the splendid *westwerk*, composed with a unity and magnificence unknown before.

An integral part of this scheme was the equally new emphasis upon the three portals and their sculptural decoration. As we shall see shortly there is little that remains of the original sculptured ensemble, and Suger is mysteriously silent about what must have been an extraordinary display, so silent that some scholars have dated the jamb statues to the mid-1150s, that is, after the death of Suger in 1151.[3]

The central portal, however, retains much of its original sculpture, though it has undergone some serious "revisions." We know from the drawings made for Dom Montfaucon and published in 1729 that there were originally twenty statue columns in the jambs of the three portals. Like the famous west portals at Chartres (1145-1155) that follow immediately in time those once at Saint-Denis, the statue columns appear to have represented the kings, queens, and prophets of the Old Testament. They are the fruit of the Tree of Jesse, the lineage of the House of David, the forbears of Christ, the representatives of the Old Law. It seems impossible that both at Chartres and Saint-Denis, as well as the other Early Gothic portals, they did not also signify the temporal power of the monarchy, in this case the French monarchy, in league with the wisdom of the church, a concept that was so important to Suger.

It is from these statues that the two heads in Baltimore and the head in the Fogg Art Museum come. Why they are not still at Saint-Denis is a sad tale, one that must be told so often about French medieval sculpture, and one whose ending almost as often involved the enrichment of an American collector or museum. The first disaster befell Saint-Denis in 1771 when the trumeau of the central portal with its statue of Saint-Denis, all three lintels, and all the statue columns were removed. This truncated version of Suger's original scheme was further damaged in the Revolution of 1789, but the mortal stroke was reserved for the insensitive attentions of an architect by the name of François Debret who, in 1839, directed the restoration of the west façade and the battered sculpture of the portals. As a result of his depredations the left and right portals were almost completely redone, while the figures of the central portal received new heads and other details.

Of the statue columns there was no trace until Mr. Ross in 1940 revealed that the two heads at the Walters

Art Gallery and the head at the Fogg were from Saint-Denis. Subsequently Marcel Aubert added to these three a series of five, and possibly six, small heads in the Louvre that probably came from the archivolts of one of the west portals.[5] They were part of a group of sculptures of unknown sources that came to the Louvre from Saint-Denis in 1881.

After the removal of extensive and disfiguring restorations that had caused the Baltimore heads to be doubted for many years, Mr. Ross was able to match them and the Fogg head in a very convincing fashion with three of the Montfaucon drawings, thus proving that the heads had originally come from the statue columns of Saint-Denis.

Based upon the Montfaucon drawings there seems little reason to doubt Ross' identification. On stylistic grounds alone, however, the differences among the three heads are noticeable. The treatment of the hair, the specific elements that form the eyes, the contours of the face, and the shape of the mouth are quite different in each case. Only the heavy ears exist as a point of agreement for the three. Yet there seems no reason to doubt the evidence of Montfaucon, and when we realize the variety of hands at work on the west portals of Chartres and consequently the number of styles evident there, the variations among the heads from Saint-Denis need not disturb us unduly.

What has bothered some scholars, however, is the condition of the Fogg head. It has often been described as having been heavily restored or extensively re-carved. When the head entered the Fogg in 1920 it bore restorations in the area of the nose and the left eye. These were subsequently removed, and little has been done to determine the actual condition of the piece. In 1940 a specimen was taken to be tested with specimens from the Walters heads, and the results indicated that the three heads, plus another small decorative fragment in the Walters Art Gallery, were all made of a stone that is quite homogeneous in composition.

As a result of the questions regarding not only the Fogg head, but other objects said to have come from Saint-Denis, in particular a small statue column in The Metropolitan Museum of Art (20.157), we decided to initiate an extensive series of tests involving spectrographic, petrographic, and chemical analysis and the examination of thin sections and cross sections. These tests will be performed by Mr. William Young of the Boston Museum of Fine Arts, an expert in stone analysis. With the co-operation of French authorities, the number and provenance of the specimens to be tested will provide a very careful control of the results. The dangers of such a procedure in relation to the decisions that can be made from the results are fully appreciated.

Stone samples will be provided from the following sources, if all goes as planned:

1. Head of a king, Fogg Art Museum.

2. Head of a king, The Walters Art Gallery, Baltimore.

3. Fragment of a decorative relief, The Walters Art Gallery, Baltimore.

4. Statue column, The Metropolitan Museum of Art, New York.

5. Samples of stone from Saint-Denis provided by Prof. Summer McK. Crosby, Yale University.

6. Head of a king, Duke University (cat. no. 54).

7. Samples from the capitals in the central portal of the west façade, Saint-Denis.

8. Samples from the four heads in the Louvre said to come from Saint-Denis.

9. Head of a king, Duke University (cat. no. 54).
   Saint-Denis.

10. Decorative fragment in the Louvre.

11. Capitals and bases in the Louvre from the cloister of Saint-Denis.

The results of these tests should be known by the Spring of this year (1969) and will be published.

Although the Fogg head agrees for the most part with one of the drawings done for Montfaucon, it is the most controversial of the three and differs from the Walters heads in significant details.[6] This may be due, as we indicate below, to the presence of a different sculptor, but the details are worth describing, nonetheless. The Fogg head is larger than the other two by some three inches. The carving of the eyes, the wrinkles in the forehead, the prominence of the upper lip, the shape of the mouth, and the strangely rigid and inorganic locks of hair are all features that differ from the two heads in The Walters Art Gallery. Yet the latter are not entirely alike either, and there are details of the Fogg head that do correspond with one or the other of the Walters heads: the ears, the corkscrew curls, the moustache and beard, the modelling of cheeks and nose. Weighing these facts in addition to the stylistic considerations discussed below and the scientific examinations carried out so far in which under an ultraviolet light there is no evidence of re-carving, we are drawn to the conclusion that the Fogg head is authentic, is relatively untampered with, and is from Saint-Denis.[7]

We have already mentioned that certain stylistic differences exist among the three heads from Saint-Denis in American collections and have pointed out that using Chartres as an example it is probable that the work of several hands may be predicated from these differences. In the development towards a more naturalistic handling of the human form as seen in the long series of jamb statues carved for Gothic portals during the second half of the twelfth and throughout the thirteenth century, the heads from Saint-Denis as well as those in the west portals of Chartres take their place at the very beginning. The relative progressiveness of a sculptor in relation to this development must always be tempered with a consideration of quality as well, while the evidence available for careful judgments in both areas is often extremely sparse.

Marcel Aubert, for example, concluded that the heads from Saint-Denis in Baltimore and at the Fogg post-dated the statue columns at Chartres because they seemed more advanced and because they possessed "une certain énergie de facture qui ne se trouve pas à Chartres."[8] Aubert supported this argument further by contending that since the western complex was not completed under Suger and since he does not mention the portal sculpture in his writings, they did not exist while he was alive. He dates the three heads to around 1155 based on this evidence. On the other hand, because of their more "archaic" appearance he concluded that the four heads in the Louvre said to have come from the archivolts of the west portals of Saint-Denis were contemporary with Suger's construction of the west façade and therefore were done around 1140.[9]

It is true that the Louvre heads are less competently handled than the three larger heads in this country, but we would maintain that this is due to a different and less able hand rather than being a question of chronology. In fact, the small Louvre heads are handled in very much the same way as the Walters head exhibited here (Walters no. 27.22). Though the Louvre heads are cruder, the manner of describing the upper and lower eyelids by means of broad, flat bands and the generalized construction of the face finds almost exact counterparts in the

NOTES

1. Erwin Panofsky, *Abbot Suger on the Abbey Church of St. Denis and Its Art Treasures*, Princeton, 1946; Marcel Aubert, *Suger*, Abbaye St. Wandrille, 1950; Sumner McK. Crosby, *L'Abbaye Royale de Saint-Denis*, Paris, 1953; Otto von Simson, *The Gothic Cathedral*, Bollingen Foundation, New York, 1956.

2. Panofsky, *ibid.*, pg. 43.

3. Marcel Aubert, "Têtes de statue-colonnes du portail occidental de Saint-Denis," *Bulletin Monumental*, vol. 103, 1945, pp. 243-248.

4. *Les monumens de la monarchie françoise*, Paris, 1929. The original drawings, which are better sources of information than the engravings made from them, are in the Bibliothèque National. They are reproduced by Ross, *op. cit.*, pp. 101-103; Arthur Kingsley Porter, *Romanesque Sculpture of the Pilgrimage Roads*, Boston, 1923, vol. X, pls. 1445-1457.

5. Aubert, *op. cit.*, pg. 248; cf. also Marcel Aubert and Michèle Beaulieu, *Description Raisonnée des Sculptures du Moyen Age*, Paris, 1950, pp. 57-58, nos. 52-56.

6. cf. Ross, *op. cit.*, fig. 18.

7. It should be taken into consideration that both in the Montfaucon drawing of the statue from which the Fogg head supposedly came and in the two Walters heads the pupils of the eyes are carved out, whereas on the Fogg head and on other Montfaucon drawings they are not.

8. Aubert, *op. cit.*, *Bulletin Monumental*, 1945, pp. 244-245; *idem.*, *La Sculpture française au début de l'époque gothique*, Paris, 1929, pp. 4 ff.; cf. also Cécile Goldscheider, "Les Origines du portail à statue-colonnes," *Bulletin des Musées de France*, vol. XI (Musée du Louvre), 1946, pp. 22-25.

9. Aubert and Beaulieu, *op. cit.*, nos. 52-55.

10. cf. the valuable report on the state of scholarship regarding Early Gothic sculpture by Louis Grodecki, "La 'Première Sculpture Gothique.' Wilhelm Vöge et l'État Actuel des Problèmes," *Bulletin Monumental*, vol. 117, 1959, pp. 265-289. cf. as well, André Lapeyre, *Des façades occidentales de Saint-Denis et de Chartres aux portails de Laon*, Paris, 1960; and a series of immensely valuable articles by Dr. Willibald Sauerländer cited by Grodecki.

Walters head (27.22).

In general, the other two heads (Walters 27.21 and Fogg 1920.30) belong to the same sculptural campaign as Walters 27.22, but do, indeed, display characteristics that could be described as being more progressive. A more plastic three-dimensionality is given to such features as the eyes; the modelling of the facial structure is also softer and contains details in the areas around the cheeks, nose, mouth, and brows that reflect a greater interest in transforming the stone into a semblance of flesh and bone. Again, we believe that this should not be ascribed to a difference in date of execution, but to a variety of sculptors, and we would date all of this work in the same period as the construction of the façade itself, that is, 1137-1140.

Finally, we do not find it possible to agree with Aubert's comparison of Saint-Denis and Chartres, nor, by the way, do we feel that the traditional division of hands in the west portals at Chartres is entirely correct. All of this material is being re-examined and has been subjected to several perceptive analyses in recent years.[10] Comparing Saint-Denis and Chartres is it possible to maintain that the three Saint-Denis heads in this country are "more advanced" or "more energetic" than the startlingly beautiful and sensitive carvings of the Headmaster at Chartres? We think not. The logical development would seem to begin at Saint-Denis between 1137 and 1140 and move to Chartres between 1145 and 1155. This is, of course, a gross over-simplification of an extremely complex situation. It is hoped that the present exhibition will aid in the investigation of these problems.

BIBLIOGRAPHY

Marvin C. Ross, "Monumental Sculptures from Saint-Denis. An Identification of Fragments from the Portal," *The Journal of The Walters Art Gallery,* vol. III, Baltimore, 1940, pp. 90-109.

idem., "Two Heads From Saint-Denis," *Magazine of Art,* vol. XXXIII, December, 1940, pp. 674-679.

Charles Rufus Morey, "Medieval Art in America," *Journal of the Warburg and Courtauld Institutes,* vol. VII, 1944, pg. 2.

Marcel Aubert, "Têtes de statue-colonnes du portail occidental de Saint-Denis," *Bulletin Monumental,* vol. 103, 1945, pp. 243-248.

idem., *La Sculpture Française au Moyen Age,* Paris, 1946, pg. 190.

Erwin Panofsky, *Abbot Suger on the Abbey Church of Saint-Denis and Its Art Treasures,* Princeton, 1946, pg. 165.

Marcel Aubert and Michèle Beaulieu, *Sculptures du Moyen Age (Encyclopédie Photographique de l'Art),* Edition "Tel," Paris, 1948, pp. 20-21, 40-41, nos. 37, 38.

idem., *Description Raisonnée des Sculptures du Moyen Age,* Musée National du Louvre, Paris, 1950, pp. 57-58, nos. 52-56.

Whitney S. Stoddard, *The West Portals of Saint-Denis and Chartres,* Harvard University Press, Cambridge, Mass., 1952, pp. 7-8, 12-13, pls. VIII, IX.

Sumner McK. Crosby, *L'Abbaye Royale de Saint-Denis,* Paris, 1953, pp. 38, 39, figs. 10, 11.

Vera K. Ostoia, "A Statue from Saint-Denis," *The Bulletin of The Metropolitan Museum of Art,* vol. XIII, no. 10, June, 1955, pg. 303.

Otto von Simson, *The Gothic Cathedral,* The Bollingen Foundation, New York, 1956, pg. 149.

Louis Grodecki, "La 'Première Sculpture Gothique.' Wilhelm Vöge et l'Etat Actuel des Problèmes," *Bulletin Monumental,* vol. 117, 1959, pg. 276.

Yves Bottineau, *Notre-Dame de Paris et la Sainte-Chapelle,* Paris, 1966, pg. 32.

Whitney S. Stoddard, *Monastery and Cathedral in France,* Wesleyan University Press, Middletown, Conn., 1966, pg. 157, fig. 203.

William D. Wixom, *Treasures From Medieval France,* The Cleveland Museum of Art, 1967, pp. 72-74, 354, no. III-14.

54. Head of a king from a statue column.
Ile-de-France. Mid-or third quarter of the twelfth century.
Limestone. h., 9⅞"; w. 8"
Art Museum, Duke University.
ex coll.: Ernest Brummer, New York.

The good fortune in being able to identify the heads from Saint-Denis (cat. nos. 52, 53) and Notre Dame in Paris (cat. no. 55) cannot be extended to this head, which is also obviously from a statue column of an Early Gothic portal. It has no close affinities with the variety of figures at Chartres carved, as we have already mentioned, by a number of sculptors with clearly distinguishable personal styles. Nor does it seem to be related to those portals that immediately follow Chartres and are its stylistics derivatives such as the south portal at Étampes (ca. 1150),[1] the south portal at Le Mans (ca. 1150-1155), the north and south portals at Bourges (ca. 1165-1180),[2] the west portal at Angers (ca. 1155-1165, according to Aubert,[3] but probably of a later date, given the greater sophistication of the figures within the development of Early Gothic sculpture), the west portal of the church of Saint-Ayoul, Provins (ca. 1157-1167), and the west portal of the church at Saint-Loup-de-Naud (1170-1175). These are only a few of the twelfth century portals adorned with statue columns that exist or once existed, and the strength of their particular relationship with Chartres varies according to the assertion of a local style or strong impulses from other regions such as Burgundy or Languedoc.[4]

To associate the half-destroyed head at Duke University with any of these monuments seems at this point virtually impossible. There is no question that it is a work of some quality, thus eliminating its association with some of the more provincial and more clumsily handled portals that still exist. Representations of now destroyed portals such as Nesle-la-Riposte or Saint-German-des-Prés, Paris,

in Dom Bernard de Montfaucon's book, *Monumens de la monarchie françoise* (Paris, 1729) provide tantalizing, but inconclusive, evidence with which to follow the process used by Marvin Ross (cat. nos. 52, 53) to identify the heads from Saint-Denis. One may see, for example, crowns that match in pattern what one supposes to have been a crown on the Duke head, but Montfaucon's engravings give no hint of the style of the figures. To attempt, therefore, to match a battered fragment of a head with inaccurate engravings of lost portals in order to arrive at an attribution would be foolhardy.

It is equally difficult to associate the head with some of the most prominent portals of the latter part of the twelfth century. If the head from the Saint Anne portal of the cathedral of Notre-Dame in Paris exhibited here (cat. no. 55) is a representative example of the style of the statue columns of that portal, it is obvious that the Duke head is not from Notre-Dame. It has no relationships with the work done at Notre-Dame-en-Vaux, Châlons-sur-Marne (ca. 1180) which has been brought to light and studied by Léon Pressouyre and Willibald Sauerländer.[5] By the end of the century and the first decade of the thirteenth century the sculpture at churches such as Mantes (central portal of the west façade, ca. 1180), Chartres (central portals of the north and south transept façades, ca. 1200-1215), Senlis (transept portals ?, ca. 1200-1215), Sens (central portal, west façade, ca. 1184-1208), and Paris, Notre-Dame (central portal, west façade, ca. 1200) has become far more advanced in terms of freer, more naturalistic modelling, thus eliminating

158

both the monuments themselves and the period of their production as possibilities of provenance for the Duke head.

It would seem that there is no alternative for the moment but to present the head, as it has been presented in two recent exhibitions, with a large question mark.[6] Perhaps the inclusion of a specimen of stone from this head in the tests to be conducted by Mr. William Young of the Museum of Fine Arts, Boston (cf. cat., nos. 52, 53) will provide new evidence toward a more specific attribution.

We have not mentioned Saint-Denis so far in this discussion because a comparison between the Duke head and the heads from Saint-Denis in Baltimore and Cambridge yields no more than did a comparison with the work at Chartres. Yet the possibility of some connection with Saint-Denis should not be entirely eliminated. Though once again the Duke head seems more advanced than those from Saint-Denis within the context of Early Gothic sculpture, it seems in some ways more related to this church than to Chartres. No counterpart can be found among the drawings for Montfaucon except for some similarities to the figure of Moses,[7] but the relationship is too vague to serve as the basis for any further speculation. There is no question, however, that the head is worthy of further investigation.

NOTES

1. We do not have the space here to comment upon the question of the history of Étampes and whether it precedes or follows Chartres; cf. Alan Priest, "The Masters of the West Façade of Chartres," *Art Studies,* vol. 1, 1923, pp. 28-44; W. S. Stoddard, *The West Portals of St. Denis and Chartres,* Harvard University Press, 1952, pp. 27-31; Marcel Aubert, *French Sculpture at the Beginning of the Gothic Period,* New York, n.d., (1929?), pp. 25-27; *idem., La Sculpture Française au Moyen Age,* Paris, 1946, pp. 185, 191-192; E. Lefèvre-Pontalis, "Étampes," *Congrès Archéologique,* Paris, 1919, pp. 6 ff.; André Lapeyre, *Des façades occidentales de Saint-Denis et de Chartres aux portails de Laon,* Paris, 1960; Louis Grodecki, "La 'Première Sculpture Gothique.' Wilhelm Vöge et l'État Actuel des Problèmes," *Bulletin Monumental,* vol. 117, 1959, pg. 278.

2. Robert Branner, "Les portails lateraux de la Cathedrale de Bourges," *Bulletin Monumental,* vol. 115, 1957, pp. 263-270.

3. *La Sculpture Française au Moyen Age,* Paris, 1946, pg. 195.

4. For a brief discussion and full list of Early Gothic portals with statue columns, both those that are still extant, and those that are lost fully or in part, cf. Marcel Aubert, *French Sculpture at the Beginning of the Gothic Period,* New York, n.d., pp. 39-48.

5. cf. the full bibliography in William Wixom, *Treasures from Medieval France,* The Cleveland Museum of Art, 1967, pp. 98, 356-357; and in the catalogue of the exhibition, *L'Europe Gothique, XII-XIV Siècles,* Musée du Louvre, Paris, 1968, pp. 6-16, nos. 3-20.

6. Robert C. Moeller III, *Sculpture and Decorative Art.* A Loan Exhibition of Selected Art Works from the Brummer Collection of Duke University, North Carolina Museum of Art, Raleigh, N. C., May 7-July 2, 1967, pg. 26, no. 7, fig. 15; Robert G. Calkins, *A Medieval Treasury,* Andrew Dickson White Museum of Art, Cornell University, Ithaca, N.Y., Oct. 8-Nov. 3, 1968, pp. 140-141, no. 57.

7. cf. Arthur Kingsley Porter, *Romanesque Sculpture of the Pilgrimage Roads,* Boston, 1923, vol. 10, pl. 1445.

BIBLIOGRAPHY

Robert C. Moeller III, *Sculpture and Decorative Art.* A Loan Exhibition of Selected Art Works from the Brummer Collection of Duke University, North Carolina Museum of Art, Raleigh, N. C., May 7-July 2, 1967, pg. 26, no. 7, fig. 15.

Robert G. Calkins, *A Medieval Treasury,* Andrew Dickson White Museum of Art, Cornell University, Ithaca, N.Y., Oct. 8-Nov. 3, 1968; Munson-Williams-Proctor Institute, Utica, N.Y., Nov. 10-Dec. 8, 1968, pp. 140-141, no. 57.

55. Paris. Cathedral of Notre-Dame.

Head of King David. Portal of Saint Anne (right portal), West façade, jamb statue. ca. 1165-1170.

Limestone. h., 11¼″

The Metropolitan Museum of Art, New York. Dick Fund, 1938. 38.180.

The difficulties encountered in attempting to understand the development of Early Gothic sculpture, especially in the second half of the twelfth century are due both to the loss of material necessary for a detailed analysis and to the complex stylistic relationships that seem to exist among those monuments that have been preserved. Problems of chronology, condition, and authenticity complicate the process still further. We have already indicated in the preceding catalogue entries of this section and in the Introduction that a line of development beginning at Saint-Denis (1137-1140) and continuing on to Chartres (1145-1155) broadens after mid-century to include a large group of portal sculptures that seem to depend most heavily upon Chartres.

The picture is not quite so simple, however, and must include the equally complex problem of the sources of Saint-Denis and Chartres. There are certain major differences that exist between the sculpture, such as it is, that is associated with Saint-Denis, its style, iconography, and composition, and the most important work at Chartres, where, it will be remembered, a variety of styles may be seen. The influence exerted by these two key monuments spreads with different degrees of intensity, encounters other traditions, mingles with local styles, and is, perhaps, rejected for the innovations of other groups of master sculptors.

We have mentioned that the best summary to date of the opinions regarding Early Gothic sculpture has been provided by Louis Grodecki,[1] who points out the separation that has been made between the " 'généologie' dionysienne" and the Chartrain tradition toward the better understanding of the genesis of more mature, and even revolutionary, developments at Mantes, Senlis, and Laon.[2]

One monument that appears to have played a major rôle in this complicated drama is the cathedral of Notre-Dame in Paris. In 1163 construction was begun on the choir of a new cathedral under the episcopacy of Maurice de Sully, who had decided to replace two ancient churches, dedicated respectively to Notre-Dame and to Saint-Étienne, by a magnificent building in the new style created at Saint-Denis and Sens. At the same time that work was begun on the east end plans were drawn up for the façade. Sometime between 1165 and 1175 the sculpture for this façade was begun. By 1177 the choir was close to completion, and on the 19th of May, 1182, the high altar was consecrated. During the remainder of the twelfth century the work of construction progressed westward, the façade as it stands today being built in the years between 1200 and 1250.

Of the twelfth century sculpture destined for the façade we possess only those portions incorporated into the right-hand portal, the portal of Saint Anne. In their final form the three western portals were carved between 1210 and 1240: left-hand portal, the Portal of the Virgin, ca. 1210-1220; central portal, the Portal of the Last Judgment, ca. 1220-1230; right-hand portal, the Portal of Saint Anne, ca. 1230-1240. The original plans for the west portals must have been altered at the beginning of the thirteenth century, but some of the sculpture that had already been executed around 1165-1175 was retained and fitted into the new scheme. The process of adapting the older sculpture to the final plan of the portals is clearly seen in the Portal of Saint Anne. The tympanum, which was too small and of the wrong shape for the new space, was used intact, the intervening spaces between its outer arc and the more pointed arch of the portal being filled by rinceaux leading up to two censing angels at the apex. The first lintel, also of the twelfth century, was too short and was enlarged by the addition of a scene at either end, the Presentation in the Temple to the left and the horses of the Three Magi on the right. A second lintel, dating ca. 1230, was then added below the first. The archivolts contain figures dating from both periods, the Elders of the Apocalypse probably having been intended for the archivolts of the central portal, which would have been similar to Chartres with its scene of the Apocalyptic Vision.

The statues that were placed within the jambs and on the trumeau of the portal had also been carved between 1165 and 1175. Unlike the upper portions of the portal, however, the statue columns did not survive the excesses of the Revolution. In 1793, or thereabouts, they were destroyed and all traces of them apparently lost. Between 1845 and 1864 the entire cathedral, which had reached a pitiable state of disrepair, was restored by Viollet-le-Duc. During the course of this rescue work much of the sculpture was replaced, including the statute columns of the portal of Saint Anne, filling the empty spaces left after the Revolution. These statues were executed under the direction of Geoffroy-Dechaume, who based his figures upon engravings in Montfaucon that preserved the general appearance of the originals.[3]

Of the twelfth century statues only a few fragments remain. The trumeau statue of St. Marcel is now in the *dépôt lapidaire* of the cathedral. The lower portions of a statue of St. Peter and the torso of a man holding a scroll are preserved in the Musée de Cluny. The only other remnant of the jamb statues is the head of King David included in this exhibition.

The identification of this head was made by James J. Rorimer in 1940.[4] The evidence mustered by Mr. Rorimer consisted of a correspondence with the figure of King David in Montfaucon and similarities in style and type of crown with certain figures on the older, or upper, lintel of the portal of Saint Anne, especially with the King Herod and the Magi to his left. Although the evidence is not overwhelming, it is all that is available, and it has generally been accepted. The crowns of both the head and the kings on the lintel lack fleurons in contrast to the Montfaucon drawing where they are present. It is possible that they were all broken from the sculpture.

Because of the uncertain nature of the comparison with the Montfaucon engraving it is the resemblance between the Metropolitan head and the figures of King Herod and the three Magi on the old lintel that provides the best evidence for attribution. What remains of the twelfth century can be divided into two groups. The tympanum with its majestic seated Virgin and Child flanked by censing angels with, to our right, King Louis VII, and, to our left, Bishop Maurice de Sully and Barbedor, dean of the cathedral chapter and secretary to the King, is by a different sculptor than the one who carved the lintel with the Presentation in the Temple, the Annunciation, the Visitation, the Nativity, The Annunciation to the Shepherds, and Herod with the three Magi. The latter sculptor was undoubtedly from the workshop of the man who carved the head of King David. Though the style of the kings in the lintel is very close to the head, they were not necessarily done by the same man, since certain minor variations in details and quality exist. These variations may be due, of course, to differences in type and scale rather than to two separate hands.

What is evident in all of this work is its close dependence upon the west portals of Chartres. As recognized initially by Wilhelm Vöge and as classified subsequently by Emile Mâle and Marcel Aubert, a direct connection may be established between the Virgin portal at Chartres and the portal of Saint Anne in Paris.[5] Vöge's belief that the two were by the same master was convincingly refuted by Mâle and Aubert. In general iconography, composition, and figural types the relationships are obvious, especially in the two figures of the seated Virgin and Child. The masters at Paris, however, have changed the iconography in many particulars, and their own styles, one might even say temperaments, are noticeably different from those at Chartres. The latter is characterized by more slender figures, a greater agitation in the draperies and the movements of the figures, and an attention to familiar details and actions that reflect very strongly a Burgundian Romanesque tradition. In Paris both the tympanum and the lintel have become more solemn, more majestic, more ceremonial. The faces are less animated than those at Chartres, though the facial types, especially in the tympanum, are decidedly Chartrain. The same may be said

for the draperies. The arrangement of folds at Paris is almost identical to that at Chartres, but the folds are multiplied, become straighter and more rigid, and in many areas seem to define more clearly the swelling volumes of the body beneath.

In the head of King David, as well, stylistic forbears may be found among the statue columns at Chartres, particularly among those by the so-called Headmaster, or atelier of the central portal. As occurred in the tympanum and lintel, however, there is the same curious combination of increased rigidity with an almost equal increase in certain aspects of physical realism, reflecting quite clearly, at so early a moment in the history of Gothic sculpture, the experimentation being carried on by sculptors still immersed to varying degrees in the traditional styles of Romanesque sculpture. The same process may be observed in the Early Gothic architecture of the second half of the twelfth century. In the head of King David the contours of the cheeks and the ridges running from either side of the nose to the corners of the mouth correspond with what seems to be the more progressive of the two heads from Saint-Denis in the Walters Art Gallery (20. 21), with certain of the heads in the central portal at Chartres, and with the heads at Angers. These features in addition to the freer handling of the hair, particularly in the locks arranged across the forehead, reflect a stage of development that prepares the way, in part, for the group of portals carved in the last two decades of the twelfth century.

In contrast to the more progressive elements of the King David head are the enormous eyes whose pupils were once probably filled with lead. Measured against any of the contemporary jamb figures from other churches, except for one of the Baltimore heads from Saint-Denis (22.22; cat. no. 52) and the archivolt heads from the same church now in the Louvre, the eyes constitute an archaic feature that is difficult to explain. The great size and perfect roundness of the eyeballs, emphasized by the loss of the pupil and isolated by the deep carving of the corners of the eyes, are the obvious reasons for their peculiarity. The rims of the eyes as well as the line of the brows are sharp and linear in strange contrast to the apparent softness of the area between the brow and the upper eyelid and, to some degree, of the contours of the cheeks. To repeat, such paradoxes can only be explained by referring to the particular moment in the development of Early Gothic sculpture when this head and the other twelfth century portions of the Saint Anne portal were carved.

NOTES

1. "La 'Première Sculpture Gothique.' Wilhelm Vöge et l'État Actuel des Problèmes," *Bulletin Monumental,* vol. 117, 1959, pp. 265-289.

2. In this area the studies of Willibald Sauerländer are crucial. cf. especially "Die Marienkrönungsportale von Senlis und Mantes," *Wallraf-Richartz Jahrbuch,* 1958, pp. 115-162, and Beiträge zur Geschichte der 'frühgotischen' Skulptur," *Zeitschrift für Kunstgeschichte,* 1956, pp. 6-26.

3. Dom Bernard de Montfaucon, *Les monumens de la monarchie françoise,* Paris, 1729, cf. esp. vol. I, pl. 8.

4. "A Twelfth Century Head of King David from Notre-Dame," *Bulletin of The Metropolitan Museum of Art,* vol. XXV, January, 1940, pp. 17-19.

5. Wilhelm Vöge, *Die Anfänge des Monumentalen Stiles im Mittelalter,* Strassburg, 1894; Emile Mâle, "Le Portail Sainte-Anne à Notre-Dame de Paris," *Revue de l'Art Ancien et Moderne,* 1897, reprinted in *Art et Artistes du Moyen Age,* Paris, 1927, pp. 188-208; Marcel Aubert, *French Sculpture at the Beginning of the Gothic Period,* 1140-1225, New York, n.d., pp. 47-50; *idem., La Sculpture Française au Moyen Age,* Paris, 1946, pp. 200-201.

BIBLIOGRAPHY

Lucien Demotte, *Sculptured Portraits,* exhibition catalogue, New York, 1930, cat. no. 9, pl. 9.

Art News, Nov. 8, 1930, pg. 4 and ill.

Illustrated London News, Dec. 6, 1930, pg. 1028.

James J. Rorimer, "A Twelfth Century Head of King David from Notre-Dame," *Bulletin of The Metropolitan Museum of Art,* vol. XXXV, January, 1940, pp. 17-19.

Marvin Chauncey Ross, "Monumental Sculpture from Saint-Denis," *Journal of the Walters Art Gallery,* vol. III, Baltimore, 1940, pg. 106.

James J. Rorimer, "Forgeries of Medieval Stone Sculptures," *Gazette des Beaux-Arts,* vol. XXVI, 6ᵉ série, July-Dec., 1944, pp. 203-204, fig. 10.

Marcel Aubert, "Têtes de statue-colonnes du portail occidental de Saint-Denis," *Bulletin Monumental,* vol. 103, 1945, pg. 247, n. 2.

James J. Rorimer and William H. Forsyth, "The Medieval Galleries," *Bulletin of The Metropolitan Museum of Art,* n.s., vol. XII, February, 1954, pp. 128, 130.

Willibald Sauerländer, "Die Marienkrönungsportale von Senlis und Mantes," *Wallraf-Richartz Jahrbuch,* vol. XX, 1958, pg. 126, abb. 70.

Louis Grodecki, "La 'Première Sculpture Gothique.' Wilhelm Vöge et l'Etat Actuel des Problèmes," *Bulletin Monumental,* vol. 117, 1959, pp. 279, 282.

Yves Bottineau, *Notre-Dame de Paris et la Sainte-Chapelle,* Paris, 1966, pg. 34.

William Wixom, *Treasures From Medieval France,* The Cleveland Museum of Art, 1967, pp. 94-95, 356.

56. Bourges (Cher).

Cathedral of Saint-Étienne.

Head of a King (a Magus?). Portal of the North Flank
(?). ca. 1165-1180.

Limestone. h., 9″; w., 4.71″; d., 5.3″

Musées de la Ville de Bourges, Hôtel Cujas, Bourges. 880.
6.1.

The provenance indicated here represents a bolder, or perhaps a more foolhardy, attitude on our part than has been shown in previous attributions, which have only suggested tentatively that this head may have belonged to the twelfth century sculptural projects destined to ornament the cathedral before it was completely re-built beginning in 1195. Our decision is based upon the fact that this head is close in style to the sculpture preserved in the portal of the south flank, (fig. 56a).

In recent studies based upon excavations Robert Branner has established that most of the sculpture of both the north and south portals was originally intended for what would have been three portals located on the west façade of the Romanesque cathedral, built in the early part of the eleventh century, and enlarged in the mid-twelfth century. The west portals, planned and partially executed between ca. 1165 and 1180, would, therefore, have comprised the third stage of the construction and enlargement of the Romanesque church.[1]

It appears, however, that a serious fire damaged the church at the end of the twelfth century, precipitating the decision to re-build the cathedral entirely. Between 1195 and 1214 the apse and choir were constructed, and between 1225 and 1255 the remainder of the church, including the nave and façade, were built. It was during this second campaign that portions of the sculpture intended for the three portals of the old façade were remounted in the portals that were located on the north and south sides of the nave. In remounting this sculpture the original iconographic scheme was ignored.

Comparing the small head of a king with the heads of the statue columns in the south portal, (fig. 56a) one is struck by the correspondence that exists in the carving of the facial structure, the hair, and the eyes. It seems plausible to suggest that this head, which entered the museum in Bourges around 1880, belonged to the group of sculptures placed in the side portals.

With strong influences from the Nivernais and Burgundy, with a Romanesque tradition that touches the Auvergne and even Western France, the sculpture of the north and south portals represents still another example of the influence of Saint-Denis and Chartres. The original plan of the portals seems to have been based upon the west portals at Chartres. Certainly most of the elements of the present south portal at Bourges would have been in the central portal of the projected west façade, and these elements are clearly derived in style and iconography from the central portal at Chartres.

The figures of the tympanum, the lintel, and the jambs are more tightly bound to the architecture than at Chartres. They are more constrained and flatter within the spaces provided for them, resulting in a certain stiffness and in forms that are broader in treatment. All of these characteristics at Bourges suggest a more conservative approach than at Chartres. If we have characterized Romanesque sculpture in part by its subservience to an architecture whose basic principle is the continuous plane of a bearing wall, it is the retention of this approach at Bourges that we see as conservative within a new style that is moving away from such constraint.

The head of a king and the statue columns of the cathedral have little relationship to the few other statue columns that exist in Berry. The tiny church at Vereaux (Cher) possesses a single western portal with a statue column on each side. Both represent females and seem to have been intended originally for their present location, perhaps in imitation of the work in progress at Bourges in the latter part of the twelfth century. The statues are clearly derived from Chartrain types. The faces of both statues are quite strange, the features being rather squashed, as if the sculptor did not really understand the scale or spatial freedom that was available to him.

The Musée du Berry possesses two very well-known statues of a Bishop and a Queen that cannot properly be called statue columns. Both are from the church of Notre-Dame-de-la-Comtale in Bourges. Their dating and stylistic origins are controversial, since they have no connection with berrichon of this period. Partially discount-

56a

ing the opinion that they may have been carved by a northern atelier and are thus linked with Saint-Denis, we would look in the opposite direction and to sculptures which, themselves, are influenced by Chartres. There are, indeed, distinct similarities between the Bourges statue of a queen and the relief of what is called by Hamann the Queen of Sheba from the portal of the chapter house at Notre-Dame-de-la-Daurade in Toulouse.[2] The statue columns from this church are dated between 1180 and 1196, providing a general date for the Bourges statues as well. The resemblance of the two statues of Queens is too close to deny some sort of connection, both being related, though somewhat distantly, to the statue columns of the Ile-de-France. In any case, the statues of a Bishop and a Queen in Bourges suggest little or no relationship with the twelfth century work done for the Cathedral of Bourges and thus with the head of a king exhibited here.

NOTES

1. cf. Robert Gauchery and Robert Branner, "La cathédrale de Bourges aux XIᵉ et XIIᵉ siècles," *Bulletin Monumental,* vol. 111, 1953, pp. 105-123; Robert Branner, "Les portails lateraux de la cathédrale de Bourges," *Bulletin Monumental,* vol. 115, 1957, pp. 263-270; *idem., La cathédrale de Bourges et sa place dans l'architecture gothique,* Bourges, 1962.

2. Richard Hamann, *Die Abteikirche von St. Gilles und ihre künstlerische Nachfolge,* Berlin, 1955, pg. 264, abb. 337; cf. also P. Mesplé, *Les Sculptures Romanes, Toulouse, Musée des Augustins.* (Inventaire des Collections Publiques Françaises, 5), Paris, 1961, no. 66. For the two Bourges statues of a Bishop and a Queen, cf. Eugène Lefévre-Pontalis, "Deux statues du XIIᵉ siècle au Musée de Bourges," *Bulletin Monumental,* vol. 77, 1913, pp. 140-143; *Cathédrales,* exhibition catalogue, Musée du Louvre, Paris, Feb.-April, 1962, pp. 40-41, nos. 25, 26; William Wixom, *Treasures From Medieval France,* The Cleveland Museum of Art, 1967, pp. 78-79, 355.

BIBLIOGRAPHY

Cathédrales. exhibition catalogue. Musée du Louvre, Paris, February-April, 1962, pp. 39-41.

Coeur de France. Kunst des Berry von der Römerzeit bis zur Gegenwart. exhibition catalogue. Darmstadt, Matildenhöhe, Oct. 14-Dec. 3, 1967; Düsseldorf, Kunsthalle, Jan. 26-March 3, 1968; München, Stadtmuseum, March 27-May 12, 1968. cat. No. 89.

57. Mantes (Seine-et-Oise).

Église Collégiale de Notre-Dame. ca. 1170-ca. 1250.

Head of a King. Central Portal of the West Façade. ca. 1180.

Limestone. h., 10⅛″; w., 5½″

Art Museum, Duke University.

ex coll.: Ernest Brummer.

We are particularly fortunate in being able to exhibit this remarkable head in the series of Early Gothic heads beginning with Saint-Denis (cat. nos. 52, 53), since it represents an important monument in the complex development of Early Gothic sculpture. Construction of the church of Notre-Dame at Mantes was begun around 1170 at the western end and then moved directly to the east. From about 1180 the work progressed steadily from east to west up to the level of the tribunes. During a second campaign between 1180 and 1190 the tribune storey was completed and the upper levels, including the vaulting, were built between ca. 1200 and ca. 1230.[1]

The erection of the façade also took a considerable amount of time, going up in various stages. Even the central and left-hand, or north, portals were the result of the efforts of several ateliers in succession. The north portal was decorated first in the years following 1170 by a group of sculptors whose work is somewhat awkward and recalls the decoration of the portal of Saint Anne at Notre-Dame in Paris (ca. 1165-1170; cat. no. 55). The central portal at Mantes was completed by two successive ateliers. The first of these two was far more accomplished than the one that had been occupied with the north portal. Between ca. 1175 and 1180 its members carved the lower portions of the central portal up to the tympanum. The tympanum and archivolts were added by the second atelier of the two between 1190 and 1195, according to Jean Bony.[2] Willibald Sauerländer, however, prefers to date the central portal as a whole around 1180.[3]

The controversy regarding dating extends beyond Mantes itself and is involved in the broader discussion of the development of Gothic sculpture between ca. 1140 and the early years of the thirteenth century, a discussion to which we have alluded in the descriptions of the other Early Gothic heads on exhibition. A clear understanding of the various genealogies of style perceptible in the growth of Gothic sculpture in France is made difficult by the terrible losses suffered during the Revolution. The portals of Mantes were mutilated in 1794, when the statue columns were destroyed and much of the sculpture in the areas above them were badly broken.[4]

Very little survives from the statue columns of the two twelfth century portals at Mantes. Three heads, at least, have been published and are preserved in the *Dépot lapidaire* of the church.[5] The head from Duke, which has been convincingly related to Mantes by Robert Moeller,[6] is thus a valuable addition to this material. Its especial value lies in the fact that it is closest in style to the most impressive of the three heads in Mantes (fig. 57a).[7] If, as we have observed, several ateliers produced the sculpture of the portals and if those involved in the central portal were more accomplished than that which carved

57a

the north portal figures, it would seem that the Mantes head that has been called Moses by Sauerländer and the Duke head would, because of differences in style and because of their higher quality, have come from the central portal, whereas the other two heads in Mantes were originally in the north portal.[8]

The Duke head matches the Moses head in almost every particular. The specific detailing of the eyes, the modelling of the facial structure, the carving of hair and beard, and the full lips are the same in both cases. Both are differentiated to some extent from the other two Mantes heads, whose details, although much the same, especially in the eyes and hair, are carved in a harder and less subtle manner.

Mantes has always played an important rôle in discussions regarding the history of Early Gothic sculpture. Since a full discussion of this knotty subject is beyond the scope of this catalogue, we can only refer briefly to the relationship between Mantes and the other important Gothic monuments of the twelfth century.[9] The iconography and composition of the tympanum and archivolts of the central portal at Mantes depend upon the cathedral of Senlis (Oise), whose sculpture may be dated, in part, ca. 1170. The lower portions of the Mantes central portal and entire north portal, however, recall the north transept portal, or "Porte des Valois," at Saint-Denis, ca. 1160-1170. At the same time the relationship between Senlis and Mantes may be generated from the slightly earlier portal of Saint Anne at Notre Dame in Paris, particularly as represented by the archivolts (ca. 1165), which, in turn, are related to the earliest sculptures at Saint-Denis.

The close communication that seems to have existed among these active centers of building and carving and the consequent interchange of styles and iconography present us with an extremely complicated picture. Mantes, itself, appears to have influenced the sculptors of the left portal of the west façade of the cathedral of Sens (Yonne), called the portal of Saint John the Baptist, carved around 1185-1190.

Our all-too-scanty exposition of the theories regarding the evolution of Gothic sculpture in the twelfth century as represented by the series of heads on exhibition here is meant to serve as an introduction to the environment within which must be placed the head from Duke. The opportunity to see all of these heads together will, we hope, generate further discussion in an area whose complexities have not yet been entirely disentangled.

Robert Moeller has identified the head at Duke as that of a prophet or a patriarch.[10] It seems to us, however, that the figure was wearing a crown, which is now battered almost beyond recognition. If this be the case, then the figure represented a king. Moeller also feels that the head may have come from an archivolt figure because it is considerably smaller than the other heads from Mantes.[11] From rough calculations it appears that the head from Duke would be too large for such a location, but it is impossible to spectulate further about its original placement or its identity. The central portal is devoted to the Virgin. On the lintel are represented her death and resurrection; in the tympanum is the Coronation of the Virgin. In the archivolts are forty-two statuettes representing the ancestors of Christ as the fruit of the Tree of Jesse. Since these include kings, prophets, and patriarchs, the Duke head would not be out of place iconographically. The problem of its size must be resolved by more precise measurements.

NOTES

1. This synopsis of the dating of construction is very general. For a more extensive account of the complex progress of the project cf. André Rhein, *Notre-Dame de Mantes*, Petites monographies des grandes edifices de France. Paris, 1932; Jean Bony, "La collégiale de Mantes," *Congrès Archéologique, Paris-Mantes,* vol. 104, 1946, pp. 163-220.

2. Bony, *ibid.,* pg. 178.

3. cf. Willibald Sauerländer, "Die Marienkrönungsportale von Senlis and Mantes," *Wallraf-Richartz Jahrbuch,* vol. XX, 1958, pp. 115 ff.; *idem.,* "Art antique et sculpture autour de 1200. Saint-Denis, Lisieux, Chartres," *Art de France,* vol. I, 1961, pp. 47-56.

4. cf. Bony, *op. cit.,* pp. 213-214.

5. cf. Marcel Aubert, "Têtes gothiques de Senlis et de Mantes," *Bulletin Monumental,* vol. 97, 1938, pp. 5-11; *Cathédrales,* exhibition catalogue, Musée du Louvre, February-April, 1962, pp. 49-51, nos. 35-36; William Wixom, *Treasures From Medieval France,* The Cleveland Museum of Art, 1967, pp. 118-119, 359.

6. Robert C. Moeller III, *Sculpture and Decorative Art. A Loan Exhibition of Selected Art works from the Brummer Collection of Duke University.* North Carolina Museum of Art, Raleigh, N.C., May 7-July 2, 1967, pp. 32-35.

7. It was this head, discovered in 1852, that was exhibited in Cleveland in 1967. cf. Wixom, *op. cit.,* pp. 118-119, 359.

8. This was already expressed in the catalogue for the exhibition *Cathédrales, op. cit.,* pg. 51.

9. We mention once again Louis Grodecki's masterful summation of the theories regarding Early Gothic sculpture: "La 'Première Sculpture Gothique.' Wilhelm Vöge et l'Etat Actuel des Problèmes," *Bulletin Monumental,* vol. 117, 1959, pp. 271-289, esp. pp. 281-289. In addition cf. Sauerländer, *op. cit., Wallraf-Richartz Jahrbuch,* vol. XX, 1958, pp. 115 ff., *idem., op. cit., Art de France,* vol. I, 1961, pg. 51; *idem., Von Sens bis Strassburg,* Berlin, 1966.

10. Moeller, *op. cit.,* pg. 32.

11. The head of Moses, for example, is 17 inches high. The other two heads from Mantes are approximately 15 inches high.

BIBLIOGRAPHY

Robert C. Moeller III, *Sculpture and Decorative Art. A Loan Exhibition of Selected Art Works from the Brummer Collection of Duke University.* North Carolina Museum of Art, Raleigh, N.C., May 7-July 2, 1967, pp. 32-35, no. 10.

58. Bourges (Cher).

Probably from one of the original jamb statues on the west façade of Bourges Cathedral.

Head (Moses?). 1230s.

Stone. h., 15^{15}⁄$_{16}$″

Musées de la Ville de Bourges, Hotel Cujas. 880.6.2

The decision to include this fine thirteenth century head in a show of twelfth century art was a fortunate one, for the twelfth century developments represented by the more familiar heads from the Walters, Fogg, and Metropolitan museums can be studied in relation to its mature Gothic style. The head, which was for years used as decoration over one of the doorways of the Musée du Berry (formerly the Hôtel Cujas) in Bourges, is undoubtedly a fragment from the west façade of Bourges Cathedral. Its size indicates that it belonged to one of the jamb statues.

The five western portals of Bourges Cathedral have suffered greatly over the centuries and many of the thirteenth century jamb statues have disappeared. In 1506 the north tower collapsed, destroying the portal at its base and part of the portal next to it. Most of the sculpture in these two portals dates from the subsequent sixteenth century reconstruction. At that time some of the original thirteenth century jamb statues were placed in niches on the new north tower. During their attack on Bourges in 1562 the Huguenots pulled down many of the jamb statues in the other three portals. Today there are only six of them on the façade, all on the right embrasure of the central portal. Five of these are from the thirteenth century, but they are not in their original places. The other jamb statues have disappeared. It is therefore not surprising that a head from the façade should have been found in another part of the town.

The sculpture of the western portals of Bourges Cathedral was carved in two major campaigns. Work began in the 1230s, soon after the design of the façade had been established. The south portal tympanum, dedicated to Saint Ursin, the tympanum of the Saint Stephen portal in the southern intermediary bay, the Genesis reliefs in the dado at the base of the façade, and many of the jamb statues were completed at this time. The head from the Musée du Berry belongs to this first campaign. A second shop of sculptors with a very different style came to Bourges in the 1240s.

Jean Favière, Conservateur des Musées de Bourges, has suggested that the head may have belonged to a figure of Moses. Horns, such as those springing from the head of Moses in the Virgin Coronation tympanum at Amiens, may have risen from the two rough circular areas on the top of the head. The figure probably stood on the right embrasure of one of the portals, facing slightly towards the doorway, for the right side of the head is not as fully developed as the left. On the left side the beard has full, curving strands. On the right the hairs are rather hastily indicated. The right eye is also less carefully done and the sculptor has omitted the bulge between lid and brow that appears over the left eye.

58a

The head was carved by a sculptor who worked on the Saint Ursin tympanum. It is almost identical to the head of one of Saint Ursin's kneeling converts in the middle register of that tympanum (fig. 58a). The facial structures are broadly conceived, with flat cheekbones and eyes and noses reduced to simple planes. The eyebrows are wedge-like and repeat the curves of the eyelids, while lining on the foreheads is rendered in shallow parallel incisions. The hair is more detailed; it is full and wavy, with short wisps at the peaks of the forehead. The ample beards grow close to the pronounced lower lips. The strands of hair in the mustaches are long and droop far down below the mouths.

The sculptor who carved this head was part of the workshop of the 1230s at Bourges. The figures created by this shop are related stylistically to the sculpture of the west façade of Amiens Cathedral, which was going up in the 1220s. The closest connections are between the Bourges Saint Ursin tympanum and the Amiens Saint Firmin tympanum, but there are many other parallels. For example, one of the kings today on the Bourges north tower is directly related to the three Magi in the Amiens Virgin portal. The Musée du Berry head is just one of numerous works done in the Amiens style at Bourges in the 1230s. Willibald Sauerländer has compared the head to that of Saint Luxor in the Amiens Saint Firmin portal.[1] It also resembles the head of the prophet Jeremiah in the central portal at Amiens. The Bourges head is an excellent example of one of the major stylistic developments in high Gothic sculpture. This style has its roots in northern France and centers around Amiens in the 1220s. The Musée du Berry head is typical of this style at Bourges in the 1230s. The sculptors at Bourges played an important role in the diffusion of the style to central and southern France in the first half of the thirteenth century.

TANIA ROLPH

NOTES

1. The façade was planned about 1228-30. cf. Robert Branner, *La Cathédrale de Bourges et sa place dans l'Architecture Gothique,* Paris, 1962, pg. 67.

2. Willibald Sauerländer, "Cathédrales: zu einer Ausstellung im Louvre," *Kunstchronik,* XV (1962), pp. 225-234, esp. p. 231.

BIBLIOGRAPHY

Cathédrales: sculptures, vitraux, objets d'art, manuscrits des XIIᵉ et XIIIᵉ siècles, Musée du Louvre, Fevrier-Avril, 1962.

Willibald Sauerländer, "Cathédrales: zu einer Ausstellung im Louvre," *Kunstchronik,* XV (1962), 225-234.

Tania Rolph, *The West Portals of Bourges Cathedral and their Sculpture,* Doctoral Dissertation, Columbia University, 1968.

Coeur de France. Kunst des Berry von der Römerzeit bis zur Gegenwart. Eine Austellung des Deutschen Kunstrates. Darmstadt, Mathildenhöhe, October 14-December 3, 1967; Düsseldorf, Kunsthalle, Jan. 26-Feb. 3, 1968; München, Stadtmuseum, Feb. 23-May 12, 1968, no. 93.

DISPUTED PROVENANCE

59. The Crucified Christ.

Spanish (Catalonian) or English(?). Mid-twelfth century.

Bronze. h., 8″

Collection of Mr. and Mrs. Martin Scher, New York.

ex coll.: Henri d'Allemagne, Paris; Wildenstein and Company, New York.

The search for stylistic companions to this unusual figure has so far proven fruitless. It is certainly unrelated to the types produced in German and the Valley of the Meuse (cf. cat. no. 51), and among those exhibited in recent years as French it seems to find no counterparts, although it was this provenance that was applied by Wildenstein to the figure. Verbal opinions from Dr. Hanns Swarzenski, Mr. Thomas Miller, and Mr. Michael Hall suggested that it might be related to English work, specifically because of the facial type, but such associations were denied by Mr. John Hunt in Ireland, who knows the English material very well, but who has only seen the crucifix in a photograph.[1]

Dr. Peter Bloch of the Berlin Museum, who is preparing for publication the catalogue of Christus figures gathered by Erich Meyer, stated in a letter that the crucifix is included in Meyer's files, but without any further information.[2] Bloch feels that the figure represents, perhaps, some sort of fusion of English and French styles, but he, too, has been unable to find any precise parallels. He gives support to the possibility that it might be English and dates it in the first half of the twelfth century.

John Hunt, while denying that it is English, does point out that "the long fall of the perizonium on the dexter side has English affinities." He feels, however, that a provenance farther south, that is in Spain, would be more accurate, and that the date should be fixed sometime late in the twelfth century.

After much investigation without many positive results it seems to us that the most likely opinion offered so far is that of Mr. Hunt. Such an assertion grows more from the cumulative sense of a style drawn from looking at monumental and small-scale Romanesque sculpture in Spain, England, France, the Valley of the Meuse, and Germany than from any specific parallels. So vague a recommendation for attribution seems hardly worth mentioning, yet in contrast to other groups of crucifixes, those done in Spain possess the same expressive qualities conveyed through the attentuation of the body, the distortion of limbs and extremeties, and the restrained, yet intense, feeling embodied in the taut silhouette, the arrangement of body axes, and the rigid composition of the body found in the Scher figure. The crucifix from Santa Clara in Palencia, now in the Cloisters, New York, and cited earlier (cat. no. 39, fig. 39a) belongs to this same general family of forms.

The most unusual characteristics of the Scher Corpus are the greatly enlarged head, hands, and feet, the latter being disquietingly enormous and a strange finale to the long, straight form of the body, broken sharply at the knees. The space formed between the bend in the legs and the back plane is filled on both sides by the fall of the perizonium, which is treated very simply and is bound up with only a single knot.

The back is hollow, and traces of several layers of paint remain in areas such as the neck, between the legs, on the eyes, and in the channels between the ribs. The right thumb appears to have broken off, but the left is bent in a way that is common among bronze crucifixes.

Placing the Scher Corpus in Spain, we would attempt an even more limited designation of provenance based, once again, on pieces that bear a general stylistic similarity. The only figure we have found that possesses some of the same distortions, such as the enlarged feet, and that is treated in somewhat the same way is a crucifix from La Seo de Urgell in Catalonia, dated 1147 and now in the museum in Barcelona.[3] This figure is, in turn, related to the fragments of an altar frontal from Farrera (Catalonia), near La Seo de Urgell, now dispersed among the Fogg Art Museum, the Museum of Fine Arts, Boston, and the Museum of Folk Arts, at Riverdale-on-Hudson, New York.[4] We would suggest that as a basis for further investigation the Scher Corpus might be placed in Catalonia and dated in the mid-twelfth century, but the adherents to a theory of English origin cannot be ignored.

NOTES

1. Letter of February 22, 1969.

2. Letter of February 12, 1969.

3. cf. Dr. Paul Thoby, *Le Crucifix des Origines au Concile de Trente. Supplément.* Nantes, 1963, pl. CCV, no. 416.

4. cf. Walter W. S. Cook, "A Catalan Wooden Altar Frontal from Farrera," *Medieval Studies in Memory of A. Kingsley Porter,* ed. by Wilhelm W. R. Koehler. vol. I, Harvard University Press, Cambridge, Mass., 1939, pp. 293-300. The Museum of Folk Arts was founded in 1926 by Mr. and Mrs. Elie Nadelman.

60. Engaged Capital.

The Weighing of Souls. Nivernais(?). Mid-twelfth century.

Limestone. h., 16″; w., 18¼″; d., 15″

The Cleveland Museum of Art, purchase from the J. H. Wade Fund. 61.407.

The dominance of the theme of the Last Judgment in Romanesque art is well-known. Although in Gothic art the subject is given no less emphasis, it is included within a far grander and more systematic scheme of iconography as part of the total composition of the cathedral, and its character changes from the more remote, abstract, and visionary quality of the Romanesque treatment of the subject to an orderly, controlled, and more rational interpretation.

Yet one of the most impressive features of Romanesque art is its inclusion of not only the fantastic and the supernatural, but aspects of human emotion and action. This is particularly true of Burgundian sculpture. At Autun the Flight Into Egypt and the Angel Appearing to the Magi on the capitals and the reactions of the resurrected to the terrors and joys of the Last Day on the lintel and tympanum of the west portal (ca. 1130) are evidence of a kind of realism rooted in a sensitive concern for an observation of the more transient physical and emotional aspects of human existence. An expression of such values is achieved with the same economy of form, the same semi-abstraction dictated by the specialized architectural environment that governs the contortions of the imaginary beings and the pure decoration. That is to say that the expressive realism of much of Romanesque sculpture does not rely for its success upon a corresponding visual realism or *mimesis*.

The theme of the Last Judgment provided endless opportunities for the Romanesque sculptor to indulge his taste for both the fantastic and the real as well as to fulfill his duty to the overall importance of the subject. The Weighing of Souls, an integral part of the traditional elements of the Last Judgment, is found on a number of Romanesque capitals (see below) as well as on the tympana of Autun, Conques, and Beaulieu-sur-Dordogne, to mention a few.

The description of judgment in such mundane terms as the weighing in a balance of the good and evil portions of a man's soul exemplifies another vital aspect of Romanesque, and, indeed, medieval art. The representation of concepts, of spiritual or supernatural beings, of scarcely imaginable events, and of literary images in visual terms requires that they be transported from the totally non-physical and pure realm of the mind and spirit to the opposite realm, that of the physical, sensual, and perishable. Such a translation, though regarded with deep suspicion not only by the Church Fathers, but by an unbroken line of purists, was inevitable if any sort of common understanding of the paradoxes of Christianity was to be achieved. Imagery, despite its concomitant danger of idolatry, was one of the most effective means of conveying the truths of the Christian religion to its present and would-be adherents. In fact, it had been the demonstrable, historical aspect of the story of Christ that had made belief in Christianity so much easier than in the still mythical bases of the other mystery religions—Mithra, Isis, Cybele, etc. The paradox of the Incarnation, itself, was an argument in favor of the transportation of the spiritual into the physical.

An apparent affront to the nature of the spiritual by expressing it in limited, physical terms is cancelled by the fact that the physical world was conceived as being merely an image of the spiritual and a means of achieving an understanding of what was not perceptible to the senses. Thus all natural objects had some meaning beyond their mere physical existence, and it was this meaning that was their *raison d'être*. The results of this approach to the physical world are the herbiaries, lapidaries, and bestiaries, that set forth the meanings of various categories of natural objects.

Understanding this mode of thought is essential to becoming more conversant with the peculiar literal-mindedness found in much of medieval art. The illustrations in the Utrecht Psalter (ca. 820) are an early and very effective example of the exact description in visual terms of literary images and the expression of emotional and spiritual states of mind. The same process takes place in Romanesque sculpture where a kind of visual fundamentalism controls the iconography. Thus souls are represented as tiny, naked humans; they are weighed in a balance, and, according to the judgment, they are either stuffed into Hell-Mouth, represented literally as a mouth, or ushered into the Heavenly Jerusalem, the crenelations and arches of whose architecture identify it as such. At Autun the artist, Gislebertus, coped with the problem of transporting the souls of the blessed, who possess all the weight and density of a living body, from an earthly to a celestial realm by having them boosted by angels up through a trap door in the bottom of a building, the souls clasping their hands in prayer and gratitude all the while. This is, indeed, another aspect of the rather special forms of realism found in Romanesque sculpture.

In the capital from Cleveland, by a kind of shorthand, the essential elements of the story of judgment are portrayed. The great scales hanging from a hook occupy the front face of the capital, and in one of its baskets, that on the side of the Blessed, stands a naked female soul. The balance has tipped in neither direction, but the defense and the prosecution, so to speak, stand at the corners of the capital, quite dramatically composed within the shape of the architectural member. To the right is the Archangel Michael, the right hand raised as if in detached anticipation of the irrevocable judgment of God, the left pointing to the reward of the Just, the Heavenly Jerusalem, which occupies, in the form of a small edifice with an arched opening, the right side of the capital. Framed by the arch is the bust of one of the Blessed while below him are seen two other souls whose attitudes are somewhat ambiguous. One, naked, appears about to enter the Holy City; the other, clothed, kneels in supplication before the angel.

Opposing this happy, but rather stolid, group is a devil on the left corner of the capital, As he strides forward, grimacing horribly, he attempts to interfere with the process of selection by leaning upon the basket of the balance that is meant to contain the sins of the resurrected soul. At the same time, with his right hand, he prepares to stuff a frightened and bewildered soul into the fish-like jaws of Hell-Mouth, which emerges into the space of the left side of the capital. Below, another soul, already damned, his arms raised in terror, flees from the scene.

Representatives of the Weighing of Souls on capitals are not infrequent, nor are they restricted to any one area in particular. Joan Evans cites several examples, among them capitals from Sainte-Marie-la-Daurade, Toulouse (ca. 1100); Duravel; Saint-Martin-de-Saujon (early 12th century); Saint-Eutrope-de-Saintes; and Vézelay, where the usual narrative vigor is displayed. Most of these capitals, as well as those representations of the scene on other portions of the architecture, tell the story in much the same way as on the Cleveland capital.

One particularly crowded version is found on a capital at Saint-Révérien (Nièvre) showing the towers and arch of the Heavenly Jerusalem, this time with three souls under the arch, the Damned being pushed into another fish-like Hell-Mouth and including, as in the Cleveland capital, a female figure, the Archangel, the balance, and a host of grinning demons.[2]

The capital from Saint-Révérien is important for another reason, since it offers the only clue, weak as it is, to the stylistic origins of the Cleveland capital. The basic form of the capital is the same, and although the example from Saint-Révérien does not form any close parallels in style with the Cleveland capital, the new similarities that exist in addition to other aspects of the style of the region lead to a tentative suggestion that the Cleveland capital was done in the Nivernais. In this case the dramatic character of the narrative should not obscure from us the heavy-handed nature of the carving.

William Wixom of the Cleveland Museum in preliminary and unpublished studies of the style of the capital has suggested that it was done in the Loire Valley in the early twelfth century on the basis of comparison with certain of the capitals at Saint-Benoit-sur-Loire, especially those representing the life of Saint Benoit. We have been unable to find the same affinities of style and have been led, albeit timidly, to the present designation of general provenance, that is, in an area not very far south of Saint-Benoit-sur-Loire.

NOTES

1. Joan Evans, *Cluniac Art of the Romanesque Period*, Cambridge University Press, 1950, pg. 69, and figs. 119a, b, 120a, b.

2. cf. Marcel Anfray, *L'Architecture Religieuse du Nivernais au Moyen Age*, Paris, 1951, pl. LI, 2, 3, 4.

BIBLIOGRAPHY

Handbook of The Cleveland Museum of Art, 1966, pg. 47.

61. **Aulnat** (Puy-de-Dôme).

Saint-Jean-d'Oulmes (?)

Portion of an archivolt. *Elder of the Apocalypse.* ca. 1150-1170.

Limestone. h., 18⅜″

City Art Museum of Saint Louis. 32.33.

A very curious problem is presented by this fragment of an archivolt and its companion (33.33) also in St. Louis (fig. 61a). The records of the Museum indicate only that both pieces are from the church of Saint-Jean-d'Oulmes, near Aulnat (Puy-de-Dôme) and in the *Bulletin* of the Museum it is asserted that despite the appearance of the two Elders, their origin is Auvergnat.[1] That such a statement was necessary is a measure of the problem involved because decorated archivolts that would contain Apocalyptic Elders of this type are totally unexpected in the Auvergne.

It is true that there is a town called Aulnat some three-and-a-half miles to the northeast of Clermont-Ferrand, and it is also true that this town contains, as the *Guide Bleu* of 1957 for *Auvergne et Centre* states, "une église moderne conservant des parties romanes."[2] Such a situation would seem to support the existence of twelfth century fragments from the church existing in an American museum.

It is practically impossible, however, to find any information about this church. In the proceedings of the Congrès Archéologique for 1895 held at Clermont-Ferrand, Henry du Ranquet, in an article entitled "École romane d'Auvergne," mentions on page 190 the *modillons* "qu'on voit encore en place à l'église d'Aulnat et de quelques autres rares monuments." He is referring to a purely non-figural or non-historiated type of *modillon,* or bracket, that is common in the Auvergne. On the following page he again refers to the "modillons d'Aulnat."

Only brief mention of Aulnat or its church is made in the standard catalogues or descriptions of monuments in the Auvergne and particularly in the Puy-de-Dôme. Mallay, in 1841, lists the church, but not its patron saint, and says that it was reconstructed in 1838, the old choir being preserved.[3] J. B. Bouillet also mentions Aulnat and its church, pointing out that it was one of the first sites in Auvergne to establish a Christian house of worship. He goes on to say that the church "a conservés, dans ses diverses restaurations, son premier caractére. Cette église est du XIe siècle, le choeur est intact."[4] He, too, does not include the dedication of the church. Both Mallay and Bouillet fail to describe any sculpture, though Mallay does say that the capitals were copied in the restoration of 1838.

At the same time it is clear that the two Elders in St. Louis are of a type and style that is found more commonly in western France. Indeed, in this area there is a place called Oulmes (Vendée), but its church is dedicated not to St. Jean, but to Notre-Dame. Is it possible that at some time the name that became attached to the Elders as Aulnat in the Puy-de-Dôme was actually Aulnay in the Charente-Maritime, that is, roughly thirty miles south of

61a

Oulmes and the site of a well-known Romanesque church?

Thus stands the mystery. Despite the inconsistencies and lack of information, it is difficult to discredit the attribution given by the Museum in St. Louis precisely because of the total obscurity of the church from which the reliefs are said to have come. The date of the church, of course, would not match the style of the sculpture said to come from it, but the dating is very vague. At the same time the inconsistencies, when considered with the type and style of the reliefs would suggest very strongly that some error was made in transcribing "Oulmes near Aulnay in the Saintonge" to "Saint-Jean-d'Oulmes near Aulnat."

Notre-Dame at Oulmes is, indeed, a Romanesque church with figured capitals in the crossing and a western portal without tympanum, but with palmette, floral, and diamond designs as decoration. Until more facts are available we shall have to put aside this portion of our examination without reaching a definite conclusion.

The church of Saint-Pierre at Aulnay has greater relevance to the St. Louis reliefs than being merely the source of a possible typographical error. It is in the archivolts of the south transept portal that we see an obvious counterpart to the St. Louis Elders. Though described as being twenty-four in number in the Revelation According to St. John (iv. 2-4; v, 8), at Aulnay the second archivolt from the top contains thirty-one figures, each identical to the next and all seated with a stringed instrument in the left hand, a vial in the right, and a crown upon the head. The pose and attributes match the two Elders in St. Louis except for the substitution of a chalice for a vial, and are common in western France. This was perhaps due to the adaptability of the subject of a series of undifferentiated figures such as the Elders to the portals of Poitou, Saintonge, and Angoumois with their heavy multiple arches covered with dense ornament that followed the radiating pattern of the stones themselves. The same treatment of the Elders seated next to one another rather than standing one above the other is found at Saint-Symphorien-de-Broue (Charente-Maritime), Avy-en-Pons (Charente-Maritime), Sainte-Croix at Bordeaux (Gironde), even farther south in the portal of Sainte-Marie at Oloron-Sainte-Marie (Basses-Pyrénées), Varaize, south portal (Charente-Maritime), and Sainte-Marie-des-Dames at Saintes (Charente-Maritime). In contrast to all of these examples, restricted, as one can see, to a specific region, and to general custom is the disturbing fact that the St. Louis Elders are beardless.

If the St. Louis Elders are similar in type to those at Aulnay, the styles have next to nothing in common. Yet the former have much stronger affinities with the style of western France and in particular with some of the churches in the Charente-Maritime and the Gironde than with the churches of the Auvergne. The sparse lines of drapery folds are similar to those found at such a church as Saintes, while the linear swirl on the abdomen may be seen on the Psychomachia figures in an archivolt at Blazimont (or Blasimon, Gironde).[5]

The appearance of the Elders is once again a reminder of the central importance to Romanesque iconography of the Apocalyptic Vision. The pictorial source for representations of the text from Revelations is generally believed to be the illuminated copies of the commentary on the Apocalypse written by Beatus, abbot of Liébana in the Asturias in 780. Based upon earlier illustrated texts of the Book of Revelation, the Beatus manuscripts were widely copied in southern France.

The central scene of the Revelation was Christ in Glory amidst the four beasts of the Evangelists and surrounded by the twenty-four Elders. As a subject for the tympana, lintels, and archivolts of Romanesque portals, this frightening vision, or some portion of it, was ubiquitous and served as a stern warning at the entrance to the building that was an image of the Heavenly Jerusalem and within whose walls the act of Redemption was repeated daily (see also cat. no. 21).

NOTES

1. Vol. XIX, no. 3, July, 1934, pp. 31-32.

2. pg. 397.

3. Armand-Gilbert Mallay, *Essai sur les églises romanes et romano-byzantines du département du Puy-de-Dôme.* 2ᵉ éd., Clermont-Ferrand, 1841, pg. 52.

4. J. B. Bouillet, "Description archéologique des monuments Celtiques, Romains et du Moyen-Age du Département du Puy-de-Dôme," *Mémoires de l'Académie des Sciences, Belles-Lettres et Arts de Clermont-Ferrand,* t. XVI, 1874, pp. 101-333. "Aulnat," pp. 115-116. Prosper Merimée, *Notes d'Un Voyage en Auvergne,* Paris, 1838, makes no mention of Aulnat.

5. cf. Arthur Kingsley Porter, *Romanesque Sculpture of the Pilgrimage Roads,* Boston, 1923, vol. VII, pl. 1041.

BIBLIOGRAPHY

Bulletin of the City Art Museum of St. Louis, vol. XIX, no. 3, July, 1934, pp. 31-32.

62. Capital.

Blasphemy and Avarice. Northern France (Cambrai ?) or Northwestern Languedoc (Perigord ?). Second half of the twelfth century.

Limestone. h., 11½″; w., 8″; d., 8″

Philadelphia Museum of Art, The George Grey Barnard Collection, 45-25-47.

The mélange of characteristics that can be associated with a number of identifiable styles in this capital makes it very difficult to place in a specific area. Martin Weinberger points out that although the capital was reported to have been acquired in the south of France, it has no typological and stylistic parallels in that region. He mentions certain features of the sculpture in Toulouse in combination with the vigor of the work at Conques. In addition he sees the influence of Northern France, that is, Early Gothic, sculpture. In the end he places the capital in Languedoc and dates it in the latter part of the twelfth century.

The vagueness of this opinion is understandable, but its general conclusion may be open to question. In fact, the off-hand suggestion of links with Northern France has more possibilities than Dr. Weinberger may have thought. The striations on the wings and hairy portions of the devils and the stippling of the serpentine portions of their bodies does seem to imitate the manner used in a great many of the capitals from Toulouse, especially those preserved in the Musée des Augustins from Notre-Dame-de-la-Daurade, Saint-Sernin, and from unknown sources.[2] The large and bulging eyes with no drilling for the pupils is also a common characteristic of Toulousan work.

Capitals of this type and composition, however, are not found at all in Toulouse nor in its immediate region. In fact, the crowded and somewhat confused rendering of the narrative makes it impossible to associate the Philadelphia capital too closely with this area. It has none of the rigid adherence to decorative principles in relation to the shape and size of the architectural member supporting the carving which is so constant a feature of the sculpture of Toulouse and its most important stylistic companions, such as the cloister and portal sculpture at Moissac.

Yet other links with this area, tenuous as they may be, do exist. The demons seem to follow the type seen in the Theophilus relief from the portal at Souillac (Lot, ca. 1130), a monument closely linked with Moissac and therefore with the main current of Languedocian sculpture. This would seem to indicate that the area of origin of the Philadelphia capital is probably located in what might be called generally northwestern Languedoc or central Guyenne.

It is remarkable, however, to find many of the characteristics linking the Philadelphia capital with Guyenne occurring in the opposite direction as well. A capital in the Musée de Cambrai published by Jacques Vanuxem[3] bears some striking resemblances to the Philadelphia capital. Probably from the church of Saint-Géry, Cambrai, the corner capital shows two male siren-like beasts with rinceaux. The form of the wings and the indication of feathers by means of many thin, incised lines seem identical in both the Philadelphia and Cambrai capitals. The large, round eyes framed by ridged lids and the general shape of the faces compare favorably. From the evidence available it is difficult to come to any solid conclusion, but the possibility that the Philadelphia capital is from a northern area and perhaps even from Cambrai, should not be overlooked. There is always the possibility, of course, that southern sculptors were active in the north.

On this capital, the agonies of the underworld are here visited upon two evildoers. As in cat. no. 9 Avarice receives an unexpected dividend for his cupidity. Standing naked with his money-bag around his neck, the sinner is fed into the jaws of Hell by two demons whose claws grasp his arms and legs, effectively displaying him upon the face of the capital.

On the opposite side a Blasphemer or Heretic suffers the just reward of having his tongue pulled out by tongs grasped in the hands of one devil while another grapples with the struggling soul. The movements of the figures are unusually involved, their limbs entangled in a complex composition that is rather difficult to read at first glance. Serpentine forms fill the two narrow sides of the capital and add to the general confusion in a way that is uncommonly asymmetrical for Romanesque sculpture.

NOTES

1. *The George Grey Barnard Collection,* privately printed, New York, n.d., (1941), pg. 10, no. 47, pls. XIV, XV.

2. cf., e.g., Pierre Mesplé, *Les Sculptures Romanes, Toulouse, Musée des Augustins* (Inventaire des Collections Publiques Françaises, 5), Paris, 1961, nos. 166-168, 224, 225, 325, 327, 328.

3. "La Sculpture du XIIe Siècle à Cambrai et à Arras," *Bulletin Monumental,* vol. 113, 1955, pg. 25, fig. 15.

BIBLIOGRAPHY

Martin Weinberger, *The George Grey Barnard Collection,* privately printed, New York, n.d. (1941), pg. 10, no. 47, pls. XIV, XV.

63. Male Head.

Southern France, Pyrenees (?). Late twelfth century.

Limestone. h., 8¾″

City Art Museum of St. Louis. 84.32.

ex coll.: Brummer Gallery.

It has been impossible so far to find any close stylistic parallels for this fine head. Without providing any convincing reasons the St. Louis Museum says that it is from the region of the Pyrenees, a vague enough designation that would have to be more carefully qualified.

The head is a sensitive piece of carving, especially in the area of the mouth with its bemused expression and softly modelled lips. The same sensitive modelling is perceived in the rest of the face despite the deterioration of the surface. The contours of the cheeks and the particular combination of parts that make up the eyes suggest more than anything else the intermediate level of sophistication attained in the Early Gothic sculpture of the late twelfth century, developing from the initial products of Saint-Denis and Chartres, and their immediate followers, and moving towards the sculpture of the Gothic portals of the first half of the thirteenth century. Another possibility in relation to Early Gothic is the sculpture of the later twelfth century in Provence.

The quality of the head cannot be denied. Our own feeling is that it dates around 1200 and that it falls into the category of sculpture generally described as being Early Gothic. As with so many other pieces in this exhibition that have been detached from their original environment and have found their way to this country without the preservation of proper records, this head must remain a subject for further speculation. The attention drawn to this head as well as to the other vaguely attributed pieces by means of this exhibit will, we hope, result in the stimulation of more expert opinions.

BIBLIOGRAPHY

M.R.R. "A Group of Medieval Sculptures," *Bulletin of the City Art Museum of St. Louis,* July, 1933, pg. 30-34, fig. 1.

BIBLIOGRAPHY

The following bibliography includes literature related to the areas of romanesque and early gothic sculpture represented in the present exhibition. The first three sections list general works on French romanesque architecture, sculpture, and iconography. The remaining sections list literature which deals with romanesque sculpture in specific regions of France, and in Tuscany and Spain, with a special section on romanesque and Early Gothic sculpture in the Ile-de-France. Any such break-down is necessarily somewhat arbitrary since regional styles and defined geographical areas frequently do not coincide and, likewise, chronological demarcations are often difficult to establish. However, it was thought that in order to provide a bibliography that would be easily usable, as well as relatively comprehensive, a division of some sort was necessary; it is hoped that the method employed will provide both layman and scholar with easy access to the material which interests him.

Bibliography included in the individual entries in the catalogue is repeated here only when it possesses a more general interest. Excepting a few important studies, articles from the *Congrès archéologique de France* are not included here. Thus, for further literature on romanesque sculpture in specific regions of France, the pertinent volumes of the *Congrès* should be consulted.

PETER FUSCO

I. GENERAL WORKS.

A. French Romanesque Architecture.

Aubert, M., *L'architecture cistercienne en France*, 2 vols., Paris, 1943; 2nd ed., 1947.

Aubert, M., and J. Verrier, *L'architecture française des origines à la fin de l'époque romane*, Paris, 1941.

Aubert, M., and S. Goubet, *Cathédrales et abbatiales romanes de France*, Paris, 1965.

Baum, J., *L'architecture romane en France*, Paris, 1931.

Besse, Dom, *Abbayes et prieurés de l'ancienne France*, Paris, 1914.

Clapham, A. W., *Romanesque Architecture in Western Europe*, Oxford, 1936.

Conant, K. J., *Carolingian and Romanesque Architecture 800 to 1200*, Baltimore, 1959.

Cotineau, Dom, *Répertoire des abbayes et prieurés de France*, s. l., 1939.

Dehio, G. and von Bezold, *Die Kirchliche Baukunst des Abendlandes*, Stuttgart, 1892.

Deschamps, P., *Églises romanes de France*, Paris, 1948.

Deshoulières, F., *Au début de l'art roman, les églises de l'onzième siècle en France*, Paris, 1943.

Evans, J., *Romanesque Architecture of the Order of Cluny*, Cambridge, 1938.

Frankl, P., *Baukunst des Mittelalters. Die frühmittelalterliche und romanische Baukunst*, Potsdam, 1926.

Gardner, A., *An Introduction to French Church Architecture*, Cambridge, 1938.

Gieure, M., *Les églises romanes de France*, 2 vols., Paris, 1953-1954.

Gromort, G., *L'architecture romane*, 3 vols., Paris, 1929-1931.

Jackson, T. G., *Byzantine and Romanesque Architecture*, 2 vols., Cambridge, 1913.

Krautheimer, R., "Introduction to an Iconography of Medieval Architecture," *Journal of the Warburg and Courtauld Institute*, vol. 5, 1942, 1-33.

Lasteyrie, R. de, *L'architecture religieuse en France à l'époque romane*, Paris, 1912.

Lenoir, A., *Architecture monastique*, Paris, 1852-1856.

Mortet, V., and P. Deschamps, *Recueil de textes relatifs à l'histoire de l'architecture et à la condition des architectes en France au moyen âge*, Paris, 1929.

Pillement, G., *Cloîtres et abbayes de France*, Paris, 1950.

Porter, A. K., *Medieval Architecture: Its Origins and Development*, 2 vols., New York, 1909; 2nd ed., New Haven, 1912.

Saalman, H., *Medieval Architecture: European Architecture 600-1200*, New York, 1962.

Vallery-Radot, J., *Églises romanes, filiations et échanges d'influences*, Paris, 1931.

Vielliard, J., *Le guide du pèlerin de Saint-Jacques de Compostelle*, Mâcon, 1938.

Viollet-le-Duc, E., *Dictionnaire raisonné de l'architecture française du XIe au XVIe siècle*, 10 vols., Paris, 1854-1868.

B. French Romanesque Sculpture.

L'art roman en France, ed. by M. Aubert, Paris, 1961.

Aubert, M., *La sculpture française du moyen âge et de la Renaissance*, Paris and Brussels, 1926.

――――, *L'art français à l'époque romane*, 4 vols., Paris, 1930-1950.

――――, *La sculpture française au moyen-âge*, Paris, 1947.

Aubert, M., and Michele Beaulieu, *Description raisonnée des sculptures du moyen âge*, Musée National du Louvre, Paris, 1950.

Aubert, M., M. Pobé, and J. Gantner, *L'art monumental roman en France*, Paris, 1955.

Baltrusaitis, J., *La stylistique ornementale dans la sculpture romane*, Paris, 1931.

――――, *Art sumérien, art roman*, Paris, 1934.

Barcelona and Santiago de Compostela, *L'art roman*, (exhibition catalogue), 1961.

Baum, J., "Die Malerei und Plastik des Mittelalters, II," *Handbuch der kunstwissenschaft*, Potsdam, 1930.

Beckwith, J., *Early Medieval Art*, New York, 1964.

Bernheimer, R., *Romanische Tierplastik und die Ursprünge ihrer Motive*, Munich, 1931.

Boston, Museum of Fine Arts, *Arts of the Middle Ages 1000-1400*, Cambridge, Mass., 1940.

Brehier, L., "Les origines de l'architecture romane, II: la naissance de la sculpture monumentale," *Revue de l'art*, 1920, 263-280.

――――, *L'art en France, des invasions barbares à l'époque romane*, Paris, 1930.

――――, *Le style roman*, Paris, 1941.

Brutails, J.-A., *L'archéologie du moyen-âge et ses méthodes*, Paris, 1900.

――――, *Précis d'archéologie du moyen âge*, Toulouse, 1908.

――――, "La géographie monumentale de la France aux époques romane et gothique," *Le Moyen Age*, 34, 1923, 1-31.

Calkins, R. G., *A Medieval Treasury: An Exhibition of Medieval Art from the Third to the Sixteenth Century*, Ithaca, New York, 1968.

Colas, R., *Le style roman en France*, Paris, 1927.

Crozat, R., "Novelles remarques sur la technique des sculpteurs romans," *Bulletin monumental*, 95, 1936, 507-511.

_____, *L'art roman*, Paris, 1962.

David, J., *Les routes de l'art roman*, Grenoble, 1924.

Delaruelle, E., *Dictionnaire d'histoire et de géographie ecclésiastique*, s.l., s.d.

Deschamps, P., "La sculpture romane en Languedoc et en Bourgogne," *Revue archéologique*, 19, 1924, 163-173.

_____, "Étude sur la renaissance de la sculpture en France à l'époque romane," *Bulletin monumental*, 84, 1925, 5-98.

_____, *La sculpture française à l'époque romane*, Paris, 1930.

Deshoulières, F., "Essai sur les tailloirs romans," *Bulletin monumental*, 78, 1914, 5-46.

_____, "Les corniches romanes," *Bulletin monumental*, 79, 1920, 27-64.

_____, "La théorie d'Eugène Lefèvre-Pontalis sur les écoles romanes," *Bulletin monumental*, 84, 1925, 197-252.

_____, *Éléments datés de l'art roman en France*, Paris, 1936.

Dictionnaire des églises de France, editions by Robert Laffont, 5 vols., Paris, 1966-1968.

Dimier, M.-A., and J. Porcher, *L'art cistercien*, La Pierre-qui-Vire, 1962.

Doren, R. van, *Dictionnaire d'histoire et de géographie ecclésiastique*, Paris, 1953-1960.

Du Colombier, P., *Les chantiers des cathédrales*, Paris, 1953.

Durand-Lefebvre, J., *Art gallo-romain et sculpture romane*, Paris, 1937.

Ebersolt, J., *Orient et occident. Recherches sur les influences byzantines et orientales en France pendant les croisades*, Paris, 1929.

Enlart, C., *Manuel d'archéologie française*, 5 vols., 2nd ed., Paris, 1919-1932.

Evans, J., *Art in Medieval France*, London, 1948; 2nd ed., Oxford, 1952.

_____, *Cluniac Art of the Romanesque Period*, Cambridge, 1950.

Flipo, V., *Mémento d'archéologie française*, Paris, 1930.

Focillon, H., *L'art des sculpteurs romans*, Paris, 1931.

_____, "Recherches récentes sur la sculpture romane en France au XIe siècle," *Bulletin monumental*, 97, 1938, 49-72.

_____, *Moyen-âge, survivances et réveils*, Montreal, 1945.

_____, *L'an mil*, Paris, 1952.

_____, *The Art of the West in the Middle Ages*, 2 vols., Greenwich, Conn., and London, 1963.

Francastel, P., *L'humanism roman. Critique des théories sur l'art du XIe siècle en France*, Rodez, 1942.

_____, "Sculpture gallo-romaine et sculpture romane," *Revue archéologique*, ser. 6, vol. 22, 1944, 134-149.

Francovich, G. de, "La corrente comasca nella scultura romanica europea," *Rivista dell'Institute Nazionale d'Archeologia e storia dell'arte*, Rome, 1936, 297-298.

_____, "Wiligelmo da Modena e gli inizii della scultura romanica in Francia e in Spagna," *Rivista del Reale Institute di archeologia e storia dell'arte*, VII, 1940.

Gaillard, G., "De la diversité des styles dans la sculpture romane des pélerinages," *Revue des arts*, 1, 1951, 77-87.

Gantner, J., *Romanische Plastik. Inhalt und Form in der Kunst des XI und XII Jahrhunderts*, 3rd ed., Vienna, 1948.

Gantner, J., and M. Pobé, *The Glory of Romanesque Art*, New York, 1956.

Garcia Romo, F., "La escultura romanica francese hasta 1090," *Archive español de arte*, 1957, 223-240; 1959, 121-141.

Gardner, A., *Medieval Sculpture in France*, Cambridge, 1931.

Gómez-Moreno, C., *Medieval Art from Private Collections, A Special Exhibition at the Cloisters*, The Metropolitan Museum of Art, New York, 1968.

Gonse, L., *Chefs d'oeuvre des musées de France, sculpture*, Paris, 1904.

Grodecki, L., "La sculpture du XIe siècle en France, état des questions," *L'information d'histoire de l'art*, III, 1958, 98-112.

Hamann, R., *Deutsche und Französische Kunst im Mittelalter*, Marburg, 1923.

Histoire général des églises de France, editions by R. Laffont, Paris, 1966.

Hubert, J., *L'art pré-roman*, Paris, 1938.

Huyghe, R., "Aux sources de l'esthetique occidentale et de l'art roman," *Centre international d'etudes romanes, bulletin trimestriel*, 1959, I, 3-7.

Kitzinger, E., *Early Medieval Art*, British Museum, London, 1955.

Laran, J., "Recherches sur les proportions de la statuaire française du XIIe siècle," *Revue archéologique*, vol. I, 1907, 436-459; vol. I, 1908, 331-358; vol. II, 1909, 75-93; special edition, 1909, 68f.

Lasteyrie, R. de, *Études sur la sculpture française au moyen âge, Foundation Piot, monuments et mémoires*, VIII, Paris, 1902.

Laveclan, P., *Histoire de l'art, moyen âge et temps modernes*, Paris, 1944.

Lefèvre-Pontalis, E., "Reportoire des architectes, maçons, sculpteurs, charpentiers et ouvriers français au XIe et au XIIe siècles," *Bulletin monumental*, 73, 1911, 423-468.

Lefort, L., "La sculpture et le travail de la pierre dans les monuments du XIe au XVIe s.," *Bulletin monumental*, 56, 1890, 236-239.

Lefrançois-Pillion, L., *Les sculpteurs français du XIIe siècle*, Paris, 1931.

_____, *Nouvelle encyclopédie de l'art français. L'art roman*, Paris, 1943.

_____, *Maîtres d'oeuvres et tailleurs de pierre des cathédrales*, Paris, 1949.

Mâle, E., "Les origines de la sculpture français aux moyen âge," *Revue de Paris*, Septmeber 1, 1895, 198-224.

_____, *Art et artistes du moyen âge*, Paris, 1928.

Marle, R. van, "Twelfth Century French Sculpture in America," *Art in America*, December, 1921, 3-16.

Martin, C., *L'art roman en France*, 3 vols., Paris, 1910-1914.

Medieval Studies in Memory of A. Kingsley Porter, ed. by R. W. Koehler, 2 vols., Cambridge, Mass., 1955.

Messener, W., *Das Relief im Mittelalter*, Berlin, 1959.

_____, *Romanische Plastik in Frankreich*, Cologne, 1964.

Michel, A., *Histoire de l'art*, vol. I, pt. 2, Haseloff, Paris, 1905.

Morey, C. R. *Romanesque Sculpture*, Princeton, 1920.

_____, *Medieval Art*, New York, 1942.

Müntz, E., "La tradition antique chez les artistes du moyen âge," *Journal des savants*, October 1887, 629-642; January 1888, 40-50.

Porter, A. K., "The Rise of Romanesque Sculpture," *American Journal of Archaeology*, 22, 1918, 399-427.

———, "Les débuts de la sculpture romane," *Gazette des beaux-arts*, 61, 1919, 47-60.

———, "Pilgrimage Sculpture," *American Journal of Archaeology*, 26, 1922, 1-53.

———, *The Romanesque Sculpture of the Pilgrimage Roads*, 10 vols., Boston, 1923.

Pradel, P., *Sculptures romanes des musées de France*, Paris, 1958.

Puig i Cadafalch, J., *Le premier art roman*, Paris, 1928.

———, *L'art wisigothique et ses survivances. Recherches sur les origines et le développement de l'art en France et en Espagne du IVe au XIIe siècle*, Paris, 1961.

Réau, L., *L'art religieux du moyen âge. La sculpture*, Paris, 1946.

Rey, R., *L'art roman et ses origines, archéologie pré-romane et romane*. Toulouse and Paris, 1945.

———, *Art des cloîtres romans*, Toulouse, 1954.

Roussel, J., *La sculpture française, époque romane*, Paris, 1928.

Saint-Paul, A., *Histoire monumentale de la France*, Paris, 1883.

Schapiro, M., "On the Aesthetic Attitude in Romanesque Art," *Art and Thought, Essays in Honor of A. K. Coomaraswamy*, London, 1947, 130-150.

Stoddard, W. S., *Monastery and Cathedral in France*, Middletown, Conn., 1966.

Swarzenski, H., *Monuments of Romanesque Art*, London and Chicago, 1954; 2nd ed., Cambridge, Mass., 1955.

Taralon, J., and R. Maitre-Devallon, *Les trésors des églises de France*, Paris, 1965.

Trouvelot, J., "Remarques sur la technique des sculpteurs du moyen âge," *Bulletin monumental*, 95, 1936, 103-108.

Vallery-Radot, J., "La sculpture française du XIIe siècle et les influences irlandaises, *Révue de l'art*, 1924.

Verrier, J., L. Gischia, and L. Mazenod, *Arts primitifs français*, Paris, 1953.

Vitry, P., and G. Brière, *Documents de sculpture française du moyen âge*, Paris, 1904.

Vitry, P., *La sculpture du moyen âge au musée du Louvre*, Paris, 1934.

Weigert, H., *Romanesque Sculpture*, London, 1962.

Weisbach, W., *Religiöse Reform und mittelalterliche Kunst*, Zurich, 1945.

Wixom, W., *Treasures from Medieval France*, Cleveland, 1967.

C. Iconography.

Adhémar, J., *Influences antiques dans l'art du moyen âge français, recherches sur les sources et les thèmes d'inspiration*, London, 1939.

Baltrusaitis, J., *Cosmographie chrétienne dans l'art du moyen âge*, Paris, 1939.

Brehier, L., *L'homme dans la sculpture romane*, Paris, 1927.

———, *L'art chrétien*, Paris, 1928.

Cabrol, F., *Dictionnaire d'archéologie chrétienne et de liturgie*, 15 vols., Paris, 1907-1953.

Cocagnac, A.-M., *Le jugement dernier dans l'art*, Paris, 1955.

Crozet, R., "Les Quatres Evangélistes et leurs symboles," *Cahiers techniques de l'art*, Strassburg, 1962.

Davy, M.-M., *Essai sur la symbolique romane*, Paris, 1955.

———, *Initiation à la symbolique romane (XIIe siècle)*, Paris, 1964.

Débidour, V.-H., *Le bestiaire sculpté en France*, Paris, 1961.

Fleury, G., *Études sur les portails imagés du XIIe siècle, leur iconographie et leur symbolisme*, Mamers, 1904.

———, "Des portails romans du XIIe siècle, et leur iconography," *Revue historique et archéologique du Maine*, 55, Le Mans, 1904, 28f.

Gilles, R., *Le symbolisme dans l'art religieux*. Paris, 1961.

Grodecki, L., "Le problème des sources iconographiques du tympan de Moissac," *Annales du Midi*, 75, 1963, 387-392.

Gutberlet, H., *Die Himmelfahrt Christi im der bildenden Kunst*, Strassburg, 1935.

Hamann, R., "Das Tier in der romanischen Plastik Frankreichs," *Medieval Studies in Memory of A. Kingsley Porter*, vol. II, Cambridge, Mass., 1939, 413-452.

Hopper, V. F., *Medieval Number Symbolism*, New York, 1938.

Jalabert, D., "La flore gothique, ses origines, son évolution du XIIe au XVe s.," *Bulletin monumental*, 91, 1932, 181-246.

———, "De l'art oriental antique à l'art roman. Recherches sur la faune et la flore romanes. Le Sphinx," *Bulletin monumental*, 94, 1935, 71-104.

———, "De l'art oriental antique à l'art roman. Recherches sur la faune et la flore romanes. Les sirenes," *Bulletin monumental*, 95, 1936, 433-471.

———, "De l'art oriental antique à l'art roman. Recherches sur-la faune et la flore romanes. L'aigle," *Bulletin monumental*, 97, 1938, 173-194.

———, *La flore sculptée des monuments du moyen âge en France, recherches sur les origines de l'art français*, Paris, 1965.

Katzenellenbogen, A., "The Representation of the Seven Liberal Arts," *Twelfth Century Europe and the Foundations of Modern Society*, ed. M. Clagett, Madison, 1961.

———, "Iconographic Novelties and Transformations in the Sculpture of French Church Facades 1160-1190," *Studies in Western Art*, vol. I, *Romanesque and Gothic Art*, Acts of the 20th International Congress of History of Art, Princeton, 1963, 108-118.

———, *Allegories of the Virtues and Vices in Medieval Art*, New York, 1964.

Künstle, K., *Ikonographie der christlichen Kunst*, 2 vols., Frieburg-i-Br., 1928.

Mâle, E., "Les influences du drame liturgique sur la sculpture romane," *Revue de l'art ancien et moderne*, 22, 1907, 81-82.

———, "La part de Suger dans la création de l'iconographie du moyen âge," *Revue de l'art ancien et moderne*, 35, 1914, 93f.

———, *L'art religieux du XIIe siècle en France*, 2nd ed., Paris, 1924.

———, *L'art religieux du XIIIe siècle en France*, 5th ed., Paris, 1923.

Marle, R. van, *L'iconographie de l'art profane au moyen âge et à la Renaissance*, 2 vols., The Hague, 1932.

Meer, F. van der, *Majestas Domini, théophanies de l'apocalypse dans l'art chrétien*, Rome and Paris, 1938.

Millet, G., *Recherches sur l'iconographie de l'Evangile*, s.l., 1916.

Moé, E. van, *L'apocalypse de Saint-Server*, s.l., 1943.

Molsdorf, W., *Christliche Symbolik der Mittelalterlichen Kunst*, Leipzig, 1926.

Pinedo, R. de, *El simbolismo religioso en la Edad media*, Burgos, 1922.

Réau, L., *Iconographie de l'art chrétien*, 3 vols., Paris, 1955-1959.

Reuter, E., *Les representations de la musique dans la sculpture romane*, Paris, 1938.

Rey, R., *Les cloîtres historiés du Midi dans l'art roman (étude iconographique)*, Toulouse, 1955.

Sanoner, G., "Iconographie de la Bible d'après les artistes de l'antiquité et du moyen âge," *Bulletin monumental*, 80, 1921, 212-238.

Schade, H., *Dämonen und Monstren Gestaltungen des Bösen in der Kunst des frühen Mittelalters*, Regensburg, 1962.

Schrade, H., *Zur Ikonographie der Himmelfahrt Christi*, Leipzig, 1928-29.

Sénécal, J. Le, "Les occupations des mois dans l'iconographie du moyen âge," *Bulletin de la soc. des antiquaires de Normandie*, 35, 1921-23, 218f.

Thibout, M., "L'éléphant dans la sculpture romane française," *Bulletin monumental*, 105, 1947, 183-195.

Thoby, P., *Le crucifix des origines au Concile de Trente*, Nantes, 1959; *Supplément*, Nantes, 1963.

Vezin, G., *L'adoration et le cycle de Mages dans l'art chrétien primitif. Étude des influences orientales et greques sur l'art chrétien*, Paris, 1950.

Webster, J. C., *The labors of the months in antique and medieval art*, Princeton, 1938.

II. REGIONAL FRENCH
A. Alsace
Durand, G., *Les églises romanes des Vosges*, Paris, 1913.

Jullian, R., "Le portail d'Andlau et l'expansion de la sculpture lombarde en Alsace à l'époque romane," *Mélanges d'archéologie et d'histoire publiées par l'École de Rome*, Rome, 1930.

Kautzsch, R., *Der romanische Kirchenbau im Elsass*, 2nd ed., Freiburg-i-B., 1944.

Rumpler, M., *Sculptures romanes en Alsace*, Strassburg, 1960.

Will, R., *Répertoire de la sculpture romane en Alsace*, Strassburg and Paris, 1955.

_____, *Alsace romane*, La Pierre-qui-Vire, 1965.

B. Auvergne and Limousin.
Amé, E., *Dictionnaire typographique du département du Cantal*, Paris, 1897.

Balme, P., *Églises romanes d'Auvergne*, Clermont-Ferrand, 1955.

Beigbeder, O., *Forey-Velay roman*, La Pierre-qui-Vire, 1962.

Blanc, A., *Brioude et sa region, notes d'art et d'histoire*, Brioude, 1944.

Bouillet, J. B., *Statistique monumentale du département du Puy-de-Dôme*, 2nd ed., Clermont-Ferrand, 1846.

Bréhier, L., "Les chapiteaux historiés de Notre-Dame-du-Port à Clermont," *Revue de l'art chrétien*, 62, 1912, 249-262, 339-350.

_____, "La sculpture romane en Auvergne," *Revue d'Auvergne*, 40, April-June 1923, 54f.

_____, "Les origines de l'art roman auvergnat," *Revue Mabillon*, 1923.

_____, "Les chapiteaux historiés dans l'art roman auvergnat," *Bulletin de la société des études locales de Thiers*, 1924.

_____, "La sculpture romane en Haute-Auvergne," *Revue de la Haute-Auvergne*, 1925, 13f.

_____, "Les traits originaux de l'iconographie dans la sculpture romane d'Auvergne," *Medieval Studies in Memory of A. Kingsley Porter*, ed. by W. Koehler, vol. II, 1939, 389-405.

Bussac, G. de, *Issoire*, Clermont, 1955.

Chabau, Abbé, *L'église d'Ydes et son symbolisme*, s.l., 1884.

Chalvet de Rochemonteix, A. de, *Les églises romanes de la Haute-Auvergne*, Paris, 1902.

Craplet, B., *Auvergne roman*, La Pierre-qui-Vire, 1958.

Delmont, H., *Guide du Cantal*, 3rd ed., Aurillac, 1948.

Fage, R., "Le tympan de l'église de Collonges," *Bulletin de la société scientifique et arch. de la Corrèze*, Brive, 1923, 209-219.

Fikry, A., *L'art roman de Puy et les influences islamiques*, Paris, 1934.

Forestier, Abbé, *L'église et la paroisse de Saint-Nectaire*, Clermont-Ferrand, 1878.

Gomot, H., *Histoire de l'abbaye royale de Mozat*, s.l., 1872.

Laborderie, A. de, *Quarante-six églises limousines*, Limoges, 1946.

_____, *Collonges, la ville rouge, son église et son tympan sculpté*, Collonges, s.d.

Lefèvre-Pontalis, E., "A quelle école faut-il rattacher l'église de Beaulieu (Corrèze)?" *Bulletin monumental*, 78, 1914, 58-87.

Mallay, A.-G., *Essai sur les églises romanes et romano-byzantines du départment du Puy-de-Dôme*, Moulins, 1841.

Mandet, *Histoire du Velay*, vol. II, Le Puy, 1860.

Maury, J., M. M.-S. Gauthier, and J. Porcher, *Limousin roman*, La Pierre-qui-Vire, 1960.

Mayeux, A. "Le tympan de Collonges," *Bulletin de la société scientifique et arch. de la Corrèze*, Brive, 1923, 164-178.

Michel, *L'ancienne Auvergne et le Velay*, Moulins, 1845-1847.

Paul, G. and P., *Notre-Dame du Puy, essai historique et archéologique*, Le-Puy-en-Velay, 1950.

Poulbrière, J. B., "L'église de Beaulieu et son portail sculpté," *Bulletin de la société archéologique et historique du Limousin*, 21, 1872, 4f.

_____, "L'église et le portail de Beaulieu, Corrèze," *Congrès archéologique de France*, 44, 1877, 582-611.

Quarré, P., *La sculpture romane de la Haute-Auvergne, decor des chapiteaux*, Aurillac, 1938.

_____, "Les corniches et les portails des églises romanes de la Haute-Auvergne," *Revue de la Haute-Auvergne*, vol. XXX, 1, 1939-1942, 16-21.

_____, "Le portail de Mauriac et le porche d'Ydes," *Bulletin monumental*, 98, 1939, 129-151.

Ranquet, H. du, *La cathédrale de Clermont-Ferrand*, Paris s.d. (1913).

Ranquet, H. and E. du, *L'église Notre-Dame du Port de Clermont-Ferrand*, Clermont-Ferrand, 1932.

Rochias, G. "Les chapiteaux de l'église de Saint-Nectaire," *Bulletin monumental*, 73, 1909, 214-242.

Thiollier, N., *L'architecture religieuse à l'époque romane dans l'ancien diocèse du Puy*, Paris and Le Puy, 1900.

C. Burgundy and Nivernais.
Anfray, L., *L'architecture religieuse en Nivernais au moyen-âge. Les églises romanes*, Paris, 1951.

Aubert, M., "La sculpture en Bourgogne," *Richesses d'art de la France*, Paris, 1930.

_____, "Eglise abbatiale de Cluny," *Congrès archéologique de France. Lyon-Mâcon*, Paris, 1935, 502-522.

Baudry, J., and others, *Bourgogne Romane,* La Pierre-qui-Vire, 1958.

Beaussart, P., *L'église bénédictine de La Charité sur Loire, fille aînée de Cluny,* La Charité, 1929.

Bruel, *Cluny, 910-1910, album historique,* s.l., 1910.

Beenken, H., "Die Tympana von La Charite-sur-Loire," *Art Studies,* 6, 1928, 145-159.

Beutler, C., "Das Tympanon zu Vezelay, Programm, Planwechsel und Datierung," *Wallraf-Richartz-Jahrbuch,* 29, 1967, 7-30.

Bréhier, L., "Questions d'art roman bourguignon," *Revue archéologique,* 29, 1929, 291-316.

Calmette, J., and H. David, *Les grandes heures de Vézelay,* Paris, 1951.

Chompton, L., *Saint-Bénigne de Dijon, les cinq basiliques,* Dijon, 1923.

———, *Histoire de l'église Saint-Bénigne de Dijon,* Dijon, 1900.

Conant, K. J., "Les fouilles de Cluny," *Bulletin monumental,* 88, 1929, 109-123.

———, "Medieval Academy Excavations at Cluny," *Speculum,* 4, 1929, 3-26, 168-176, 291-304, 443-450.

———, "Cluny. The Date of the Ambulatory Capitals," *Speculum,* 5, 1930, 77-94.

———, "The Iconography and the Sequence of the Ambulatory Capitals of Cluny," *Speculum,* 5, 1930, 278-287.

———, "Le problème de Cluny d'après les fouilles récentes," *Revue de l'art ancien et moderne,* 1931.

———, "The Apse at Cluny," *Speculum,* 7, 1932, 23-35.

———, "The Third Church at Cluny," *Medieval Studies in Honor of Arthur Kingsley Porter,* vol. II, Cambridge, Mass., 1939, 327-358.

Deschamps, P., "Notes sur la sculpture romane en Bourgogne," *Gazette des beaux-arts,* 64, 2, 1922, 61-80.

———, "L'age des chapiteaux du choeur de Cluny," *Revue de l'art ancien et moderne,* 58, 1930, 157-176.

Deshoulières, F., "La date des chapiteaux du choeur de l'église abbatiale de Cluny d'après un article de M. Paul Deschamps," *Bulletin monumental,* 40, 1931, 83-89.

Dickson, M. and C., *Les églises romanes de l'ancien diocèse de Chalon, Cluny et sa région,* Mâcon, 1935.

Domke, H., *Burgund,* Munich, 1963.

Evans, J., *Monastic Life at Cluny, 910-1157,* Oxford, 1931.

———, *Cluniac Art of the Romanesque Period,* Cambridge, 1950.

Freeman, M., "A Romanesque Virgin from Autun," *The Metropolitan Museum of Art Bulletin,* vol. VIII, no. 4, 1949, 112-116.

Géry, A., *L'abbaye Saint-Martin de Nevers,* s.l., 1902.

Graham, R., and A. W. Clapham, "The Monastery of Cluny, 910-1155," *Archaeologia,* 80, 1930, 143f.

Grivot, D., *Autun,* Lyon, 1967.

Grivot, D., and G. Zarnecki, *Giselbertus Sculpteur d'Autun,* Paris, 1960.

Hamann, R., *Das Lazarus-grab in Autun,* Marburg, 1935.

Jalabert, D., "L'Ève de la cathédrale d'Autun. Sa place dans l'histoire de la sculpture romane," *Gazette des beaux-arts,* 35, 1949, 247-274.

Katzenellenbogen, A., "The Central Tympanum at Vézelay," *The Art Bulletin,* 26, September 1944, 141-151.

Kerber, B., "Burgund und die Entwicklung der Franzosischen Kathedralsculptur in zwölften Jahrhundert," *Munstersche Studien zur Kunstgeschichte,* 4, 1966.

Lefèvre, L. E. "Le symbolisme du tympan de Vézelay," *Revue de l'art chrétien,* 56, 1906, 253f.

Lücken, G. von, *Die Anfänge der burgundischen Schule,* Basel s.d. (1922).

———, "Burgundische Skulpturen des XI and XII Jahrhunderts," *Jahrbuch fur Kunstwissenschaft,* 1923, 103-124.

Malo, C., "Les églises romanes de l'ancien diocèse de Chalon-sur-Saône," *Bulletin monumental,* 90, 1931, 371-435.

Mathews, M., "Gislebertus Hoc Fecit," *GESTA,* no. 1 and 2, 1964, n.p.

Mayeur, P., "Le tympan de l'église abbatiale de Vézelay," *Revue de l'art chrétien,* 58, 1908, 103-108.

———, "Les scènes secondaires du tympan de Vézelay, *Revue de l'art chrétien,* 59, 1909, 326-332.

———, "L'église de l'ancien prieuré clunisien de Charlieu: symbolisme des sculptures ornant la petite baie de la façade septentrionale du narthex," *Revue de l'art chrétien,* 59, 1909, 33-35.

Mayeux, A., "Le tympan du portail de Montceaux l'Étoile," *Bulletin monumental,* 80, 1921, 239-244.

Monot, H., *Charlieu,* Roanne, 1934.

Oursel, C., "Le rôle et la place de Cluny dans la renaissance de la sculpture en France à l'époque romane," *Revue archéologique,* 17, 1923, 255-289.

———, "La genèse monumentale de l'église abbatiale de Vézelay," *Art Studies,* 5, 1927, 31-50.

———, *L'art roman en Bourgogne, études d'histoire et d'archéologie,* Dijon and Boston, 1928.

———, "La Bourgogne dans l'art roman," *Revue du moyen âge latin,* 6, 1950, 347-354.

———, *L'art roman de Bourgogne,* Grenoble, 1953.

Oursel, R. and A.-M., *Les églises romanes de l'Autunois et du Brionnais, Cluny et sa région,* Mâcon, 1956.

Pasquet, R. J., *Le Haut-Morvan et sa capitale Château-Chinon,* Nevers, 1955.

Petit, R. V., *Les villes et campagnes de l'Avallonnais,* Auxerre, 1916.

———, "L'architecture religieuse au XIe et au XIIe siècle dans l'ancien diocèse d'Auxerre," *Bulletin monumental,* 68, 1904, 42-92.

Philippe, A., "L'église de la Charité-sur-Loire," *Bulletin monumental,* 69, 1905, 469-500.

Porée, C., *L'abbaye de Vézelay,* Paris, 1909.

Porter, A. K., "La sculpture du XIIe siècle en Bourgogne, *Gazette des beaux-arts,* 2, 1920, 73-94.

Quantin, M., *Répertoire archéologique du department de l'Yonne,* Paris, 1868.

Quarré, P., "La sculpture des anciens portails de Saint-Bénigne de Dijon," *Gazette des beaux-arts,* 50, 1957, 177-194.

———, "La sculpture du tombeau de Saint Lazare à Autun," *Cahiers de la civilisation médiévale,* 1962, 169-174.

———, "Les apports languedociens et rhodaniens dans la sculpture romane de Bourgogne," *Bulletin du Centre International d'Études Romanes,* 1965, 1f.

Raeber, R., *La Charité-sur-Loire*, Berne, 1964.

Salet, F., "La Madeleine de Vézelay et ses dates de construction," *Bulletin monumental*, 95, 1936, 5-25.

———, "La Madeleine de Vézelay. Notes sur la façade de la nef," *Bulletin monumental*, 99, 1940, 223-237.

———, "La sculpture romane en Bourgogne à propos d'un livre récent," *Bulletin monumental*, 119, 1961, 325-343.

Salet, F., and J. Adhémar, *La Madeleine de Vézelay*, Melun, 1948.

Sanoner, G., "Portail de l'abbaye de Vézelay," *Revue de l'art chrétien*, 54, 1904, 448-459.

Schurenberg, L., "Spätromanische und frühgotische Plastik in Dijon und ihre Bedeutung für die Skulpturen des Strassburger Münster Querschiffes," *Jahrbuch der preussischen Kunstsammlungen*, 1937.

Serbat, L., "La Charité-sur-Loire," *Congrès archéologique de France*, 80, 1913, 374-400.

Soultrait, G. de, *Guide archéologique dans Nevers*, Nevers, 1856.

Sunderland, E., "The History and Architecture of the Church of Saint Fortunatus at Charlieu in Burgundy," *The Art Bulletin*, 21, 1939, 61-88.

———, *Histoire monumental de l'abbaye de Charlieu*, Charlieu, 1953.

Talobre, J., *La construction de l'abbaye de Cluny*, Mâcon, 1936.

———, "La reconstitution du portail de l'eglise abbatiale de Cluny," *Bulletin monumental*, 102, 1944, 225-240.

Terret, V., *La sculpture bourguignonne aux XIIe et VIIIe siècles, ses origines et ses sources d'inspirations: Cluny*, Cluny, 1914.

Terret, V., *La sculpture bourguignonne aux XIIe et VIIIe siécles, ses origines et ses sources d'inspirations: Autun*, 2 vols., Autun, 1925.

———, "La cathédral Saint-Lazare d'Autun," *Mémoires de la Société Éduenne*, 43, 1919.

———, *Saulieu*, Autun, 1919.

Thiollier, F. and N., *L'art roman à Charlieu et en Brionnais*, Montbrison, 1892.

Thiollier, F. and N., *L'art roman à Charlieu et en Brionnais*, Montbrison, 1894.

Vallery-Radot, J., "La limite meridionale de l'école romane de Bourgogne," *Bulletin monumental*, 95, 1936, 273-316.

———, "L'iconographie et le style des trois portails de Saint-Lazare d'Avallon," *Gazette des beaux-arts*, 52, 1958, 23-34.

Viollet-le-Duc, E., *Monographie de l'abbaye de Vézelay*, s.l., 1873.

Virey, J., *L'architecture romane dans l'ancien diocèse de Mâcon*, Paris, 1892.

———, *Paray-le-Monial et les églises du Brionnais*, Paris, 1926.

———, *L'abbaye de Cluny*, Paris, 1927.

———, *Les églises romanes de l'ancien diocèse de Mâcon, Cluny et sa région*, Mâcon, 1934.

Vittenet, A., *L'abbaye de Moutier-Saint-Jean (Côte d'Or)*, Mâcon, 1938.

Waxweiler, N., *Die Kapitäle des Übergangs Stiles der Kirche Ste. Madeleine in Vezelay in Burgund*, Strassburg, 1914.

D. Central France, Val-de-Loire, and Berry.

Aymard, O., A. Surchamp, E. Devaux, R. Gamard, and C. Jean-Nesmy, *Touraine roman*, La Pierre-qui-Vire, 1957.

Banchereau, J., *L'église Saint-Benoît-sur-Loire, et Germigny-les-Près*, Paris, 1930.

Chenesseau, G., *L'abbaye de Fleury à Saint-Benoît-sur-Loire*, Paris, 1931.

Crozet, R., *L'abbaye de Noirlac et l'architecture cistercienne en Berry*, Paris, 1932.

———, *L'art roman en Berry*, Paris, 1932.

———, "Chapiteaux berrichons en Touraine et en Poitou, *Bulletin monumental*, 94, 1935, 237-240.

Defarques, B., *Val de Loire roman*, La Pierre-qui-Vire, 1956.

Deshoulières, F., "Les églises romanes du Berry," *Bulletin monumental*, 93, 1909, 469-492.

———, "Nouvelles remarques sur les églises romanes du Berry," *Bulletin monumental*, 81, 1922, 5-27.

———, "Les églises romanes du Berry," *Bulletin monumental*, 90, 1931, 5-33.

———, *Les églises de France, Cher*, Paris, 1932.

Génermont, M., *Souvigny et Bourbonnais*, Moulins, 1945.

Génermont, M., and P. Pradel, *Les églises de France, Allier*, Paris, 1938.

Guery, R. A., *L'Anjou à travers les ages*, s.l., 1947.

Herbécourt, P. d', *Anjou roman*, La Pierre-qui-Vire, 1959.

Hubert, E., *Dictionnaire topographique de l'Indre*, s.l., 1884.

———, *Le Bas-Berry, histoire et archéologie du départment de l'Indre*, Paris, 1908.

Hubert, E. and J., *Le Bas-Berry, Chateauroux et Déols*, Paris, 1930.

Kersers, R. Buhot de, *Histoire et statistique monumental du Cher*, Bourges, 1883.

Lacrocq, L., *Les églises de France, Creuse*, Paris, 1934.

Lesueur, F., "Saint Martin de Tours et les origines de l'art roman, *Bulletin monumental*, 107, 1949, 7-84.

Malo-Renault, M., "Les sculpteurs romans de Saint-Benoît-sur-Loire," *Revue de l'art*," 1927, 209-222, 319-322.

Michel, R. E., *Monuments religieux, civils, et militaires en Gâtinais*, s.l., 1877.

Plat, G., "La Touraine, berceau des écoles romanes du Sud-Ouest," *Bulletin monumental*, 77, 1913, 347-378.

———, *L'art de batir en France, des Romans a l'an 1100, d'apres les monuments anciens de la Touraine, de l'Anjou, et du Vendômois*, Paris, 1939.

Port, C., *Dictionnaire du Maine-et-Loire*, 2nd ed., s.l., 1964.

Pradel, P., *Le Bourbonnais*, Paris, 1938.

Saint-Benoît-sur-Loire, introduction by M. Thibout and Dom J. Leclerq, Paris, 1945.

Surchamp, A., *Val de Loire roman*, La Pierre-qui-Vire, 1956.

Thiollier, F. and N., *Art et archéologie dans le départment de la Loire*, Saint-Étienne, 1898.

Vivier, *La Touraine artistique*, Paris, 1926.

E. Languedoc and Guyenne.

Allègre, V., *L'art roman dans la région albigeoise*, Albi, 1943.

———, *Les vieilles églises du Béarn. Étude archéologique*, 2 vols., Toulouse, 1952.

Angles, A., *L'abbaye de Moissac*, Paris, 1910.

Aubert, M., "Moissac," *Congrès archéologique de France*, 92, 1929, 494-525.

192

_____, "Saint-Sernin," *Congrès archéologique de France,* 92, 1929, 9-68.

_____, *L'église Saint-Sernin de Toulouse,* Paris, 1933.

_____, "L'église de Conques," *Congrès archéologique de France,* Figeac-Cahors-Rodez, 100, 1937.

_____, *Conques-en-Rouergue,* Paris, 1939, 459-523.

Auriol, R. A., and R. Rey, *Saint-Sernin de Toulouse,* Toulouse, 1930.

Balsan, L., *Conques et son trésor,* Rodez, 1956.

Barrière, R., *Histoire religieuse et monumentale du diocèse d'Agen depuis les temps les plus reculés jusqu'à nos jours,* s.l., 1856.

Bernoulli, C., *Die Skulpturen der Abtei Conques-en-Rouergue,* Bâle, 1956.

Bonnet, E., "Antiquités et monuments du départment de l'Hérault," *Geographie générale du department de l'Hérault,* vol. 3, Montpellier, 1905.

Bouillet, A., *L'église et le tresor de Conques,* Rodez, s.d.

Bousquet, L., *Le jugement dernier au tympan de l'église Saint-Foy de Conques,* Rodez, 1948.

Boyer, C., Notice in *Répertoire archéologique de l'Aude, période romane,* Montpellier, 1941.

Brutails, J.-A., *Les vielles églises de la Gironde,* Bordeaux, 1912.

Cetto, A. M., "Explication de la porte Miègeville de Saint-Sernin a Toulouse," *Actes du XVIIᵉ congrès d'histoire de l'art,* vol. I, La Haye, 1955.

Dainville, M. de, *Monuments historiques de l'Hérault,* Montpellier, 1933.

_____, *Les églises romanes du diocèse de Montpellier,* Montpellier, 1937.

Daras, C., "L'évolution de l'architecture aux façades des églises romanes d'Aquitaine," *Bulletin dé la société des antiquaires de l'Ouest,* 1953, 470f.

Delaruelle, É., "Les bas-reliefs de Saint-Sernin," *Annales du Midi,* 41, 1929, 50-60.

Deschamps, P., "L'autel roman de Saint-Sernin de Toulouse et les sculptures du cloître de Moissac," *Bulletin archéologique du comité des travaux historiques,* 1923, 239-250.

_____, "Notes sur la sculpture monumentale en Languedoc et en Espagne," *Bulletin monumental,* 82, 1923, 305-351.

_____, "Étude sur les sculptures de Sainte-Foy de Conques et de Saint-Sernin de Toulouse, et leurs rélations avec celles de Saint-Isidore de Léon et de Saint-Jaques de Compostelle," *Bulletin monumental,* 100, 1941, 239-264.

_____, "Les sculptures de l'église Sainte-Foy de Conques et leur decoration peinte," *Monuments Piot,* 38, 1941, 156-185.

Desgraves, L., *Évocation du vieux Bordeaux,* Paris, 1960.

Dictionnaire topographique du Gard, Paris, 1868.

Dufourcet, R., Camiade, and Tallebois, *Aquitaine historique et monumentale,* s.l., 1890.

Durliat, M., *La sculpture romane en Roussillon,* 4 vols., Perpignan, 1948-1954.

_____, "Saint Pons-de-Thomières," *Congrès archéologique,* Montpellier, 1950, 271-289.

_____, *Arts anciens du Roussillon,* Perpignan, 1954.

_____, *Les Christs romans du Roussillon et de Cerdagne,* Perpignan, 1956.

_____, *La sculpture romane en Cerdagne,* Peripignan, 1957.

_____, *Roussillon roman,* La Pierre-qui-Vire, 1958.

_____, "Aux origines de la sculpture romane languedocienne. Les chapiteaux et le portail de Saint-Michel de Lescure," *Cahiers de civilisation mediévale,* 5, 1962, 411-418.

_____, "Les debuts de la sculpture romane a Toulouse," *Centre international d'etudes romanes,* 3, July 1962, 9-12.

_____, "La construction de Saint-Sernin de Toulouse au XIᵉ siècle," *Bulletin monumental,* 121, 1963, 151-170.

_____, "L'église abbatiale de Moissac des origines à la fin du XIᵉ siècle," *Cahiers archéologiques,* 15, 1965, 155-177.

Enlart, C., and L. Bréhier, *Les églises à coupoles d'Aquitaine,* s.l., 1927.

Fau, J.-C., *Les chapiteaux de Conques,* Toulouse, 1956.

Gaillard, G., *Rouergue roman,* La Pierre-qui-Vire, 1963.

Griffe, E., *Histoire religieuse des anciens pays de l'Aude,* Paris, 1933.

Héliot, P., "Les portails polylobés de l'Aquitane et des régions limitrophes," *Bulletin monumental,* 104, 1946, 63-89.

_____, "Sur les façades des églises romanes d'Aquitaine à propos d'une étude récente," *Bulletin de la société des antiquaries de l'Ouest,* 1952, 254f.

Lafargue, M., "Les sculptures du premier atelier de la Daurade et les chapitaux du cloître de Moissac," *Bulletin monumental,* 97, 1938, 195-216.

_____, *Les chapitaux du cloître de Notre-Dame de la Daurade,* Paris, 1940.

Lahondès, R. J. de, *L'église Saint-Étienne,* Toulouse, 1890.

_____, "Les chapiteaux de Saint-Sernin," *Memoires de société archéologique du Midi de la France,* 15, 1894-1896, 258-283.

_____, *Les monuments de Toulouse,* Toulouse, 1920.

Lavedan, P., and R. Rey, *Luchon, Saint-Bertrand-de-Comminges et la région,* Toulouse and Paris, 1931.

Lefèvre-Pontalis, E., "L'école du Périgord n'existe pas," *Bulletin monumental,* 82, 1923, 7-35.

Mâle, E., "Les chapiteaux romans du Musée de Toulouse et l'école toulousaine du XIIᵉ siècle," *Revue archéologique,* 20, 1892, 28-35, 176-197.

Malo-Renault, J., "Musée des Augustins de Toulouse. La porte de la Daurade," *Bulletin des musées de France,* vol. II, no. 4, 1930, 91-94.

Marboutin, R., *La cathedrale d'Agen,* s.l., 1931.

Marignan, A., *Histoire de la sculpture en Languedoc du XIIᵉ-XIIIᵉ siècle,* Paris, 1902.

_____, *La decoration monumentale des églises de la France septentrionale du XIIᵉ au XIIIᵉ siècle,* Paris, 1911.

Mesplé, P., "L'art roman decadent du Sud-Ouest," *Bulletin monumental,* 115, 1957, 7-22.

_____, *Toulouse, Musée des Augustins, Les sculptures romanes,* Paris, 1961.

Mesuret, R., *Évocation du vieux Toulouse,* Paris, 1960.

Polge, R. H., *Topobibliographie monumentale du Gers,* Auch, 1952.

_____, *Bibliographie des monuments religieux et civils du Gers,* Auch, 1959.

Porter, A. K., "Spain or Toulouse," *The Art Bulletin,* 7, 1924, 3-25.

Rachou, H., *Catalogue des collections de sculpture et d'épigraphie du Musée de Toulouse,* Toulouse, 1912.

_____, "Saint-Étienne de Toulouse," *Congrès archéologique,* 92, 1929, 69f.

———, *Pierres romanes toulousaines,* Toulouse, 1934.

Rey, R., *Les vieilles églises fortifiées du Midi de la France,* Paris, 1925.

———, *La cathédrale de Cahors et l'architecture à coupoles d'Aquitaine,* Paris, 1925.

———, "Quelques survivances antiques dans la sculpture romane meridionale," *Gazette des beaux-arts,* 70, Sept.-Oct., 1928, 173-191.

———, *La cathédrale de Toulouse,* Paris, 1929.

———, "Sainte-Marie-la-Daurade," *Congrès archéologique de France,* 92, 1929, 105-108.

———, *La sculpture romane languedocienne,* Toulouse and Paris, 1936.

Rupin, E., *L'abbaye et les cloîtres de Moissac,* Paris, 1897.

Sabarthès, *Dictionnaire topographique de l'Aude,* Paris, 1912.

Sahuc, J., *Saint-Pons-de-Thomières, les archives, l'abbaye, l'évêché,* Bergerac, 1895.

———, *L'art roman à Saint-Pons-de-Thomières,* Montpellier, 1908.

Schapiro, M., "The Romanesque Sculpture of Moissac, Part I," *The Art Bulletin,* 13, 1931, 249-351, 464-532.

———, "The Sculptures of Souillac," *Medieval Studies in Memory of A. Kingsley Porter,* ed. by W. Koehler, vol. II, 1939, 359-387.

Schurenberg, L., "Die romanischen Kirchenfassaden Aquitaniens Das Munster," *Zeitschrift für christliche Kunst und Kunstwissenschaft,* 1951, 257-268.

Scott, D. W., "A Restoration of the West Portal Relief Decoration of Saint Sernin of Toulouse," *The Art Bulletin,* 46, September 1964, 271-282.

Secret, J., *Les églises du Riberacrois,* Perigueux, 1958.

———, "Les façades à arcatures dans les églises du Périgord," *Bulletin monumental,* 118, 1960, 89-109.

———, *Périgord roman,* La Pierre-qui-Vire, 1968.

Seidel, L., "A Romantic Forgery: The Romanesque 'Portal' of Saint-Étienne in Toulouse," *The Art Bulletin,* 50, March 1968, 33-42.

Tholin, G., *Études sur l'architecture religieuse de l'Agenais du Xe au XVIe s.,* Paris, 1874.

Vallery-Radot, J., "Les églises romanes de Rouergue," *Bulletin monumental,* 99, 1940, 5-68.

Vidal, M., *Quercy roman,* La Pierre-qui-Vire, 1960.

F. Normandy and Brittany.

Anfray, M., *L'architecture normande, son influence dans le nord de la France aux XIe et XIIe siècles,* Paris, 1939.

Banéat, P., *Le départment d'Ille-et-Vilaine, histoire, archéologie, monuments,* 4 vols., Rennes, 1927-1930.

Couffon, R., *Répertoire des églises et chapelles du diocèse de Saint-Brieuc et Tréguier,* Saint-Brieuc, 1939-1947.

Daoust, J., *L'abbaye Saint-Georges de Boscherville,* s.l., 1954.

Debidour, V.-H., *La sculpture bretonne,* Rennes, 1953.

Dictionnaire historique et archéologique de Pas-de-Calais, Arras, 1873-1884.

Duhem, G., *Les églises de France, Morbihan,* Paris, 1932.

Engerand, L., "La sculpture romane en Normandie," *Bulletin monumental,* 68, 1904, 405-416.

Fage, R., "La decoration geometrique dans l'école romane de Normandie," *Congrès archéologique,* vol. II, Caen, 1908, 615-633.

Fossey, Abbé, and J. Longnon, *La Haute-Normandie,* Paris, 1912.

Grand, R., *Mélanges d'archéologie bretonne,* Paris, 1921.

———, *L'art roman en Bretagne,* Paris, 1958.

Grodecki, L., "Les débuts de la sculpture romane en Normandie," *Bulletin monumental,* 108, 1950, 7-67.

Héliot, P., *Les églises du moyen âge dans le Pas-de-Calais,* 2 vols., Arras, 1951-1953.

Huard, G., *L'art roman en Normandie,* Paris, 1928.

Jalabert, D., *L'art normand au moyen âge,* Paris, 1931.

Lambert, E., *Caen roman et gothique,* Caen, 1935.

Lefèvre-Pontalis, E., "Les influences normandes au XIe et au XIIe siècle dans le Nord de la France," *Bulletin monumental,* 70, 1906, 3-37.

———, "Les influences poitevins en Bretagne et l'église de Pont-Croix," *Bulletin monumental,* 73, 1909.

Lisle de Dréneuc, *Dictionnaire archéologique de la Loire-Inférieure,* Nantes, 1882.

Mottay, G. du, *Iconographie et hagiographie bretonnes,* Saint-Brieuc, 1869.

———, *Repertoire archéologique de départment des Côtes-du-Nord,* Saint-Brieuc, 1883-1884.

Musset, L., *Normandie romane, la Basse Normandie,* La Pierre-qui-Vire, 1967.

Porée, Abbé, "La statuaire en Normandie," *Bulletin monumental,* 64, 1899, 381-436.

Prentout, H., *Caen et Bayeux,* Paris, 1909.

Rodière, R., et P. Héliot, "Essai de bibliographie monumentale du Pas-de-Calais et de la Somme," *Revue du Nord,* 24, 1939.

Ruprich-Robert, V., *L'église Ste-Trinité et l'église Saint-Étienne à Caen,* Caen, 1884.

———, *L'architecture normande aux XIe et XIIe siècles en Normandie et en Angleterre,* 2 vols., Paris, 1884-1889.

Wacquet, H., *L'art breton,* Grenoble, 1933.

Warren, H. de, *La Bretagne cistercienne,* Paris, 1946.

G. Northern France and The Valley of the Meuse.

L'art mosan, ed. by P. Francastel, Paris, 1953.

Borchgrave d'Altena, J. de, *Sculptures conservées au pays mosan,* s.l., s.d.

Dehaisnes, Mgr., *Histoire de l'art dans la Flandre, l'Artois et le Hainaut avant le XVe siècle,* 3 vols., Lille, 1886.

———, *Le Nord monumental et artistique,* Lille, 1897.

Devigne, M., *La sculpture mosane du XIIe an XVIe siècle,* Brussels and Paris, 1932.

Enlart, C., *Monuments religieux de l'architecture romane et de transition dans la region picarde,* s.l., s.d.

Houdoy, *Histoire artistique de la cathédrale de Cambrai,* Lille, 1880.

Lambert, E., *Les relations artistiques entre la Belgique et le Nord de la France d'après les monuments du XIe et du XIIe siècles,* Brussels, 1936.

Liège, *Art mosan et arts anciens du pays de Liège,* Liège, 1951.

Tollenaere, L., *La sculpture sur pierre de l'ancien diocèse de Liège à l'époque romane,* Gembloux, 1957.

194

H. Provence and the Rhone Valley.

Aubert, M., "Les dates de la façade de Saint-Gilles," *Bulletin monumental,* 95, 1936, 369-372.

Bailly, *Dictionnaire des communes, Vauclause,* Avignon, 1961.

Benoît, F., *Arles, ses monuments, son histoire,* Lyon, 1927.

———, *La Provence et le combat Venaissin,* Paris, 1949.

Berenguier, R., *Abbayes de Provence,* Caisse nationale des monuments historiques, 1960.

Bergounhoux, E., and P. Masson, *Les Bouches-du-Rhône, encyclopedie départementale,* vol. XV, Paris, 1933.

Bernoulli, C., *Die romanische Portalarchitektur in der Provence,* Strassburg, 1906.

Besse, Dom, *Abbayes et prieurés de l'ancienne France, province de Vienne,* vol. 9, Paris, 1932.

Brun, L., "Presentation de la Provence romane," *Centre international d'études romanes,* 2, April 1962, 5-10.

Charles-Roux, J., *Arles, son histoire, ses monuments, ses musées.* Paris, 1914.

Débidour, V.H., *Trésors cachés du pays niçois,* Paris, 1961.

Déniau, J., *Histoire de Lyon et du Lyonnais,* Paris, 1951.

Dictionnaire illustré du départment du Rhone, s.l., 1902.

Doré, R., *L'art en Provence dans le comtat Venaissin et le comté de Nice,* Paris, 1929.

———, *L'art en Provence,* Paris, 1930.

———, *L'architecture et la sculpture monumentale au moyen âge dans le department des Bouches-du-Rhone,* Marseille, 1933.

Féraud, J. M., *Sites et monuments de Haute Provence, le pays de Forcalquier,* Forcalquier, 1963.

Gaillard, G., *Visages du Dauphiné,* Paris, 1948.

Gouron, M., "Dates des sculptures du portail de l'église de Saint-Gilles," *Bulletin de la société d'histoire et d'archéologie de Nîmes,* 1935.

Guigue, R. M. C., *Topologie historique du départment de l'Ain,* Trevoux, 1873.

Hallays, A., *Avignon et le comtat Venaissin,* Paris, 1921.

Hamann, R., "The Facade of St. Gilles : a reconstruction," *Burlingtin Magazine,* 64, 1934, 19f.

———, *Die Abteikirche von St. Gilles und ihre künstlerische Nachfolge,* 3 vols., Berlin, 1956.

Horn, W., *Die Fassade von St. Gilles,* Hamburg, 1937.

Jouve, E.-G., *Statistique monumentale de la Drôme,* Valence, 1867.

Jullian, R., "L'art de la draperie dans la sculpture romane de Provence," *Gazette des beaux-arts,* 70, Sept.-Oct., 1928, 241-258.

Labande, L.-H., *Études d'histoire et d'archéologie romanes, Provence et Bas-Languedoc,* s.l., 1902.

———, "Étude historique et archéologique sur Saint-Trophime d'Arles du IVe au XIIIe siècle," *Bulletin monumental,* 67, 1903, 459-497; 68, 1904, 3-42.

———, *L'église Notre-Dame des Doms d'Avignon, des origines au XIIIe siècle,* Paris, 1907.

———, "Saint Gilles," *Congrès archéologique de France,* 76, 1909, 168-181.

———, *L'église Saint-Trophime d'Arles,* Paris, 1930.

Les Paroisses du diocèse d'Aix, Aix, 1911.

Marignan, A., *L'école de sculpture en Provence du XIIe au XIIIe siècle,* Paris, 1899.

Revoil, H., *L'architecture romane du Midi de la France,* 3 vols., Paris, 1867-74.

Roman, J., *Répertoire archéologique des Hautes-Alpes,* s.l., s.d.

Schapiro, M., "New Documents on St. Gilles," *The Art Bulletin,* 17, 1935, 415-431.

———, "Further Documents on St. Gilles," *The Art Bulletin,* 19, 1937, 111-112.

Stockhausen, H. A. von, "Die romanischen Kreuzgänge der Provence, II, Die Plastik," *Marburger Jahrbuch fur Kunstwissenschaft,* 1936, 97-107.

Vallery-Radot, J., "La domaine de l'école roman en Provence," *Bulletin monumental,* 103, 1945, 5-63.

Villard, A., *Art de Provence,* Paris, 1957.

I. Western France: Poitou, Saintonge, and Angoumois.

Brouillet, P. A., *Notice des objets composant les collections de la ville de Poitiers,* s.l., 1884-1885.

Brutails, J.-A., *Les vieilles églises de la Gironde,* Bordeaux, 1912.

Chagnolleau, R. J., *L'église d'Aulnay-de-Saintonge,* Grenoble, 1938.

Chasseloup-Laubat, F. de, *Réflexions sur la Saintonge romane,* La Rochelle, 1961.

Coatanoan, N., *Chapiteaux de Saint-Pierre de Chauvigny en Poitou,* Monaco, 1959.

Crozat, R., *Textes et documents relatifs à l'histoire des arts en Poitou,* Poitiers, 1942.

———, *L'art roman en Poitou,* Paris, 1948.

———, "Survivances antiques dans le décor roman du Poitou, de l'Angoumois, et de la Saintonge," *Bulletin monumental,* 114, 1956, 7-33.

———, *Chauvigny et ses monuments, étude archéologique,* Poitiers, 1958.

Dangibeaud, C., "L'école de sculpture romane saintongeaise," *Bulletin archéologique,* 1910, 22-49.

Daras, C., "L'orientalisme dans l'art roman en Angoumois," *Bulletin et mémoires de la société archéologique et historique de la Charente,* Angoulême, 1937.

———, *La cathédrale d'Angoulême, chef-d'oeuvre monumental de Girard II,* Angoulême, 1943.

———, "Les églises au XIe siècle en Charente," *Bulletin des antiquaires de l'Ouest,* 1959, 190f.

———, "Les façades des églises romanes ornées d'arcatures en Charente, leur origine, leur filiation," *Bulletin monumental,* 119, 1961, 121-138.

———, *Angoumois roman,* La Pierre-qui-Vire, 1961.

Gaborit, G., *Inventaire archéologique de l'arrondissement de Jonzac,* Angoulême, 1950.

George, J., *Les églises de France, Charente,* Paris, 1933.

George, J., and A. Guérin-Boutaud, *Les églises romanes de l'ancien diocèse d'Angoulême,* Paris, 1928.

Héliot, P., "Les portails polylobés de l'Aquitaine et des regions limitrophes," *Bulletin monumental,* 104, 1946, 63-89.

Hubie, S., *Les merveilles de la Saintonge romane,* Paris, 1962.

Labande-Mailfert, Y., *Poitou roman,* La Pierre-qui-Vire, 1957.

Maillard, E., "Les sculptures de la façade occidentale de la cathédrale de Poitiers," *Gazette des beaux-arts,* 62, 2, 1920, 289-308.

Mendell, E. L., *Romanesque Sculpture in Saintonge,* New Haven, 1940.

Michon, Abbé, *Statistique monumentale de la Charente,* s.l., 1844.

Sauvel, T., "Tympans de l'Angoumois," *Bulletin monumental,* 95, 1936, 203-213.

———, "La façade de Saint-Pierre d'Angoulême," *Bulletin monumental,* 103, 1945, 179-199.

Vicaire, P., "Y-a-t-il un humanisme de l'art roman du Poitou et de la Saintonge?," *Bulletin de la société des antiquaires de l'Ouest,* 14, 1946-1948, 436-454.

Urseau, C., *La cathedrale d'Angers,* Paris, 1929.

III. SPAIN AND CATALONIA.

A. Spain.

Ainaud de Lasarte, J., "Noticias de San Pedro de Roda," *Revista de Gerona,* 9, 1959, 33-35.

Alcolea, S., *La catedral de Santiago,* Madrid, 1948.

Del Arco y Garay, R., *El arte románico en la región pirenaica,* s.l., 1932.

Durliat, M., *L'art dans le royaume de Majorque,* Toulouse, 1962.

———, *L'art roman en Espagne,* Paris, 1962.

Gaillard, G., "Sculptures espagnoles de la seconde moitié du douzième siècle," *Studies in Western Art,* vol. I, Princeton, 1963, 142-149.

———, "Notes sur la date des sculptures de Compostelle et de Léon, *Gazette des beaux-arts,* I, 1929, 341-378.

———, *Les débuts de la sculpture romane espagnole: Léon, Jaca, Compostelle,* Paris, 1938.

———, "La sculpture du XIe siècle en Navarre avant l'influence des pélerinages," *Bulletin monumental,* 113, 1955, 237-249.

Gómez-Moreno, M., *Catalogo monumental de España. Provincia de León,* 2 vols., Madrid, 1925-1926.

———, *El arte románico español,* Madrid, 1934.

Gudiol-Ricart, J., and J. A. Gaya Nuño, "Arquitectura y escultura románicas," *Ars Hispaniae,* vol. V, Madrid, 1948.

Lambert, E., *L'art gothique en Espange aux XIIe et XIIIe siècles,* Paris, 1931.

Monsalvatje y Fossas, F., *Nomenclator histórico de las iglesias parroquiales y rurales, santuarios y capillas de provincia y diócesis de Gerona,* 3 vols., Olot, 1908-1910.

Naesgaard, O., *Saint-Jaques-de-Compostelle et les débuts de la grande sculpture vers 1100,* Copenhagen, 1962.

Perez Carmona, J., *Arquitectura y escultura románicas en la provencia de Bourgos,* Bourgos, 1959.

Porter, A. K., "Compostela, Bari, and Romanesque Architecture," *Art Studies,* (Princeton), 1, 1923, 7-21.

———, "Leonesque Romanesque and Southern France," *The Art Bulletin,* 8, 1926, 235-250.

———, *Spanish Romanesque Sculpture,* 2 vols., Paris and Florence, 1928.

———, *La escultura románi ca en España,* 2 vols., Florence and Barcelona, 1929.

Subías Galter, J., *El monestir de Sant Pere de Roda,* Barcelona, 1948.

Whitehill, W. M., *Spanish Romanesque Architecture of the Eleventh Century,* Oxford, 1941.

B. Catalonia.

L'art català, ed. by J. Folch i Torres, 2 vols., Barcelona, 1955-1957, 1958.

Duran, F., *La escultura medieval catalana,* Madrid, s.d.

Durliat, M., *L'art catalan,* Paris, 1963.

Gaillard, G., *Premiers essais de sculpture monumentale en Catalogne aux Xe et XIe siècles,* Paris, 1938.

Gudiol-Ricart, J., J. Ainaud de Lasarte, and S. Alcolea Gil, *Arte de España. Cataluña,* Barcelona, 1955.

Junyent, E., *Catalogne romane,* 2 vols., La Pierre-qui-Vire, 1960-1961.

Puig i Cadafalch, J., *Le premier art roman. L'architecture en Catalogne et dans l'occident méditerranéen aux Xe et XIe siècles,* Paris, 1928.

———, *La géographie et les origines du premier art roman,* Paris, 1935.

———, "L'escultura romànica a Catalunya," *Monumenta Cataloniae,* 3 vols., Barcelona, 1949-1952.

Puig i Cadafalch, J., A. de Falguera, and J. Goday y Casals, *L'arquitectura romànica a Catalunya,* 3 vols., Barcelona, 1909-1918.

Zervos, C., and J. Gudiol-Ricart, *L'art de la Catalogne de la seconde moitié du neuvième siècle à la fin du quinzième siècle,* Paris, 1937.

IV. TUSCANY (IN RELATION TO CATALOGUE NUMBER 40).

Biehl, W., *Toskanische Plastik des Frühen und Hohen Mittelalters,* Leipsig, 1926.

Crichton, G. H., *Romanesque Sculpture in Italy,* London, 1954.

Decker, H., *L'art roman en Italie,* Paris, s.d.

Lavagnino, E., *Storia dell'arte medioevale italiana,* Turin, 1936.

Salmi, M., *La scultura romanica in Toscana,* Florence, 1928.

———, *Églises romanes de Toscane,* Paris, 1961.

Sheppard, C. D., "Romanesque Sculpture in Tuscany," *Gazette des beaux-arts,* 54, 1959, 97-108.

V. ROMANESQUE ILE-DE-FRANCE AND EARLY GOTHIC.

Abdul-hak, S., *La sculpture des porches du transept de la cathédrale de Chartres,* Paris, 1942.

Adenauer, H., *Die Kathedrale von Laon,* Dusseldorf, 1934.

Aubert, M., "Le portail occidental de la cathédrale de Senlis," *Revue de l'art chrétien,* 1910, 157-172.

———, *Monographie de la cathédrale de Senlis,* Paris, 1910.

———, *Senlis,* Paris, 1922.

———, *La cathédrale de Chartres,* Paris and Grenoble, s.d.

———, *La sculpture française au début de l'époque gothique, 1140-1225,* Paris, 1929.

———, "Le portail royal et la façade occidentale de Chartres," *Bulletin monumental,* 100, 1941, 177-218.

———, "Têtes de statues-colonnes du portail occidental de Saint-Denis," *Bulletin monumental,* 103, 1945, 243-248.

———, "Têtes gothiques de Senlis et de Mantes," *Bulletin monumental,* 97, 1938, 5-11.

Bony, J., "La collégiale de Mantes," *Congrès archéologique de France,* 106, 1947, 163-220.

———, "Introduction to the Transition from Romanesque to Gothic," *Studies in Western Art,* vol. I, Princeton, 1963, 81-84.

Borries, E. von, *Die Westportale von St. Denis Versuch einer Rekonstruktion,* Dissertation, Hamburg, 1955.

Bouvier, H., *Histoire de l'église et de l'ancien diocèse de Sens,* Amiens, 1906.

196

Bouxin, A., *La cathédrale de Laon*, Laon, 1902.

Branner, R., "Les portails lateraux de la cathédrale de Bourges," *Bulletin monumental*, 115, 1957, 263-270.

———, *La cathédrale de Bourges et sa place dans l'architecture gothique*, Bourges and Paris, 1962.

———, "Gothic Architecture, 1160-1180, and its Romanesque Sources," *Studies in Western Art*, vol. I, Princeton, 1963, 92-104.

Broche, L., *La cathédrale de Laon*, Paris, 1926.

Bulteau, Abbé, *Monographie de la cathédrale de Chartres*, 2nd ed., Chartres, 1887-1892.

Cahier, C., *Monographie de la cathédrale de Bourges*, Paris, 1841-1844.

Chartraire, E., "La sculpture du grand portail de la cathédrale de Sens," *Bulletin archéologique*, 1914, 499f.

———, *La cathédrale de Sens*, Paris, 1920.

Crosby, S. Mc K., "Fouilles executées recémment dans la basilique de Saint-Denis," *Bulletin monumental*, 105, 1947, 167-181.

———, *L'abbaye royale de Saint-Denis*, Paris, 1953.

———, "Abbot Suger's St. Denis. The New Gothic," *Studies in Western Art*, vol. I, Princeton, 1963, 85-91.

Delaporte, C., *La cathédrale de Chartres*, 2 vols., Paris, 1959.

Deschamps, P., *La cathédrale de Sens*, Paris, 1943.

Dumolin and Outardel, *Les églises de France: Paris et la Seine*, Paris, s.d.

Farcy, R. L. de, *Monographie de la cathédrale d'Angers*, 4 vols., s.l., 1901-1926.

Fichot, C., *Statistique monumentale du départment de l'Aube*, 5 vols., Troyes, 1883-1907.

Formigé, J., *L'abbaye royale de Saint-Denis, recherches nouvelles*, Paris, 1960.

Fourrey, R., *Sens, ville d'art et d'histoire*, Lyon, 1953.

Frankl, P., "The Chronology of Chartres Cathedral," *The Art Bulletin*, 39, March, 1957, 33-47.

———, "Reconsiderations on the Chronology of Chartres Cathedral," *The Art Bulletin*, 43, March, 1961, 51-58.

Gall, E., *Die gotische Baukunst in Frankreich und Deutschland. Vol. I: Die Vorstufen in Nord Frankreich von der Mitte des elften bis gegen Ende des zwölften Jahrhunderts*, 2nd ed., Brunswick, 1955.

Gaussen, *Portefeuille archéologique de la Champagne*, Bar-sur-Aube, 1861.

Giesau, H., "Stand der Forschung über das Figurenportal des Mittelalters," *Beiträge zur Kunst des Mittelalters*, Berlin, 1950, 119-129.

Goldscheider, C., "Les origines du portal à statues-colonnes," *Bulletin des musées de France*, 1946, No. 6-7, 22-25.

Gosebruch, D., "Die portale in St. Lazare in Avallon und St. Benigne in Dijon," *Jantzen-schulferfestschrift*, unpublished manuscript, 1951.

Grodecki, L., "The Transept Portals of Chartres Cathedral: The Date of their Construction According to Archaeological Data," *The Art Bulletin*, 33, September, 1951, 156-164.

———, "À propos de la sculpture française autour de 1200," *Bulletin monumental*, 115, 1957, 119-126.

———, "Chronologie de la cathédrale de Chartres," *Bulletin monumental*, 116, 1958, 91f.

———, "La 'première sculpture gothique.' Wilhelm Vöge et l'état actuel des problèmes," *Bulletin monumental*, 117, 1959, 265-289.

———, *Chartres*, Paris, 1963.

Hamann-MacLean, R., "Les origines des portails et façades sculptées gothiques," *Cahiers de civilisation médiéval*, 2e trimestre, 1959, 162f.

Harvey, J. H., *The Gothic World, 1100-1600, a Survey of Architecture and Art*, London, 1950.

Heimann, A., "The Master-Sculptor of the West Facade in Chartres, *Acts of the International Congress of History of Art*, London, 1939, 20f.

Houvet, E., *Cathédrale de Chartres*, 7 vols., Chelles 1919.

Jullian, R., *La sculpture gothique*, Paris, 1966.

Katzenellenbogen, A., *The Sculptural Programs of Chartres Cathedral*, Baltimore, 1959; 2nd ed., New York, 1964.

Kidson, P., *Sculpture at Chartres*, London, 1958.

Lambert, E., "Les portals sculptés de la cathédrale de Laon," *Gazette des beaux-arts*, 17, 1937, 83-98.

Lapeyre, A., *Des façades occidentales de Saint-Denis et de Chartres aux portails de Laon*, Macon, 1960.

Lefèvre-Pontalis, E., *L'architecture religieuse dans l'ancien diocèse de Soissons au XIe et au XIIe siècle*, 2 vols., Paris, 1894-1896.

———, *Les architectes et la construction de la cathédrale de Chartres*, Paris, 1905. (extract from *Memoires de la société nationale des antiquaires de France*, 64, 1903, 69f.).

———, "Les campagnes de construction de Notre-Dame d'Etampes," *Bulletin monumental*, 73, 1909, 5-31.

———, "Le pretendu style de transition," *Bulletin monumental*, 76, 1912, 242-252, 556-561.

Mâle, E., "Le portail de Senlis et son influence," *Revue de l'art ancien et moderne*, 1911, 161-176; reprinted in *Art et artistes au moyen âge*, Paris, 1927, 209-255.

———, "Le portail Sainte-Anne à Notre-Dame de Paris," *Art et artistes au moyen âge*, Paris, 1927, 188-208.

———, *Notre-Dame de Chartres*, Paris, 1948.

Martindale, A., *Gothic Art from the Twelfth to the Fifteenth Centuries*, New York, 1967.

Martinell, C., "L'art de transició al gòtic," *L'art català*, ed. by J. Folch i Torres, vol. I, Barcelona, 1957.

Marriage, M. and E., *Les sculptures de la cathédrale de Chartres*, Cambridge, 1909.

Merlet, R., *La cathédrale de Chartres*, Paris, s.d.

Micheli, G. L., *Le décor géometrique dans la sculpture de l'Aisne et de l'Oise au XIe siècle*, Paris, 1939.

Montaiglon, A. de, "Antiquités et curiosités de la ville de Sens," *Gazette des beaux-arts*, 22, 1880, 125f.

Moreau, A., *La cathédrale de Sens*, Paris, s.d. (1960 ?).

Mussat, A., "Les origines du style gothique de l'Ouest," *L'information d'histoire d'art*, 6, 1961.

———, *Le style gothique de l'Ouest de la France: style plantagenet ou gothique angevin, XIIe-XIIIe siècles*, Paris, 1963.

Panofsky, E., *Abbot Suger on the Abbey Church of St. Denis and Its Art Treasures*, Princeton, 1946.

———, *Renaissance and Renascences in Western Art*, Stockholm, 1960.

Paris, *L'art en Champagne au moyen âge*, Paris, 1957.

———, *Cathédrales, sculptures, vitraux, objets d'art, manuscrits des XIIe et XIIIe siècles*, Louvre, Paris 1962.

———, *L'europe gothique, XIIe-XIVe siècles*, Louvre, Paris, 1968.

Porré, C., "Sens, la cathédrale," *Congrès archéologique de France,* 74, 1907, 209-225.

Pressouyre, L., "Sculptures du premier art gothique à Notre-Dame-en-Vaux de Châlons-sur-Marne," *Bulletin monumental,* 120, 1962, 359-366.

Priest, A., "The Masters of the West Facade of Chartres," *Art Studies,* Princeton, 1923, 28-44.

Quantin, M., *Notice historique sur la cathédrale de Sens,* Auxerre, 1842.

_____, "Le grand portail de la cathédrale de Sens," *Annuaire de l'Yonne,* 1850, 313f.

Salet, F., "La cathédrale de Sens et sa place dans l'architecture medievale," *Comptes rendus de l'Academie des Inscriptions et Belles-Lettres,* 1955, 182f.

Sauerländer, W., "Beitrage zur Geschichte der 'frühgotischen' skulptur," *Zeitschrift fur Kunstgeschichte,* 19, 1956, 1-34.

_____, "Die Marienkronungsportale von Senlis und Mantes," *Wallraf-Richartz-Jahrbuch,* 20, 1958, 115f.

_____, "Die kunstgeschichtliche Stellung der Westportale von Notre-Dame in Paris," *Marburger Jahrbuch für Kunstwissenschaft,* 17, 1959, 1-12.

_____, "Von Sens bis Strassburg," *Kunstchronik,* 13, 1960, 279f.

_____, "Art antique et sculpture autour de 1200," I, *Art de France,* 1961, 47-56.

_____, "Skulpturen des 12 Jh. in Châlons-sur-Marne," *Zeitschrift für Kunstgeschichte,* 25, 1961, 97f.

_____, *Das Königsportal von Chartres,* Munich, 1962.

_____, "Twelfth Century Sculpture at Châlons-sur-Marne," *Studies in Western Art,* vol. I, Princeton, 1963, 119-128.

_____, *Von Sens bis Strassburg, Beitrag zur kunstgeschichtlichen Stellung der strassburger Querhausskulpturen,* Berlin, 1966.

Schlag, G., "Die Skulpturen des Querhauses der Kathedrale von Chartres," *Wallraf-Richartz-Jahrbuch,* 5, 1943, 115-164.

Schreiner, L., *Die Frühgotische Plastik Südwestfrankreichs,* Cologne, 1963.

Schürenberg, L., "Spätromanische und frühgotische Plastik in Dijon und ihre Bedeutung für die Skulpturen des Strassburger Munsterquerschiffs," *Jahrbuch der preussischen Kunstsammlungen,* 58, 1937, 13f.

Sedlmayr, H., *Die Entstehung der Kathedrale,* Zurich, 1950.

Seymour, C. Jr., "Têtes gothiques de la cathédrale de Noyen," *Gazette des beaux-arts,* 74, Oct. 1937, 137-142.

_____, "XIII Century Sculptures at Noyon and the Development of the Gothic Caryatid," *Gazette des beaux-arts,* 86, 1944, 163-182.

_____, *Notre-Dame of Noyon in the Twelfth Century,* New Haven, 1939; 2nd ed., New York, 1968.

Simson, O. von, *The Gothic Cathedral: Origins of Gothic Architecture and the Medieval Concept of Order,* New York, 1956; 2nd ed., New York, 1964.

Stoddard, W. S., *The West Portals of St. Denis and Chartres,* Cambridge, Mass., 1952.

Tarbé, T., *Description de l'église metropolitaine de St.-Etienne de Sens,* Sens and Paris, 1941.

Urseau, C., *La cathédrale d'Angers,* Paris, 1930.

Vanuxem, J., "Autour du triomphe de la vierge du portail de la cathédrale de Senlis, les portails détruits de la cathédrale de Cambrai et de Saint-Nicolas d'Amiens," *Bulletin monumentale,* 103, 1945, 89-102.

Vöge, W., *Die Anfänge der monumentalen Stiles im Mittelalter,* Strassburg, 1894.

_____, *Bildhauer des Mittelalters, Gesammelte Schriften,* Berlin, 1958.

Woilley, E., *Répertoire archéologique de l'Oise,* Paris, 1862.